Well Built?

A forensic approach to the prevention, diagnosis
and cure of building defects

© Robert William Houghton-Evans, 2005
Published by RIBA Enterprises Ltd, 15 Bonhill Street, London EC2P 2EA

ISBN 1 85946 122 0
Stock Code 4241

The right of Robert William Houghton-Evans to be identified as the Author of this Work has been asserted in accordance with the Copyright, Design and Patents Act 1988.

British Library Cataloguing in Publications Data
A catalogue record for this book is available from the British Library.

Publisher: Steven Cross
Commissioning Editor: Matthew Thompson
Project Editor: Anna Walters
Editor: Ian McDonald

Designed by Ben Millbank
Typeset by Academic + Technical, Bristol
Printed and bound in Great Britain by MPG Books, Bodmin

Cover illustration taken from *The City*, 1998, oil on canvas, by Olga Moscow

Cartoons drawn by Ian McDonald, based on original ideas by Ray Scally

Well Built?

A forensic approach to the prevention, diagnosis
and cure of building defects

Robert William Houghton-Evans

RIBA Enterprises

Acknowledgements

The author wishes to thank his colleagues for their support and assistance and particularly Ray Scally for contributing to the drawn illustrations, Ann Glacki for finding much of the reference material used and Roger Knowles for checking the sections dealing with legal procedures. Thanks also to Sue Gilbert who corrected and improved the initial drafts.

The author is grateful to Peter Trotman of the BRE who provided some of the statistical information used in this book.

This book is dedicated to Dr. William Houghton-Evans MA PhD RIBA MRTPI, whose support and collaboration was fundamental to getting it off the ground. Sadly he died in 2002, before the book was finished.

Contents

Introduction   ix

Prologue   xi

Terminology   xii

1: Roles and Relationships Defined   1

2: Errors Before Construction   27

3: Errors During Construction   65

4: Errors After Construction   85

5: Symptom and Cause   93

6: Diagnosis of Defects   141

7: Remedial Works   169

8: Damage and Remedy   193

9: Litigation and the Alternatives   215

10: Arbitration and Adjudication   241

11: The Expert   269

12: Liability – Insurance and Limitation   287

Bibliography   315

Useful Organizations/Addresses   319

Index   321

Introduction

Forewarned is forearmed

This book offers practical guidance through the minefield of building defects and disputes.

New pitfalls appear daily, as modern technologies supplant tried and tested traditions. As both building and legal practices evolve alongside rising standards and more demanding regulation, it is not safe to assume that what worked yesterday is good enough for tomorrow.

The book is intended as a practical guide. It is based on the author's experience gained through over 200 commissions, in eight different legal jurisdictions – investigating, collecting evidence and resolving over £30m-worth of defects and a similar amount of wrongly alleged shortcomings in built work.

Dealing with building failures requires various degrees of familiarity with science, law and practice. This book is not intended to provide a basic training in these areas. Rather, it draws together key aspects from each to provide an overview of the principles of the prevention, diagnosis and cure of defects and the related aspects of legal remedy and liability. References are given to publications which go into aspects of technical or legal matters at greater length than practicable here.

The author does not hold himself out to have greater legal or scientific expertise than is appropriate for a practising architect, and does not offer in this book to provide comprehensive answers to each and every problem which may arise. Each defect and dispute needs to be considered on its own. The guidance given is not a substitute for taking qualified legal and technical advice as and when appropriate.

Prologue

Once upon a time a man built a hut. He employed no architect, hired no builder and entered no contracts. If it worked, he was happy – if not he fixed it.

With industrialisation, self-reliance declines. Construction becomes an enterprise to be procured by clients who do not themselves build and may not occupy the completed buildings. They may borrow to finance and sell projects on concepts and promises long before they are built. To fulfil their undertakings, clients draw from the building trades and professions to form project teams which are bound by contract, regulated by statute and judged by the written authorities found in ever-evolving codes and standards. This division of tasks brings scope for misunderstanding, dispute over errors and the apportionment of blame.

Defective building provides fertile grounds for the costly exercise of the lawyers' arts – where damage is the compensation payable for fault rather than the deterioration it causes and effort is diverted from practical to legal remedy. Discovering the root cause of the breaches in the performance of buildings is fundamental to the expedient application of proper legal and technical remedies.

In 1976 it was estimated that one third of the output of the building industry was for maintenance and repair. Of this, as much as one fifth arose from the rectification of avoidable defects caused by poor workmanship or design – equating to over £400 million waste expenditure per year, excluding consequential costs and losses.[1]

By 1998, when the Egan Report[2] was published, over a third of projects were reported to be held up by defects, with fewer than one in six being defect free on completion.[3] The current UK Government, by adopting the Egan Report, have proposed an annual reduction in defects of 20 per cent as part of a drive, launched under the title 'Achieving Excellence', towards the elimination of retentions.[4]

In many countries, especially those with codified legal systems, there are requirements for suitably qualified people – including contractors, designers and inspectors – to fulfil specific roles on construction projects. Although intended to prevent defects due to unsuitably skilled or qualified people managing, supervising, inspecting and designing buildings, experience shows this does not ensure defect-free work. In the UK there is currently a drive towards closer teamwork, involving all parties working together in partnership to achieve best results. Complete freedom from error may remain unattainable, but a better understanding of how faults are introduced into construction would form a good basis from which to minimise defective work.

Whilst poor communication is at the root of much of what goes wrong, it is closely accompanied by undue haste and false economy as persistent widespread underlying causes of bad construction.

Obtaining the highest return at the lowest cost is the goal of consumerism. The purchase of goods on this basis involves controllable risk. The thing which is being bought can be examined beforehand and its quality and cost objectively assessed before a bargain is struck.

In a building project, the thing being bought does not exist when a client agrees to buy it. The client engages people to produce it – a provision of a service leading to the supply of a product. The final product is dependent on the performance of all of the service providers.

Choosing the lowest quoted price is, on the face of it, consistent with accepting lowest quality. In many spheres experience teaches that you get what you pay for.

> *It's unwise to pay too much, but it's worse to pay too little. When you pay too much you lose a little money, that is all. When you pay too little, you sometimes lose everything because the thing you bought was incapable of doing the thing it was bought to do.*[5]

Generally, clients commissioning building work ask for a quality product and those bidding for the work promise just that. But there remains an inherent divergence in expectations between specifying good quality and seeking the lowest price. This leads to much debate over the interpretation of specifications, when the service providers find limits on expenditure prevent their profitably meeting client expectation. Optimum quality, where unnecessary extravagance is avoided whilst sufficient funds are allocated to each task, is a skilled balance which requires co-operation and good communication.

On paper, the profitability of a project often benefits from the shortest possible time elapsing between the first payment being made and the work being completed. Competition to win business encourages optimistic projections of what can be achieved – followed by cutting corners to overcome the delays which routinely occur in building.

The combination of poor communication, cost cutting and rushed work is the prevalent cause of work going wrong and being left uncorrected until its consequences so severely mar performance that the faults have to be addressed. Often this is too late to allow the application of economic and expedient remedies.

Terminology

Because this book addresses both technical and legal issues, some of the terms used need to be clarified. For example, 'fault' may be used to describe a deficiency in a material, a product or an action. In common usage, a fault may be caused by a defect or a defect may be the result of a fault. Similarly, 'damage' may be the symptom from which we discover defective work but its plural, 'damages', may be used in legal terminology to mean the compensation payable for a breach of contract. In this book the following usage has been adopted:

Faults

Imperfections or blemishes in a material or structure, in workmanship or in appearance, which are the primary physical causes of the failure of a building component. These may be departure from good practice in design or construction, or deficiencies in a material or product selected. Where responsibility for a failure is to be allocated, 'fault' may refer to something wrongly done to which blame is attached; that is, the delinquent or culpable action which caused the fault to be incorporated or retained in the built work.

Defect

The absence of something essential to completeness, a lack or a deficiency arising from an incorrectly designed or built component of a building – a product of fault. Not all defects give rise to perceptible problems. For example, mortar bridging a wall cavity is a defect whether or not rain crosses the cavity, causing wet plaster.

Failure

Incorrect or deficient behaviour, giving way, cessation of function – the consequence of a defect where and to the extent that the defect impairs performance or appearance: in the above example, rain penetration across a wall cavity.

Damage

The harm, injury or impairment of value resulting from a failure: in the above example, the water damage to plaster and the need to correct the fault and repair the plaster. Where legal terminology is used, 'damages' is a sum of money claimed or awarded in compensation for loss or injury. In this latter context, 'damages' is the legal remedy for a breach of contract.

Loss

The quantification of damage. This may be the cost of accommodating failures, mitigating damage or eliminating faults. The usual measure, where damages result from a breach of contract, is the cost of putting the wronged party in the position they would have been in had the breach not occurred. We will see later on that while this may form the basis of calculation, it is rarely, if ever, the net reward for successful litigation.

---

[1]   H. J. Eldridge, *Common Defects In Buildings*, p. 1.
[2]   *Rethinking Construction*, The report of the Construction Taskforce, July 1998.

3   1998 Conference to launch the Construction Best Practice Programme following the Egan recommendations.

4   Money held back at handover for a fixed period as a security for the employer against latent defects – see Chapter 1, Payment, p. 24 and Chapter 4, Defects liability/maintenance period, p. 86.

5   Attributed to John Ruskin (1819–1900).

Roles and Relationships Defined

Individuals' responsibilities for potential failures arise out of their relationships with one another. Their roles and responsibilities may be agreed voluntarily or imposed by statute or common law. In this chapter, the written and implied duties of all involved are reviewed with reference to standard forms of contract and to ordinary standards of competence and other legal duties.

Roles

The building team has evolved with the development of civilisation. Once, no clear division could be made among those who together fulfilled today's basic roles of user, client, designer and builder.

The first significant distinction comes with the separation of the builder. Separation of the role of designer is less clear – and is still by no means complete. According to the Renaissance architect Alberti, *'anything that is immediately necessary for any particular purpose, and about which there is no doubt of what sort it should be, or of the ability of the owner to afford it ... is not so much the business of the architect as of a common workman'*. It is with the elaboration of structures like fortifications, temples and palaces that the design specialist begins to emerge. Sometimes a statesman or scholar, sometimes a skilled craftsman, designers have developed by different routes and been known by a variety of names ever since.

Today's still-growing specialisation results in further distinctive roles. Clients are now rarely themselves users, and range from speculative developers to public corporations. Designers may be generalist architects, engineers, or specialists in one or another aspect of their discipline. 'Surveyor' – the designation considered appropriate for Christopher Wren – is now used to cover specialisations ranging from mapping to estimating and cost control. And the task of 'overseer' – which is what surveyor really means – is now shared with site managers, foremen, supervisors, building inspectors and clerks of works. Builders are often themselves developers, and divide what was once a unified role into those of general contractors and specialist subcontractors – who in turn range from those who only supply to those who design, supply and fix.

Today's complex relationships require adequate definition of roles and responsibilities, which may be specified in standard forms of contract or bespoke agreements. The former, striking a variety of balances between brevity and comprehensiveness, are published by professional bodies and committees drawn from across the industry – but however precisely these are worded, there will always be room for dispute. They can never unambiguously embrace all that may happen in the building process.

Building professions

With the exception of architects, who are subject to the standards set for them by the Architects' Registration Board (ARB), there are no mandatory minimum standards for entry into building professions in the UK. Nor is there any mandatory requirement to use qualified professionals to design, inspect and manage building work.

Insofar as standards exist, these are the self-regulating standards imposed by professional bodies for their members and summarised in their codes of practice, model contracts and other published guidance. As there is no requirement, in the UK, for a building professional to join a professional body, compliance with these standards is, necessarily, entirely voluntary.

The standards set by the professional bodies for their members are likely nonetheless to be used as benchmarks to judge practitioners trading openly as building professionals. For example, anyone, with no qualification, may call themselves a surveyor and ply for business as such. However, if their competence is called into question, it is the standards set by chartered surveyors, embodied in the guidance issued by their chartered society, which is likely to be accepted as defining what may reasonably be expected of a practising surveyor. It is therefore worthwhile considering the roles of building professionals in terms of the practices established by their institutes and professional bodies.

Professional competence

Many trades and professions have long required prospective members to serve a probationary period to gain entry to their ranks. Increasingly the building professions have moved toward academic qualification, to the point that it is now rare for new members of the older professions to start with less than a bachelor's degree. As soon, however, as newly qualified professionals begin to practise, it is their actions – not qualifications – which become the gauge of their competence.

In common law, professional competence is assessed in comparative rather than absolute terms. For a professional to be in error is not of itself grounds for a claim for professional negligence. Unless the express terms of the contract state to the contrary, or in cases where there is an implied or statutory duty to achieve 'fitness for purpose', it is not sufficient merely to show that a defect has arisen from someone's errors or omissions.

For example, many engineers have, in the recent past, wrongly specified high-alumina cement. However, they did so at a time when a large part of the profession believed this to be sound. The mere fact that they were wrong and that damage has resulted from this error does not make them liable for the consequential losses. Each engineer, in common with other design professionals, is judged by comparison with their peers. Thus, for an engineer to be liable for the cost of a defect they would have to have performed their duties to a lower standard than could be expected of a representative body of ordinarily competent engineers.

The standard of skill and care in all cases is similar. The duty owed to a client is to act with the skill and care of the ordinary prudent person holding themselves out as possessing the particular skill offered. It is not simply a question of giving correct or incorrect advice, but of demonstrating a standard of skill commonly found in persons of like discipline.

Legal opinion on this can be found in various decided court cases.[6]

To quote from the privy council in *Chin Keow* v *Government of Malaysia*:

... where you get a situation which involves the use of some special skill or competence, then the test whether there has been negligence or not is not the test of the man on the top of the Clapham Omnibus, because he has not got this special skill. The test is the standard of the ordinary skilled man exercising and professing to have that special skill ... it is well established law that it is sufficient if he exercises the ordinary skill of an ordinary competent man exercising that particular art.

The applicable common law is well set out in the following:

The law requires of a professional man that he live up in practice to the standard of the ordinary skilled man exercising and professing to have his special professional skills. He need not possess the highest expert skill; it is enough if he exercises the ordinary skill of an ordinary competent man exercising his particular art[7]

... No matter what profession it may be, the common law does not impose on those who practise it any liability for damage resulting from what in the result turn out to have been errors of judgement, unless the error was such as no reasonable well-informed and competent member of that profession could have made.[8]

It can be drawn from the decided cases on negligence that a professional should:

* command the corpus of knowledge which forms part of the professional equipment of the ordinary member of their profession;
* not lag behind other ordinarily assiduous and intelligent members of a profession in knowledge of new advances and developments in their field;
* have such awareness as an ordinarily competent practitioner would have of the deficiencies in their knowledge and the limitations on their skill;
* be alert to the hazards and risks inherent in any professional task they undertake to the extent that other ordinarily competent members of their profession would be;
* bring to any professional task they undertake no less expertise, skill and care than any other ordinarily competent members of that profession would bring, but no more.

The standard is that of the reasonable average. The law does not require of a professional to be exceptional (unless, perhaps, if in plying for work they hold themselves out to be exceptional).

In deciding whether someone has fallen short of the standards observed by ordinarily skilled and competent members of their profession, it is the standards prevailing at the time of acts or omissions that provide the relevant yardstick.

He is not ... to be judged by the wisdom of hindsight. This of course means that knowledge of an event which happened later should not be applied when judging acts and/or omissions which took place before that event ...; ... it is necessary, if the Defendant's conduct is to be fairly judged, that the making of [any] retrospective assessment should not of itself have the effect of magnifying the significance of the ... risk as it appeared or should reasonably have appeared to [an] ordinarily competent practical man with a job to do at the time.[9]

In applying a test of skill and competence, circumstances also need to be taken into account. Negligent advice which is not relied upon or which self-evidently ought not to be relied upon is not a good basis for a claim in negligence. The same negligent advice given in circumstances where it is relied upon may form the basis for a sustainable claim.

For example, in relation to a proposed building project, Archie, the project architect, asked Edward, the project engineer, to carry out a soils investigation. The investigation was limited to shallow test holes. Edward advised Archie accordingly, noting that deeper test holes were required before the capacity of the ground to support the proposed building could be established with confidence. This action was not negligent, because the limits of the reliance that could be placed on the test results were stated.

Figure 1.1: **Failure to qualify professional advice can be negligent.**

Later, Owen, the employer, requested a copy of the report. Edward wrote to Owen supplying the requested information, but omitted to warn of the need for deeper trial holes. In writing to Owen, Edward gave his opinion of the load-bearing capacity of the soil. In subsequent legal action it was held that Edward was in breach of his duty of care for not advising Owen that it would be prudent to take further tests before drawing firm conclusions on the bearing capacity of the ground.

The level of the duty of care will depend on the way in which the people concerned hold themselves out. For example, designers who are not qualified architects but who hold themselves out in all respects to be competent to carry out the work of an architect may owe a duty of care equal to that owed by an architect taking on similar work.

Such claims of special expertise may be made orally, in letter headings, in brochures, etc. For example, many builders implicitly hold themselves out to be competent to design as well as to build by stating in their letter headings that they are a 'Design and Build Contractor'. It is arguable that builders who represent themselves as being competent to design and build a house without their customers needing the services of architect or engineer stand to be judged negligent if, in the design of the house, they do not exercise the same skill as may reasonably be expected of ordinarily competent architects and engineers.

Professionals may similarly alter the standards required of them by advertising special skills. Building professionals who promote their services by claiming some special knowledge or an exceptional level of skill may correspondingly extend their obligations to their clients beyond that of ordinary professional competence. For example, architects who claim that they specialise in the design of commercial buildings and have great experience in optimising returns from office developments may be judged by a higher standard when carrying out such work than architects who, whilst no doubt regarding themselves as competent to design offices, claim no special skill or experience in this type of building.

It is unnecessary to enter a contract in order to take on a duty of skill and care. People who hold themselves out to be expert in a field and give advice, whether or not they do so for reward, may be liable to the people they advise if their advice is both wrong and negligent.[10]

This standard for assessing the performance of experts often gives rise to the need for expert evidence in disputes over professional competence. UK courts rely on experienced practitioners to give guidance on what constitutes a level of ordinary professional competence and opinion on whether what was done conformed therewith.[11]

Roles in the supervision/inspection of work on site

Supervision of work in progress is a necessary part of a contractor's role, usually involving employment of foremen or site supervisors. But contractor's employees are answerable to the contractor, not the client, and supervision in the client's interest may involve designers, site inspectors, clerks of works, etc. either engaged as independent consultants or directly in the client's employ.

Arrangements in which a client employs an architect to oversee the building works are described in various publications of the Royal Institute of British Architects (RIBA) and other professional organisations, and defined in standard forms of building contract. It is interesting to note the change of language which has occurred in standard contracts such as those published by the Joint Contracts Tribunal (JCT) and the RIBA. Whereas architects, until more than halfway through the last century, undertook ordinarily to 'supervise' building works, they now more commonly restrict their services during construction to administration and inspection. Supervision has been seen by the courts in England and Wales as a continuous and substantial duty, which goes far beyond the interim inspections provided for in the architect's standard terms of appointment.

Many architects and engineers still speak, in conversation with their clients, of their 'supervising' a project, and many clients expect to be able to leave such matters entirely in the hands of their professional consultants. Difficulty arises where 'supervision' as used in these conversations is not understood to have the same meaning as that given to it after the work has gone wrong and the duties of the parties has become a matter for legal debate.

It is safer to restrict the use of the term 'supervision' to site-based management, which is capable of constantly monitoring building work and has the authority to take immediate action to correct error.

A key consideration is the division of responsibility

Most standard forms of building contract make 'supervision' the responsibility of main contractors, who are likely – following current practice – to make each sub-contractor they employ responsible for the supervision of their own work. A general foreman may lack the detailed knowledge of a subcontractor's work required to supervise all aspects of it, leaving a potential vacuum in the overall co-ordinating role of the general contractor in supervision.

Inspection may involve a variety of people with overlapping duties. For example, a clerk of works may, as a matter of course, inspect precisely the same parts of construction as the project architect. Where errors in architects' inspections occur, the architects may say that they were relying on the more frequent inspections of the clerk of works to excuse their paying too little attention to an aspect of the construction which was being wrongly built during their visits to site.

The appointment of a clerk of works does not ordinarily reduce the architect's inspection responsibilities. If architects believe that their duties in inspection are reduced by the presence of a clerk of works, it would be better for them to have this set out in their contracts of employment and agreed with their clients.

Where architects engage clerks of works on their clients' behalf, those architects may be liable to their clients for any shortcoming in the inspection whether the fault lies with the architect or the clerk of works. Where a client engages the architect and clerk of works directly in separate contracts the shortcomings of the clerk of works are less likely to be the architect's liability, although they may still be so if they arose through the architect's failure adequately to inform and direct the clerk of works.

Where the architect or clerk of works is an employee of the client, their negligent action might be seen to make the employer liable for the consequences. This may bring into play the rules of law relating to contributory negligence.[12] To the extent that the employer, through their employees, has materially contributed to a defect in a building, their ability to recover damages from others who have similarly contributed to the defect may be reduced.

Roles in design development on site

Many difficulties arise from modifications and details designed after the commencement of work on site. Although, traditionally, building contracts have been written on the presumption that the design is completed and then the building is built, 'lump-sum' contracts written on this basis have developed to allow design information to be completed as construction is under way without changing the underlying approach of 'design first, build afterwards'. This, however, readily leads to dispute over post-tender design.

Contracts based on the assumption that there will be an interplay between the building and design processes more closely mirror what typically happens in a building project, and allow for more realistic arrangements to be made.

The alteration and elaboration of designs as building work progresses is often a pragmatic, common-sense approach – and does not necessarily indicate that the designs are defective or the designers acting incompetently. Contractors may nevertheless argue that it does, in furtherance of claims for extensions of time and additional payments. This may discourage designers from working closely with builders, an arrangement which is vital for good quality and trouble-free buildings. Anything which inhibits this collaboration is conducive to a claims-ridden project and defective construction.

Experienced and practical professionals often complete projects without reference to the detailed provisions of standard forms of contract. It is nevertheless advisable to have them there in the background to provide a method for resolving problems without recourse to lawyers. A clear contract which sets out the rules for dealing with issues as they arise helps to keep things in the hands of the project team and out of the barristers' chambers.

Relationships

Although rarely referred to directly in contract documents, the most significant relationship for successful design is that between 'designer' and 'user'. Where the client is to be the principal user and the designer is a self-employed architect, this should be relatively straightforward – but even here there can be difficulties.

Many a building fails to satisfy because the client never adequately explained what was wanted or the designer didn't ask the right questions or ensure that their proposals were understood. Architects could be held responsible for what 'ordinarily competent' like professionals ought to know, but only with thorough preliminary investigation can they unearth the likely requirements and expectations of every potential user – most of whom are today unlikely to be available for consultation.

Anticipation and discovery of user needs is vital for successful design but not something easily definable in legal terms. Ideally, records should be kept of consultations and decisions – typically in the form of agreed minutes of meetings, schedules of accommodation, target costs and dates, and drawings of agreed proposals.

An abattoir floor was designed to be hygienic, washable and slip resistant. Flooring products were selected with that in mind but there was much complaint over the slipperiness of the floor. Eventually an employee sliced off one of his fingers when he slipped whilst cutting meat.

Coarse particles were sealed into the floor's surface to provide traction. The floor was washed daily. All employees were required to wear special footwear and to use a sterilising boot wash on entering and leaving. It was found that residual water from sterilising and washing reduced the traction between the selected footwear and the sealed surface to the floor.

Although the specified floor finishes had worked well elsewhere, they proved not to be compatible with the processes being carried out in the building and the choice of footwear. Without better knowledge of the processes the building was to house, the designer could not have anticipated and prevented the problem.

Partnerships

Not every designer is a self-employed loner. Many nowadays are in partnerships where a client's contractual relationship is with the partners, not the individual designer. With a conventional partnership responsibility lies equally with all the partners, each of whom can be held totally liable for any contractual failure by any partner or employee.

The Partnership Act 1890 sets out the basic structure of partnership law and has remained largely unchanged for over 100 years. The Limited Partnerships Act 1907 introduced a second form of partnership, in which the liability of one or more of the partners could be limited whilst also retaining general partners with unlimited liability.

Companies

Where designers work as directors of a limited company – which for architects has only recently become professionally acceptable – responsibility lies collectively with the company through its directors, whose liabilities are defined under company law. The executive directors are, under UK law, ordinarily employees of the company and, as such, gain some protection from liability whilst acting as employees of the company.[13] Employees who hold equity in the company may at the same time be owners.

A company, by registering, becomes a corporation, thus acquiring an independent legal identity.[14] There are, in English law, corporations which are not companies and which also have independent legal identity, including such bodies as the Crown and local authorities. There are distinctions between these corporations and registered companies. For example, a local authority which negligently approves, as compliant with the Building Regulations, work which is defective may enjoy public-interest immunity from claims against it. Such a defence is not ordinarily available to a commercial company, such as a firm of approved inspectors.

Whilst a registered company may enter into contractual relationships with other companies and people, its members may relate to others both as the 'voice' of the company and as individuals. In this way, architect employees of a company may be seen both as representing the company and as acting in their own right.

Where designers work as employees, their primary responsibility is to their employers, not to those whom their employers are contracted to serve. Like all citizens, they have the duty to avoid breaking the law. They will also, if professionally qualified, run the risk of being 'struck off' if they fail to observe professional standards. But any failings in their service to clients have to be dealt with by their employers, under the terms of their employment, which normally can at worst result in their being sacked.

Other relationships

Where a client's contractual relationship is with developers or builders, who engage designers to assist them, responsibilities are more complex. Where designers are salaried employees, roles and responsibilities are those of employer and employee. But where they are fee-earning consultants, clients should be made aware that their role as designers is to satisfy both client and developer – a situation in which conflicts of interest may easily arise.

Where designers are employed by developers intending to market their products, user needs are determined in terms of anticipated marketability and the designer's role becomes mainly one of advising how to satisfy potential purchasers within the limits imposed by statutory requirements and commercial profitability.

Specialisation today usually requires separate disciplines to design structures, services, etc. These may be employed directly by the client, the contractor, a subcontractor or the principal designer. Again, it is essential that roles and responsibilities be adequately defined.

It is now common to rely extensively on specialist suppliers, manufacturers and subcontractors to advise on those parts of a building design which use their proprietary products or specialist services. This is a trend where, all too often, little attention is paid to co-ordination and communication.

The design of the cladding of a new paper mill had been given to the project structural engineer who passed it on to the cladding subcontractor. The cladding corroded quickly because of the high internal temperature and humidity maintained for the manufacturing process housed in the building. Unfortunately for the engineers, the subcontractor on whom they relied was not sufficiently solvent to bear the cost of the ensuing claim.

The transfer of the design via engineer to subcontractor was not accompanied by adequate information on the nature of the processes to be housed. The designers were unaware of the special conditions with which they had to deal, and the design was such as might be produced for an ordinary building. It was faulty only insofar as it was unsuited to the special conditions created by the manufacturing process.

Had the traditional method of building procurement been followed, with a lead designer clearly in charge of the process, better communication and co-ordination of the design team might have prevented the use of a design which was fatally ill-suited to the building's intended function.

Roles and relationships defined in contract

Various types of contractual relationship may come into play in construction projects, and to facilitate this there are suitable standard forms and many bespoke variants. These include:

- consultant agreements;
- main (head) contracts between the employer and the main contractor;
- subcontracts between the main contractor and their subcontractors (both for subcontractors selected by the employer and for other subcontractors);
- sub-subcontracts between a subcontractor and their sub-subcontractors;
- design agreements between an employer and a specialist designer;
- forms of tender for issue by an employer to prospective main contractors, for issue by a main contractor to prospective subcontractors, and for issue by a subcontractor to prospective sub-subcontractors;
- forms of contract for the supply of goods; and
- forms of bond (including performance bonds) and collateral warranties.

The parties to these contracts may take on both 'express' and 'implied' duties.

It is well to bear in mind the distinction between the essential terms on which a contractual relationship is based and other conditions and obligations which may exist by the virtue of the contract.

> Take for example, the construction of a podium to allow civic dignitaries to present a speech at 4.00 p.m. on the afternoon of Tuesday 7 January. After the speech it is to be demolished and will serve no further purpose. Here time clearly is of the essence. The completion of the podium any later than the time at which the speeches are to be given would serve no purpose.
>
> If, however, the construction of the podium was to allow a speech at the time stated but it was thereafter to be retained to allow speeches to be given at intervals over the next several years, it is more debatable whether or not time is of the essence. The podium finished late would still serve a purpose.
>
> If those commissioning the work wished to make time of the essence they could say so in the contract, but then they would have to be wary themselves of any action they undertook which impeded completion by the prescribed time. If time truly is of the essence then a failure to complete by the prescribed time could be said to invalidate the whole contract.
>
> If completion by the prescribed time is not of the essence then late completion may give rise to an entitlement to damages, but not the right to effectively cancel the whole contract.

Those terms of the contract which are essential to its performance can be regarded as being in a separate category from other obligations which may be incorporated into a contract. On this view, there is a hierarchy to the obligations set out on the parties under a contract, as follows:

1. those which are essential to the purpose of the contract, the non-performance of which would so frustrate the contract that there was no purpose in entering into it in the first place;
2. the terms and conditions which one party or the other considers desirable, but which do not go to the root of the contract.

Thus it may be said that the employer's obligation to pay for the work is fundamental. In the absence of a promise to pay, there is no reason for the contractor to enter the contract. However, an agreement to make payments on a certain basis at certain times may not go to the essence of a contract and small irregularities in following a prescribed regime of payment may be remedied without invalidating the whole contract.

Under some jurisdictions, this is set out in law in clear terms. For example, the Hungarian Civil Code imposes certain obligations on employer and contractor, and states where a breach of those obligations will be remedied without causing the contract, as a whole, to fail. In legal systems which are based on common law, there is less certainty. In contrast to the Hungarian system, the English courts pay regard to legal precedent and, in assessing a contract, have to use judgement in balancing the requirements of equity and fairness with those of commercial certainty.

A requirement can be made 'of the essence' by agreement between the parties but, if this is done, there is need for consistency. For example, the JCT family of contracts allows time for completion to be varied under certain circumstances and contains provisions for remedies for delays which are less draconian that determination of the contract. In a contract which contains such provisions it would be difficult to make time of the essence.

If something is of the essence then, in principle, any alteration to it will fundamentally alter the nature of the contract and may jeopardise its validity. A contract may therefore set up relationships between the contracting parties which are, in the terms of the contract, unalterable – as well as relationships which can be altered. It may stipulate the circumstances in which non-essential conditions may be altered and incorporate controls over the implementation of such changes. Ultimately, the contracting parties may agree changes to the essential provisions of a contract but an agreement thus altered may be better regarded as a new contract rather than an amended variant of the original agreement.

The majority of requirements set out under building contracts are dealt with as not being of the essence and mechanisms are provided to get round minor breaches of the contract requirements without invalidating the whole contract. It is always difficult where persistent minor breaches occur to decide whether their accumulation amounts to grounds to repudiate the whole contract or whether to persist with the contract and seek to remedy each breach, employing the mechanisms allowed for in the contract.

For example, if a contractor continually and persistently fails to correct defective work, it may be argued that it is reasonable to replace them with another contractor on the grounds that it is no longer possible to have faith in their ability to discharge their obligations. Where no essential term of the contract has been breached, it is usually safer to persist in an attempt to make the contract work than to abandon it.

This is embodied in the concept of 'partnering contracts' where the intention is that the parties take on, as a common objective, the successful completion of the project rather than the pursuit of their own diverse interests. Although this is no different from the sensible way to approach any contract, it is notable that those forms which predate the vogue for partnering tend to contain ever-increasing detail about how to resolve conflicts arising from the different commercial interests of the contracting parties, rather than guidance on how to co-operate in the pursuit of a common interest.

Standard forms of building contracts

There are a limited number of permutations of approaches to building contracts. The underlying principles are whether there are to be hierarchical or parallel contracts for individual trades and design consultants and the degree to which the outcome is to be fixed at the outset or developed as matters progress. A further distinction can be made between single projects carried out as single contracts and a series of contracts which may be for the completion of one project or spread over several projects. Secondary considerations include whether tenders are to be obtained by competitive bids or negotiation.

To accommodate these alternatives there are many variants of standard forms of agreement for construction work. The detail they contain is usually proportional to the value and complexity of the work being undertaken. Formal building contracts can be categorised broadly as follows:

- traditional/conventional;
- design and build;
- management.

Traditional/conventional supply-and-build contracts

Since the establishment of architecture, engineering and surveying as autonomous professions standing apart from the building trades, and the emergence of the general contractor there has been a tradition of separating design from construction and of retaining designers to act as independent consultants to supervise the building of their designs on behalf of their clients. This has led to a variety of approaches which are characterised by the design process being separated from construction, and substantial documentation being required before the contractor can be invited to tender for carrying out the work. This way of building has been an established convention in the UK for at least 150 years, but has recently been diminishing in popularity.

For traditional procurement there are three main types of contract:

1. lump sum;
2. measurement;
3. cost reimbursement.

In a lump-sum contract the contract sum is settled before construction work starts. The contractor undertakes specified works in return for the payment of an agreed sum. Such contracts may be 'with quantities' and priced on the basis of drawings and a firm bill of quantities or 'without quantities' and priced on a combination of drawings, specifications and schedules.

In a measurement contract, the contract sum is not finalised until after building work is complete. Payments are assessed on re-measurement of the work done. The basis for this should be agreed at the outset and stated in the contract. The work which the contractor undertakes is not measured accurately before tenders are invited. Design needs to be reasonably complete and an accurate picture of the quality required should be included in the invitations to tender. Usually the variants based on drawings and approximate quantities give greater certainty to the employer over the outcome than those which substitute specifications and schedules for bills.

A variant of this is the 'measured term' contract, under which individual works can be initiated by instructions as part of a programme of work and priced according to rates related to the categories of work likely to form part of the programme.

In a cost-reimbursement, cost-plus or prime-cost contract, the contract sum is arrived at on the basis of the actual (prime) costs of labour, plant and materials, with additional payments to cover overheads and profit. The amount of fee added can be agreed on any basis, but is usually either a fixed sum or a percentage of the prime sums. In its basic form this is a relatively high-risk option for the employer but it can be combined with an agreed fixed maximum price, so limiting the employer's exposure.

Design-and-build contracts

This is also usually lump-sum, fixed-price contracting. A greater proportion of the risk is taken by the contractor and less by the employer than is usually the case in conventional building contracts. The contractor is responsible for undertaking both the design and the construction of the work in return for a lump-sum price. There are variants on this option depending on the degree to which the initial design is shown in the client's requirements.

For design-and-build procurement there are three main types of agreement:

1. package deal or turnkey;
2. design and build;
3. contractor's design for specific elements only.

A package deal or 'turnkey' contract is one where the client buys a complete package.

Design and build or contracts with contractor's design place responsibility on the contractor to design, supply and build the works. Under English law, unless expressly excluded, there will be an implied requirement that the work be fit for its intended purpose. The JCT, for example, prevents such a term being implied in their 'With Contractor's Design' form of contract. In this form the contractor's design liability is limited to 'the like liability of an architect or as the case may be other appropriate professional designer engaged independently under a separate contract with the employer to supply designs for a building contractor who was not the supplier of the design'.[15]

These contracts differ fundamentally from traditional 'work-and-materials' contracts in that they expressly provide for contractor's design obligations.

Contractor's design for specific elements only combine defined elements of design-and-build with traditional 'work-and-materials' contracts.

Management contracts

Overall design is the responsibility of the client's consultants, and the contractor is responsible both for defining packages of work and then for managing the carrying out of this work through separate trades or works contractors, who are contractually accountable to him.

For management procurement there are two main types of contract with many variants, usually from commercial sources:

1. management contracts;
2. construction management.

The contract will usually include both a pre-construction and a construction phase. Project drawings, a project specification and a cost plan will be used to produce the documents on which competitive tenders can be obtained for the work packages. Management contractors are then responsible for the administration and operation of the works contracts. However, they are not liable for the consequences of any default by a works contractor so long as the management contractor has complied with the particular requirements of the management contract. The management contract and the works contracts for each package must be compatible.

In construction management, the construction manager undertakes to manage the carrying out of the work through trade contractors but the client is involved in the directing of the project, and contracts directly with the trades contractors.

The Construction Management Agreement will cover the services as defined in that document. Although the trades contracts are arranged and administered by the construction manager, contractually they are the client's risk. The Construction Management Agreement and the Trade Contract for each package must be compatible.

Design–Manage–Construct variants of management procurement have been specially drafted to suit certain projects.

There are hybrid approaches which combine elements from each of the above to form alternative ways of defining the roles and relationships of the members of a project team.

Ad hoc contracts

Contract terms may be imported by reference. For example, a letter confirming that work is to be carried out in accordance with the terms and conditions of the JCT Minor Works form may, if properly set out and accepted, import those terms into an agreement without the standard form itself being executed. Such arrangements are common but they can lead to difficulties: for example, an imported form of contract may contain an arbitration clause. Where the terms of a contract are imported by reference but not executed there may be arguments about whether either of the parties have the right to arbitrate in preference to litigation.[16]

Additionally, in standard forms there are often options to be selected and items to be filled in. Unless the letter which imports the standard terms sets out the selection of options and the information required to fill in the blanks in the standard form, there will be difficulty in relying fully on the imported contract.

Where contracts are entered into on the basis of an exchange of correspondence, whether or not a standard form is used, it is important to be clear what parts of the correspondence have effect in the final agreement.

Many firms, when tendering for work, do so on their own bespoke forms which set out their terms and conditions of trading. Likewise, many invitations to tender set out the terms and conditions required for the submission of tenders. The 'small print' on these tenders and invitations to tender may be mutually exclusive. Unless there is a mutually agreed statement of which terms and conditions apply to the final agreement, later documents will ordinarily take preference over earlier. Where later documents are not in conflict with earlier documents, both may stand equally as parts of the agreement which has been entered into.

Often the exchange of correspondence will involve discussions over the nature and extent of the work which, if not clarified in a final agreement, may lead to differences over the quality and extent of what is to be done under the contract. For example, a tenderer may carry out the work in accordance with what they have proposed in their letters, only to find that their work is said to be deficient because it does not accord with conflicting requirements contained in the invitation to tender – a recipe for legal dispute because what is perceived to be defective depends on which conditions are relied upon.

It is common practice for all parties' standard terms and conditions to state that they are final and will override any other terms and conditions. This is equally true of standard forms of contract, which similarly seek to ensure that their terms and conditions take precedence. The larger standard forms also usually set out the order of priority of the documents contained and referred to within them. This allows any conflict – say between a specification, a drawing and a bill item – to be resolved according to preset rules rather than becoming an issue for legal argument. Joint signatures on the final agreement, making clear which documents apply and confirming the order of priority to be given between any documents which are in conflict, is the surest way of limiting such legal conflict.

Building work may be commissioned as a series of trade contracts without employing a general contractor or using any standard form for the purpose. Although essentially a simple approach, this contains its own pitfalls. For example, the start of one tradesman's work may depend on the completion of another's. If the first trade contract finishes late and the second one is consequently delayed, the employer (not the first tradesman) will be responsible to the second tradesman for any consequences of the delay. Any requirement that the contract be finished by a set date is likely to carry with it an implied requirement that the employer facilitates the carrying out of the work so that completion by the due date is achievable.

> In a building, joiners undertook to carry out certain work on an agreement which stipulated that they would execute the specified work for a specified sum and undertake to finish by a certain date. The start of the joiners' work was delayed by late plastering. The terms under which the plasterers were working did not contain a requirement to complete by a certain date. It was found that the completion date agreed to by the joiners could not be enforced as being of the essence.[17]

Contract documents

Typically, the first part of a formal contract is the signed agreement between the parties and the remainder the terms and conditions to which the signatories are bound. Other documents which form part of the contract 'bundle' are usually not part of the standard forms but are referred to in them as appropriate.

The agreement typically sets out the functions of the parties, i.e. who is the employer, the contractor, the designer, etc. Where the employer is not represented by an agent such as an architect, engineer or surveyor, the parties described in the agreement will be the employer and contractor only.

At its minimum, a building contract is an agreement between an employer and a builder and nothing more. An example is the JCT Standard Building Contract for a Home Owner/Occupier: a four-page simple document which does not provide for the employer engaging an architect or other agent to manage the work.

Ordinarily, where the building contract provides for the employer to act through an agent, any failure of the employer's agents to carry out their duties under the building contract is a breach of contract by the employer. That is, the employer warrants that their agents will do those things that the contract defines as the agent's duties. For example, under the JCT Standard Forms (With or Without Quantities, the Intermediate and Minor Works) the employer is responsible to the contractor for any failure by the architect to supply the information required of them under the contract. Under a separate contract of employment the architect may be responsible for this failing to the employer but this does not alter the employer's liability, under the building contract, to the contractor.

For all but the smallest, simplest work, contracts based on the standard forms comprise three parts: the agreement, conditions and such documents as are required to describe the work, e.g. drawings, specifications, schedules.

Where design-and-build forms are used or where there are elements of contractors' design work, these are better covered by a design brief. Commonly, design-and-build contracts are started after some consideration has been given to the design and here the design brief may appropriately be superseded by the employers' requirements – combining design brief, such design information as has been prepared pre-tender, performance specification and any stipulations or restrictions on the way things are to be done.

In commonly used standard forms of contract, the employer's agent's terms of employment is a separate agreement. It is important to ensure that agents' obligations to the employer are consistent with the obligations they undertake on the employer's behalf under the building contract. This is straightforward where mutually supportive forms of agreement are used, such as the RIBA Standard Terms for the Appointment of an Architect and the JCT Standard Form of Building Contract. Where this is not done, skilled legal drafting is required.

The current practice of employing a general contractor who in turn employs subcontractors has led to the use of collateral warranties. These are separate contracts (although they may be referred to in the main building contract and be a condition attaching to subcontracting). They establish direct contractual relationships (warranties) between the employer and the subcontractors. They are separate from, and additional to, the contracts between the employer and general contractor and between the general contractor and their subcontractors.

Such warranties usually give the employer the right to pursue the subcontractors directly for defects in their work without reducing the employer's rights of action against the main contractor. This direct relationship between employer and subcontractor can also facilitate direct payments between them, which can be useful if the main contractor ceases trading or if the main contract is determined before the work is complete.

Where subcontractors have a design input, direct employer-subcontractor relationships can assist in getting the design work under way at an early stage and can help integrate the subcontractors into the design team. Bringing designers together at the right time and achieving a good working relationship is fundamental to the co-ordination of the design and permits the efficient use of design resources and skills.

All but the simplest contract forms will identify who is involved, the duties they are to undertake and the obligations they are to accept.

For example, in the JCT family of contracts reference is made to some or all of the following:

- architect;
- contract administrator;
- employer's agent;
- quantity surveyor;
- planning supervisor; and
- clerk of works.

Where individuals are not named, provisions for the actions of an identifiable function may be made. For example, the contractor may be required to provide access or to co-operate in other ways with inspectors or to provide accommodation for a clerk of works.

The contract may also make clear the effect of directions issued by inspectors, architects, contract administrators, etc. To avoid defects being built in, it is advantageous for resident inspectors to be able to issue appropriate directions where they find incorrect work. Under typical forms of contract such directions are not binding unless promptly confirmed by the employer or their agent: traditionally the architect, engineer or contract administrator, who may have to consider – in addition to the technical issues – the cost and programming effects of condemning work.

To limit the scope for subsequent dispute it is important to ensure that the authority and duties of named individuals are made clear. For example, since the introduction of planning supervisors there has been some controversy over their actions on site.

Here, responsibility and authority to act is to some extent defined by statute. Where the role of a planning supervisor is dealt with in a building contract, it is important that the way in which this is done is consistent with statutory provision. There is some deliberate flexibility in these statutory provisions so as to allow the details of how to implement the regulations to be tailored to suit each project.

Traditionally the employer's obligation is to make payments as detailed in the contract and the contractor's reciprocal obligation is to perform the work in accordance with the contract requirements. These obligations contain the essential terms on which the contract is based. A breach of these terms can cause the contract to break down completely.

The employer's obligations may be extended to encompass requirements which are not of the essence, such as providing access or information as may be appropriate to facilitate the work.

The contractor's basic obligations to supply and build in accordance with the contract may be qualified to include any of the following: submission of valuations, submission of design proposals, carrying out of performance-specified work, sub-letting of specified work to named or nominated contractors, completion of the work by a given date or sectional completion in accordance with a set of scheduled dates.

At the outset, it is the employer's duty to obtain the necessary planning consents and Building Regulations approvals. This may be delegate to professional consultants or the employer may require the contractor to do this. Either way, the contractor is obliged by statute to build in compliance with applicable laws. Where, as is common, the employer's design team makes the necessary written and drawn submissions to the building control authority, this does not reduce the builder's duty to comply with the Building Regulations. Work which is constructed in breach of the regulations may therefore evidence deficiencies in the designer's work, the builder's work, or both.

Statutory obligations will apply regardless of the wording of a contract. This is recognised in many standard forms. See, for example, the references where appropriate in JCT forms to the Housing Grants, Construction and Regeneration Act 1996 and the Construction (Design and Management) Regulations. Such over-riding statuary provisions are often now referred to in standard forms of contract, making clear how they are to be dealt with under the terms of the contract.

Express terms

Although, technically, a contract does not have to be expressed in words to come into existence, it is the express terms which are looked to first when a dispute arises. It is nonetheless possible for terms of a contract to lack verbal expression. Agreement to a contract may be evidenced by action and terms may be implied.

For example, a householder may discuss with gardeners whether or not they would be willing to undertake some landscaping work. The gardeners may understand that conversation to be an invitation to do the work discussed and start working the following day. The householder may see the gardening start and do nothing. At the end of the week the gardeners may apply for payment. There may be an enforceable contract despite the lack of clear verbal agreement. The scope for dispute over the detail of the contract could hardly be greater but, at the root of the matter, the gardeners starting work evidences their acceptance of the contract they think the householder offered – and by opening the gate to let the gardeners in to start work the householder evidenced an implicit recognition of the existence of a gardening contract, requiring neither further discussion nor documentation.

In theory it makes no difference in law whether a contract is evidenced by action, agreed orally or written. The written agreement has the obvious virtue that the discipline of writing requires clarity of expression and will tend to throw up misunderstandings earlier in the process than will alternatives. It also offers the firmest reference point (contemporaneous record) if later disagreement arises over understanding the parties' intentions.

An agreement letter

For many projects a straightforward letter setting out the essential elements of the agreement to ensure that a contract is formed is often satisfactory. The key is to treat such a letter with the same care and attention to detail as a formal contract based on the standard forms. The letter should list what the builder is to undertake and be formally acknowledged and understood by all parties. The following illustrates what should be covered:

- a brief description of the project, stating clearly what the end product is to be;
- the design/specification information which is to be followed;
- the price of the work – if not a lump sum, then the basis for pricing;
- anything excluded from the price, e.g. who is to be responsible for unforeseen problems;
- access to the site and hours of work;
- any special terms of payment, such as interim payments, payments for unfixed materials, off-site work, etc;
- the programme, i.e. start and finish dates and any interim partial completion dates;
- whether the work can be varied without breaking the contract, and the effect of variations on price and programme;
- whether permissions have been obtained and, if not, who is responsible for obtaining permissions, for example statutory consents, relief from restrictive covenants, etc;
- who is responsible for design where it is not yet fully completed;
- any insurance matters;
- how any disputes will be resolved.

It is preferable for this to be done by exchange of letters, or for two copies of the one letter to be signed by each party and exchanged.

The standard forms of agreement

Unless suitable legal expertise is applied to the task, it is usually safer to use one of the standard forms of contract rather than to write them from scratch. Many are to industry-accepted standards and known by professionals and contractors. There are many standard printed forms of agreement intended for projects of a few thousand pounds upward.

Whether or not these standard forms are used, the most important consideration is good communication. Complex forms of contract which are difficult to understand are inherently unsatisfactory. Simplicity and clarity of language is the most desirable quality in all written agreements. Formal acknowledgement of contract documents helps avoid misunderstandings. Where contracts are formally executed, this is confirmed by all parties signing all parts of the contractual agreements.

Contracts where no professional is appointed

The simplest form of building contract is one between client and builder without any other parties, agent, etc. being named. The JCT publish a form for this called the 'Building Contract for a Home Owner/Occupier' which is intended to be for householders who engage a builders without any professional agent such as an architect to look after the job for them. As a general rule such agreements need to cover the following:

- The work to be done – this may be as set out in the invitation to quote, the quotation, specifications, drawings and any other relevant documents. The documents relied upon should be stated and, if appropriate, their order of priority and responsibilities for dealing with anything which is necessary but omitted from these documents.
- Identify who will be responsible for obtaining planning, building regulation and party wall approvals, etc.
- Identify the facilities which the contractor may use, e.g. electricity, toilets, telephone and water.
- State the agreed price and mechanism, if any, for variations.
- State how and when payments will be made to the contractor.
- State the date at which the contractor can take possession of the site and when the work is to be fully complete.
- If warranties are required these should be specified and the beneficiary of the warranty stated
- State insurance requirements and who is responsible for obtaining cover.
- Any limits on the contractor's hours on site should be stated.

- State how the works are to be accessed and precautions against intruders.
- The routes of dispute settlement can be stated if a particular method is preferred.
- State health and safety requirements.

Forms for architect (or engineer, etc.) designed and run projects

This approach is most suitable where clients:

- lack certainty over what they want;
- intend to participate fully in the design process;
- wish to explore design options and alternative strategies;
- require high-quality bespoke designs well developed before committing to a building project;
- prefer control and flexibility throughout the works;
- need to be able to vary their requirements during the contract period;
- want the building work to be independently monitored and controlled.

The JCT publish various forms for this, including The Agreement for Minor Building Works, The Intermediate Form and the 'With' and 'Without Quantities' variants of the main form. Typically such a contract should make the following clear, as a minimum, if the risk of disputes and failures are to be minimised.

The agreement

It is important to ensure that the agreement is consistent with the intentions of the parties as set out and amplified in its attached conditions.

> In a major central European building renovation project, the very copious terms and conditions made the contractor responsible for producing certain parts of the drawings but the agreement failed to make clear that the contractor had design responsibility. Much time and cost was wasted once the contract was entered into, and after disputes had arisen over the contractor's responsibilities for design. Had the wording of the agreement been more carefully considered and been written to be fully consistent with the attached terms and conditions, much costly dispute would have been avoided.

Intentions of the parties

The intentions of the parties should be set out to the extent that they have not been fully amplified in the agreement.

Chapter 1

Contractor's obligations

Typically the contractor will undertake to carry out and complete the work to certain specifications, drawings, schedules, etc. to an agreed standard, for an agreed cost and within the agreed time.

Employer's obligations

The employer will undertake to make payments at agreed times and on an agreed basis. Depending on the type of contract used, either the employer or the contractor may undertake to supply various documents dealing with the design of the works. It is important to be clear about the extent of each party's input into, and responsibility for, the design. It is also usually necessary to agree the access that the employer will provide to the contractor to carry out the work, when such access may start and whether it is to be continuous.

Programme

Commencement and completion should be clearly agreed. If the employer does not provide access on the commencement date, the consequence of this should be set out. If a completion date is not given there will normally be an implied term that the contractor will complete the work within a reasonable time.

The consequence of delay and late completion is best set out, as otherwise the almost inevitable deviations from the planned programme can lead to lawyers being engaged to resolve the most routine disputes.

Control of the works

Who can vary the specification, and under what circumstances, must be established. The terms of the contract can be varied by agreement, but not unilaterally unless provided for in the agreement. An employer may change their mind or a specified item may prove to be unavailable. A mechanism for dealing with this is usually desirable.

Payment

The price for the agreed works may be recited within the agreement. When and how payment is to be made is generally detailed in a contract clause. Note the basis of the price. A builder may have given an estimate, a quotation or a best guess. The agreement, if properly completed and executed, can fix the price for the works described in the contract to the sum stated in the contract, (unless the contract allows re-measurement and variation). Failure to confirm the price and payment method in a written contract leaves the builder's tendered prices open to interpretation and dispute.

Interim payments, while common practice in building, are not necessarily an implied right under a contract. If any payment is to be made before the work is properly completed – whether by way of advanced payments, payments for work off site, interim payment for work completed, etc. – this is best made clear in the contract.

Although it is common to hold retention money from each payment until the final payment, there is no implied right to do this. Ordinarily, five per cent of the sum due for each interim payment is retained, with half of this being released when the building is put into use and the remaining retention released after a fixed period – variously described as the 'defects liability' or 'maintenance' period. Who owns this retained money can be a matter for dispute. For it to come into existence it has to be agreed that it is due to the builder, but that payment of it is to be deferred. The employer retains it, as it were, on trust for the contractor who, arguably, has no right to use it for any other purpose and, insofar as it accrues interest, it is arguable that this is morally the builder's. There may be, as a consequence, a requirement for retention money to be held by an independent party.

Statutory obligations

All parties have an unavoidable obligation to comply with statute. Who does what to achieve compliance needs to be made clear. For example, if fees have to be paid for Building Regulations and planning approvals, directions as to payment should be included.

Injury, damage and insurance

Many contract forms place the contractor under an obligation to indemnify the employer against any claims arising out of, or in connection with, the works and to take out insurance to cover the obligation. This is to make sure that there is no gap in the insurance cover for the employer. An important point is that the insurance is the property of the contractor and a loss may initially be suffered by the property owner as any claim may be directed at them, especially if the contractor has ceased trading. Joint-names insurance is usually appropriate. Where external funds, mortgagors, etc. are involved, they will have an interest which may have to be acknowledged in the insurance arrangements.

Determination

These clauses set out what happens if it becomes necessary for either party to end the contract unilaterally before the parties' duties under the contract have been fully discharged. Such clauses should be invoked sparingly and then only where one party has fundamentally breached the contract. There are often other, less draconian, remedies for a breach of contract which should be considered first.

Dispute resolution

The current route to dispute resolution for most work in the UK is initially through adjudication. For most types of work, this will be an implied term unless dealt with expressly in the contract. Conciliation and arbitration clauses can be added, but these cannot remove the right to adjudication where statute requires this.

[6] For example: *Marshall* v *Lindsey County Council* (1935) 1 KB 516, 540 (CA), *Greaves and Co (Contractors) Ltd* v *Banham Mikle and Partners* (1975) 3 ALL ER 104 and McNare, J. *in Bolam* v *Friern Hospital Management Committee* [1957] 2 All ER 118.

[7] *Bolam* v *Friern Hospital Management Committee* [1957] 1 WLR 582.

[8] *Saif Ali* v *Sydney Mitchell & Co.* [1980] AC 198 at 220 D per Lord Diplock.

[9] Bingham, L. J. dissenting opinion in the Court of Appeal in the Abbeystead case (*Eckersley & Others* v *Binnie & Partners, Edmund Nuttall Ltd. & North West Water Authority* [1990] 18 ConLR 1).

[10] Damages for professional negligence are discussed in more detail in Chapter 8.

[11] This expert witness role is dealt with more fully in Chapter 11.

[12] See the Law Reform (Contributory Negligence) Act 1945, which is dealt with more fully in Chapter 12.

[13] Limitation to liability is dealt with more fully in Chapter 12.

[14] Companies Acts (1985, 1989).

[15] JCT Standard Form of Building Contract With Contractor's Design 1998 Edition, incorporating amendments 1 to 5 inclusive, Clause 2.5.1.

[16] See, for example, *Aughton Limited* v *M. F. Kent Services Ltd.* (1992) 57 BLR 1.

[17] *T. & R. Duncanson* v *The Scottish County Investment Company*; AC: 1030942 (1915).

Errors Before Construction

Inception/feasibility

The preparatory stages of a project are subdivided, in the RIBA Plan of Work, into work stages A and B. They are defined respectively as:

Appraisal –
Identification of the Client's requirements and possible constraints on development. Preparation of studies to enable the Client to decide whether to proceed and to select probable procurement method.

and

Strategic briefing –
Preparation of strategic brief by, or on behalf of, the client confirming key requirements and constraints. Identification of procedures, organisational structure and range of consultants and others to be engaged for the project [Identifies the strategic brief (as CIB Guide) which becomes the clear responsibility of the client].

Much in this relies on the client engaging fully with the designers. Where clients are inexperienced in construction, the building professionals engaged need to guide them through the role they have to play.

A poor understanding of client requirements and user needs can lead to flawed proposals. The best results come from wide-ranging preliminary discussion of a client's requirements and the exploration of alternative solutions, which may reveal possibilities greatly different from those originally envisaged.

This could lead to the preparation of alternative designs, or the abandonment of building altogether. Records of what is agreed should be kept.

The brief

A successful project starts in good co-ordination and the development of an effective brief. Briefs evolve with studies of feasibility and develop to embrace the design team's ideas, but they are initially an expression of client aspirations or needs. The firmer the clients' idea of what they want at the outset the more straightforward it is to write the initial brief.

Those uninitiated in building may, when first taking on the role of client, have difficulty in expressing their objectives clearly, causing the brief to develop through several stages. On large jobs, as the client's ideas coalesce they can be collated in writing for development into an initial brief. On jobs of all sizes, good communication is required to ensure the developing brief is understood and agreed.

Owen, determined to extend his house, took a pencil plan neatly ruled on graph paper to Archie, an architect. Saying he wanted to use the extension for formal dining, Owen showed his plan to Archie. Shortly after accepting the commission, Archie demonstrated that, by improving the use of the existing building, with a little adjustment to the circulation routes, he could, for the cost of altering two internal doorways and moving some furniture, achieve all that was wanted without extending the house at all. This proposal fully met the stated brief at a fraction of the cost Owen would have to pay to build what he had drawn.

The householder was not happy with Archie's ideas and kept coming up with new reasons why he still needed an extension. Archie returned and after looking around finally realised why his client was not convinced by designs based on function and economy.

Figure 2.1: **Defect-free building is as much a matter of understanding client goals as it is of achieving competent detailing and construction.**

The Jones's next door had just remodelled the front of their house to make it a splendid place to receive and entertain guests. Owen was impressed and wanted to match them in the extravagant-party-throwing stakes. Thinking it sounded silly to build an extension to keep up with the Jones's, he had come up with what he thought were practical reasons to extend the house. Central to what he wanted was a grander reception and entrance – the very opposite of Archie's practical and economic response to his stated brief.

Once the real purpose of the work was established, architect and client collaborated in remodelling the house front with flamboyant splendour.

Along with developing the brief and exploring the possibilities it is usually necessary to agree probable cost and available budgets at an early stage, to reduce the risk of later disappointment and dispute. Even where this is done, a failure to respect the client's requirements can lead to dispute and dissatisfaction.

A city commissioned a theatre from an architect at a fixed maximum budget for both fees and build cost.

The architect prepared a design and, assisted by a quantity surveyor, reported the projected build cost within budget. When tenders came in well over budget, the architect promised adequate savings during construction. In mistaken reliance on these assurances, the client agreed to build.

The architect, eager to make a name as a grand designer, found ambition incompatible with monetary constraint, and not only failed to achieve the promised savings but piled up additional cost – doubling the budget overrun.

In the resulting legal action, the architect argued that his building was of such merit that his actions were justified; indeed, it would have been worth paying even more to obtain such excellent architecture.

After the dispute had run some distance, the architect's insurers conceded a payment to compensate the city for the architect's misdemeanours but the compensation fell far below the overspend on the project.

In this case the architect benefited from the nature of his client. Had they been a commercial organisation, and the theatre built for profit, a larger claim might have been sustained against him.

The lack of standard formats for briefing documentation confuses many clients and adds to the difficulty of producing consistently good briefs.

Briefs need to contain four elements:

1. General – covering the broad parameters and functional requirements for the facilities, and matters of quality and form.
2. Financial – cost and expenditure as items in themselves but also related to the quality parameters in the General Brief.

3. Timescale – the project development and construction programme related to cost and quality.
4. Lifetime assessment – operating expectations, life expectancy, management and maintenance.

These four components require review at all stages of the evolution of the brief and require within the design team the different skills of designer, cost consultant, project planner and facility manager.

Site investigation

Design will eventually require investigation of one or more possible locations. These may be entirely vacant, or have existing structures on them requiring alteration or removal. They may or may not have been built on before. Preliminary investigation of vacant sites can profit from inspection of ordnance survey maps and other records – especially those held by local authorities and bodies responsible for water, drainage and other services.

No architect should need to be reminded that design has to take full account of its location and surroundings.

In Jersey a two-storey house with a cellar was built close to the sea. Shortly thereafter the periodic emergence of water and build-up of white deposits indicated all was not well in the cellar.

Investigation showed that this was due to sea water. A buried stream passed close to the house and drained into the sea. Tidal conditions periodically reversed its flow. At these times the reinforced concrete cellar was subject to attack due to the salt in the water and to hydrostatic pressure.

With hindsight it was obvious that a more thorough investigation would have revealed the need to design for this condition. The outlet of the stream was a few hundred metres from the house and clearly visible from the beach at low tide. The sea rose, at its highest monthly level, above the outlet from the buried stream, the high tide mark being discernible on the embankment around the outlet.

Because of the lack of care in inspecting the site and its immediate surroundings, the problem was not foreseen. A basement which was periodically sitting in sea water was incorporated in the design with insufficiently robust detailing. Sea water gradually worked through the concrete and the initial symptoms of localised occasional damp and growing salt deposits developed into periods of flooding. These were nothing compared to what was to follow, as the salt-laden concrete began to fracture beneath its surface.

It is necessary also to examine the site's surroundings. This has always been true but its importance is now broadened by statute in the requirements of the Construction (Design and Management) Regulations. The designer must take into consideration the health and safety implications of developing the chosen site as well as those that arise from the way in which the site is to be developed.

A failure to give proper consideration to all significant matters that constrain and influence a development in any particular location can greatly reduce the success of a building project.

Inadequate assessment of the potential of a proposed site for a project can lead to substantial wasted investment, which no amount of subsequent diligence and skill may be able to recover.

> A development in Israel required the construction of a highway, the positioning of which was constrained by the local geology and the need to tunnel part of it. The result was that the road was planned to pass close to existing flats and the tunnel had to be dug not far from them. Due to the geology and topography, construction – particularly vibration from the tunnelling – was likely to disturb the residents and traffic noise might cause annoyance.
>
> The developer had to contend with local regulations (which were changed during the early stages of the project) as well as potential claims from the residents. To address this, acoustic studies were required which led to advice on modifying the method of construction and on carrying out landscaping to limit the propagation of traffic noise in the open air – all of which increased the cost of the proposed development, and some of which extended the programme.
>
> The need to address noise and vibration was missed by the designers but raised by the residents when they learnt of the proposed development. By this time, the developer had entered building contracts and invested too much to pull out.
>
> A more thorough preliminary study would have raised awareness of these technical impediments and the impending change in the regulations during the inception of the scheme. This would have allowed a more measured appraisal of the commercial viability of the scheme before large sums were invested and building contracts placed.

Many problems can be foreseen and managed if proposed building sites are carefully appraised at the outset. It is beneficial to ascertain the limitations attaching to possible locations as precisely as practicable. This includes the wider environment as well as the building plot itself.

A Mediterranean coastal development suffered from a lack of regard to climate and terrain.

The mountainous backdrop to the development modified the weather patterns, often trapping humid air and occasionally funnelling driving rain through the site. The local building traditions were ill-suited to the site's microclimate, while similar construction further along, where the coast opened up, performed acceptably.

The style of building used was no more prone to condensation damage and rain ingress than other buildings along the coast, and in the sunshine they all performed equally well. This development unfortunately endured worse rain storms and longer periods of high humidity than was typical for the area. As a result, its performance was inadequate.

The nature and condition of the subsoil, drainage and vegetation can all affect the advisability of a development. The accessibility of the site and whether or not it is, or can be, supplied with mains services are often significant constraints on development potential.

It is increasingly likely for development to involve previously used 'brownfield' land where it may be necessary to deal with contamination, built-up ground and the buried remnants of demolished buildings. Geotechnical surveys, library research and general enquiry can all assist here.

It is often possible to find out much about the likely levels of contamination, risk of subsidence, possibility of flooding, etc. from local knowledge. Similarly, researching local history can provide some guidance on the likelihood of geological activity disturbing the site, flooding and the like.

Even more important than research and site investigation is the use made of the information obtained.

In a housing development in Wales, an action was brought against a developer of five houses which proved to be susceptible to flooding. The research, which this developer could have made but did not, was carried out retrospectively. This showed that the field on which he had built had flooded in the past. From this it was argued that he should have known not to build to the lower end of the field.

Fortunately for the developer the claim against him was unsuccessful, although he lost the cost he was put to in presenting his arguments in court. To prepare his case for the court hearing, he found himself paying for the same research, investigation and design analysis that would have been needed at the outset had he properly assessed flood risk before proceeding with the development.

Each of the Building Research Establishment (BRE)'s building elements series gives advice on typical defects, their symptoms, causes and remedies. With foundations, items prior to construction are especially significant. Checks on the adequacy of site surveys, previous flooding, shrinkable soils and proximity of trees are especially advised.

Settlement can be caused by building too close to trees, and heave by their removal. Inadequate stripping of existing vegetation may cause problems, as also may commencement of work too soon after tree removal, inappropriate pollarding and trees dying.

Choice of appropriate foundations should follow thorough investigation of ground conditions. Water tables, natural and piped drainage, frost hollows, vegetation and proximity to other buildings should be checked. The most common difficulties are reported to arise from building on fill, on shrinkable clay, or on compacted soils.

Foundations should be designed to accommodate unavoidable movement without unacceptable consequences – total immobility is impossible. For most buildings, typical unacceptable consequences include comparatively minor matters like unsightly cracks and difficulties with opening doors and windows. However the concern that such cracking and distortions causes to building occupants is far from minor – it can be difficult to accept that cracking and movement is not symptomatic of structural failure.

Even where a sensible level of investigation is made before work commences, there are risks of failure if the information obtained is not properly interpreted and applied.

A housing development in the north of England was built on made ground and shortly after completion some cracking occurred to a few of the houses. The cracking was sufficient to cause concern; although there was no evidence of likely collapse, there was immediately some difficulty in obtaining mortgages and building insurance for the cracked houses. The householders grew worried as property values dropped.

The houses were founded on piles. Prior to building, a geotechnical survey had been carried out and the piles had been tested sufficiently to show that they were capable of carrying the design load. The piles were driven down to firm bearing strata and linked by reinforced concrete capping beams, which supported masonry cavity walls.

One of the dynamic pile tests had given an anomalous result but nonetheless the piles had been shown to be capable of safely carrying the design load and work proceeded with no further investigation. Failure to consider the cause of this anomaly was the oversight which led to the cracking.

Whilst all of the piles, when loaded, would mobilise their end bearings and carry the applied load, they would not all mobilise skin friction to the same degree. Under load the piles will shorten. The deflection of each will depend on the support it gains from the ground throughout its height, with soft pockets of ground giving less support than firmer soil. Discontinuous patches of soft ground existed at high level and some piles passed through these patches.

Each wall was typically supported by three piles. Where the adjoining piles passed through markedly different ground conditions, this would result in differential shortening which, in turn, would cause deflection in the capping beam.

There is written authority that piles, when loaded, may typically deflect by 2–10 mm. That is, there is known to be a potential for up to 8 mm difference in the deflection of loaded piles. By calculation it was shown that the probable order of differential deflections on this site was 3–4 mm – sufficient to fracture the masonry without precipitating collapse. As the piles deflected and walls cracked, the loads were redistributed and the construction stabilised.

Once started, the cracks in the brickwork acted as movement joints, opening and closing as the temperature changed. These reciprocal movements caused the cracks to grow, giving the appearance of continuing progressive failure.

Figure 2.2: **Cracking through masonry owing to movements in the foundations.**

Had the foreseeable differences in the behaviour of the piles been allowed for in the design, the damage could have been averted. The geotechnical survey and pile tests contained all the information necessary to predict and prevent this mode of failure, particularly had attention been paid to the anomalous pile test result.

It was predictable that houses built for sale would be bought by people who required mortgages and building insurance, the providers of which are reluctant to take risks with buildings that appear to be suffering structural distress. In these circumstances, a relatively minor but very visible technical problem could severely compromise saleability.

Legal constraints

Statutory obligations

Failure to comprehend and accommodate statutory and civil obligations can lead to abortive work and expensive mistakes.

Statutory obligations grow steadily and include such things as, for example, the Town and Country Planning Act, the Building Act, Licensed Premises, the Party Wall Act, the Health and Safety at Work, Etc. Act, and numerous regulations promulgated under these acts, such as the Construction (Design and Management) Regulations.

The statutory instruments are relatively straightforward in that they are set down in written documents, limited to precisely what they say and often elaborated by official guidance notes or approved codes of practice (ACoP). In many cases these supporting documents contain an introduction stating their legal status.

For example, the Construction (Design and Management) Regulations are accompanied by an ACoP which has special legal status. It is a criminal offence not to comply with the regulations, and while following the code of practice is not mandatory it is proof of compliance with the regulations. If some way to comply with the regulations is achieved by means other than those set out in the approved code of practice, this is equally lawful.

Ordinarily it is the approved documents, codes and guides to the regulations which are relied on by those designing and constructing buildings. It is important nonetheless to remember the difference between the law, which is mandatory, and the guidance, which is not.

The Building Regulations were historically limited to a consolidation of health and safety requirements. This is confirmed in regulation 8, which states that '*the purpose of the regulations is to secure reasonable standards of health and safety for persons in or about buildings*'. More recent changes to the regulations have extended their remit to include such things as controls over water contamination, the conservation of fuel and power, and access and facilities for disabled people. This has the effect of bringing many more things under the control of the regulations than had historically been the case. As a consequence, there is an ever-increased risk that work may be carried out which requires approval under the regulations but for which approval has neither been sought nor given. For example, the replacement of a window in a house is now subject to Building Regulations approval although its repair may not be.

Whether or not a matter is covered by the Building Regulations is sometimes difficult to establish. The same is often true when considering the scope and application of other legislation such as the Construction (Design and Management) Regulations, etc.

A nursing home lacked common facilities. An architect, commissioned to correct its deficiencies, designed an extension to accommodate dining. A proprietary conservatory system, selected for the extension, was built by the supplier to their own details.

The health authority questioned the suitability of an uninsulated, fully-glazed room, with neither heating nor cooling, as all-year-round accommodation for the frail and old. They were not convinced that the residents' dining should be dependent on outbreaks of clement weather, and declined to accept this extension as bringing the nursing home up to standard.

The piped hot-water central heating system was extended into the conservatory. At about this time the local authority challenged compliance with the Building Regulations. Under their interpretation of the regulations, were it a conservatory it need not comply, but if habitable compliance was mandatory.

At the time this work was carried out, the Building Regulations did not contain a definition of what constituted a conservatory. The meaning of 'conservatory', taken from the dictionary, was based on its use and not its form: *'a greenhouse for tender plants; a room, esp. attached to a house, designed for growing or displaying of plants'*[18] and not, as is now the case under the regulations, defined by the amount of the enclosure which is glazed.

Three engineers were asked to prepare structural calculations for submission to the local authority to gain retrospective approval for the conservatory. The engineers diligently established that the conservatory structure, as it had been built, could not be justified by any science known to them. To obtain approval, as well as arguably to make the conservatory safer, a structural frame had to be built inside the conservatory and the conservatory attached to the frame.

The nursing home owner was successful in his claims against both architect and conservatory company.

Things such as mobile lifting gantries, and other machinery which is permanently installed in and attached to building structures, are an area of potential ambiguity in the application of regulations that apply strictly to building.

In a theatre refurbishment, a stage machinery suspension structure was to be installed to allow loudspeakers, stage lighting, etc. to be lifted and lowered, as needed, for each production. This was to be a pentagonal arrangement of aluminium lattice-work pocketed into and attached to the walls with moment connectors in five positions. It was not acceptable to make the lattices deeper than specified and not safe to attach them to the building roof to provide intermediate support.

The specified beams were too weak for the spans involved.

Because of the way the contract was written, if this work was covered by the Building Regulations the contractor was responsible for modifying it as necessary to ensure compliance. If it was not a matter controlled under the Building Regulations then it was less clear that the cost associated with the redesign of the beams should be borne by the contractor.

The client saw it as part of the regulated building work. After all, it was designed by the structural engineer, installed by the building workers and permanently connected to the building: 'If it looks like building work, it is building work and therefore subject to Building Regulations'. Further, it was argued that as the Building Regulations are in their essence a consolidation of health and safety requirements, and as the need to redesign this beam was essentially a matter of safety, this was properly the province of the Building Regulations.

A contrary argument was put forward on the following basis:

Screwing a bracket to the wall which was to hold, say, a loudspeaker or a lamp would not ordinarily be regarded as requiring approval under the Building Regulations. The aluminium lattice beams constituted no more than a large bracket to carry more than one loudspeaker or light. By analogy it was reasoned that this was not a matter covered by the Building Regulations.

It was also pointed out that, in accordance with regulation (2)(a), it is clear that the regulations distinguish between buildings, services and fittings. Certain services and fittings only are controlled and these are set out in parts (g), (h) and (j) of schedule 1 to the regulations. As the proposed work may be regarded as the installation of a service or fitting or both and as the work is not such that it would be covered by parts (g), (h) and (j) of schedule 1, it cannot be controlled by the Building Regulations.

The matter was settled and the contrary views on the applicability of the regulations were not tested in court.

Regulatory provisions often overlap, in which case it is ordinarily necessary to find solutions which comply simultaneously with all applicable regulations. Compliance with one applicable regulation is no excuse for non-compliance with another unless this is stated in the regulations themselves.

Property rights

English law of property is derived from custom, overlaid with statute, and can be confusing. A property right is a durable and transmissible right over property. These derive not only from ownership but also by way of easements, covenants, etc.

An important starting point in most building projects is to establish ownership of the land or buildings to be developed. It is also often necessary to research the ownership of adjoining property. This can include freehold or leasehold interests and any way in which these interests are compromised by licenses, easements and covenants. Commencing work on a development which cannot proceed because of, for example, a right of way results in abortive work. A client may regard such an action as negligent and seek to recover their losses from those employed to assist in the development.

Establishing the legal status of land is more a matter for solicitors than designers and builders but if the project team proceeds on the assumption their client has an unencumbered title to the land they may be wrong. It is better to confirm with the client that the necessary enquiries have been made and to recommend the client takes competent legal advice. The alternative, particularly with inexperienced clients, is that they will assume the designers and builder know what they are doing and that they have all of the knowledge and skills required to deal fully with the legal and technical aspects of the project.

Party structures

Party wall legislation is a particular area of difficulty.

A roofer undertook the renewal of a roof on a terraced house in Manchester. One edge of the roof was continuous with the adjoining house roof. The adjoining roof had deteriorated over the party wall and it was necessary to make minor adjustments to the adjoining roof to allow the renewed roof to be properly completed.

The roofer was a run-of-the-mill small roofing and cladding contractor and the householder was a single woman with no prior experience of building work. Neither had more than the lay person's grasp of the law. Predictably, no competent professional was consulted until matters went wrong.

The neighbour refused permission for the work to be carried into the edge of her roof. Leaking occurred at the party wall to the detriment of both properties.

The householder, when engaging the roofer, had assumed he could complete the work with no further input from her. The roofer made the contrary assumption that the neighbouring owners would resolve any problem at their party boundaries together. With unerring lack of foresight, they had not discussed the matter until compelled by the circumstances.

The current party wall legislation provided a mechanism to resolve the matter. The rights and obligations created by this legislation attach to the property owners. The woman whose roof was renewed was in breach of the Party Wall Act and was unwilling to take the necessary steps to use the Act to resolve the matter. The adjoining owner would not voluntarily co-operate, without which co-operation neither roof could be rectified. The roofer was held by both owners to be at fault but could not himself, as a matter of law, use the Party Wall Act to resolve the matter.

The roofer told his client what was necessary and offered, after the nearly completed roofing work had been stopped, to refer her to an architect who could advise on the relevant legislation and act as party wall surveyor under the Act. She declined both the offer and the architect's fee account which would inevitably have followed.

The developing owner, ostrich-like, was steadfast in maintaining her breach of the Act and in declining any troublesome advice which might expose her to further cost or acceptance of responsibility.

The roofer's hands were tied. As he had no title to the properties he had no right to invoke the mechanisms provided by the Act or otherwise to interfere in what was essentially a property dispute.

The householder had relied on the roofer and in so doing had assumed a level of legal expertise which he did not possess. The advice given by the roofer, which corrected this misapprehension, was given late.

The result: an impasse under two gently leaking roofs.

Even where proper attention is paid to legal boundaries in design, difficulties can arise on site.

A development in Worcester was hemmed in by surrounding properties. For maximum return, the development was taken to the very edge of the legal boundaries. To prevent dispute, the foundations were designed not to cross the boundaries into the land of those neighbouring owners who were opposed to the development. This created difficulties in construction.

> The site team did not appreciate the significance of this aspect of the design, particularly as the legal boundaries were to them nought but invisible concepts passing though muddy excavations.
>
> In constructing a basement, the builder ran the bottom layer of concrete wide of the site boundaries.
>
> The tanking was to be in asphalt and a non-traditional detail had been designed to avoid a toe of concrete and asphalt projecting over the boundary. The asphalter, seeing the projecting concrete, reverted to familiar tradition and ignored the drawings.
>
> The resident clerk of works, more familiar with traditional building than with property law, was unaware of the potential consequences and took no action.
>
> The fault was discovered by the architect during a routine visit after it was well advanced. Technically there was nothing wrong with the work other than its projection into land owned by others.
>
> However well built, the cellar could not be allowed to continue its trespass. Over two weeks were lost in cutting out the erroneous work and making good just because those on site did not properly appreciate the wider legal implications of departing from the drawn detail.

A common problem with the application of the Party Wall Act is boundary disputes. It is not clear under the Act whether or not party wall surveyors can settle boundary disputes, but knowing the position of the party boundaries is central to the correct application of the Act.

Estates in land

An 'estate in land' is more commonly called land ownership and is an interest in land, which is endowed with certain rights and obligations and carries a right to occupy or receive the benefit of that land.

In addition, there are non-proprietary interests in land, such as licences. There are also proprietary interests that fall short of being estates – mortgages, easements, etc. It is not always easy to distinguish an estate (particularly a lease) from a lesser form of interest, and courts are often called upon to make rulings in such cases.

There are now two forms of land ownership ('legal estates'). These are: freehold ('fee simple absolute in possession') and leasehold (the ownership of 'a term of years absolute').[19]

Freehold is a form of land ownership that is not derived from, or conditional on, the estate of another.

A lease is a form of estate in land in which the landlord confers the right of occupation of the land on the tenant for a fixed period of time. The lease is a limited form of ownership. The landlord continues to have an interest in the land. A lease has both contractual and tenurial features, and can be difficult to identify.

Identifying the existence of a valid lease is often important because it is capable of being enforced not only by the original landlord and tenant against one another, but against their successors in title. In addition, covenants entered into by landlord and tenant are also capable of 'running with the land', i.e. binding their successors in title.

The person from whom the leaseholder's title derives may be the freehold owner or another leaseholder with an earlier title.

In general, leases must be written to be valid.[20] Leases of over seven years may be registered.[21]

Flying freehold

'Flying freehold' is a colloquialism used for a freehold property that does not stand on its own land. For example, a two-storey house could be converted into two flats, one on each floor. The upper floor could be regarded as a flying freehold. The freehold for the upper flat would be of value only so long as the lower flat was properly maintained. In addition, a way to enter and leave the top flat that was not dependent on the owner of the lower flat would be required.

There are potential difficulties with flying freeholds. Restrictive covenants can be used, for example, to prevent the freeholders blocking each others' staircases. Imposing positive obligations on freeholders that would be binding through multiple sales of the properties may prove impracticable. For example, if several freeholders needed to jointly maintain a shared roof, they could not compel each other to contribute and co-operate. This difficulty could deter mortgage lenders and undermine the commercial value of such developments.

Easements

An easement is the right or privilege of using something not one's own. In English property law, easements are defined as an entitlement to rights over another's land. The right may attach to one piece of land, the 'dominant tenement', and be exercised over another piece of land, the 'servient tenement'. The right is limited to allow the dominant tenement to make a specific use of a property owned by another, for example a right of way across the property.

Easements are, as with much English property law, based on historic custom rather than statute. They may have come into use as a method to allow landowners to sell parts of their land whilst retaining rights over them.

An owner of a Victorian house with extensive grounds on the outskirts of Leeds wished to sell the house but keep some of its garden to build himself a more modern home for his retirement. The part of the garden which the householder wished to keep was at the back and the only access was from the highway at the front. To reach the retained ground he had to cross the land he wished to sell.

If this project had gone ahead without retaining a suitable right for vehicular access, the new house might, at best, have a much reduced market value or, at the worst, be unusable. A contract between the house owner and the purchaser might not create a permanent right of access as the agreement would exist between the contracting parties and not attach to the land. Either could sell their part of the land, potentially extinguishing the right of access.

Easements are obligations that 'run with the land', and are therefore attached to the title, not the owner. By creating an easement for the use of an extended drive, an enduring right of access is created.

A similar problem arose with the loss of an opportunity for 'back-lands' development in Kent. An inherited house in the hills above Folkestone came with some adjoining agricultural land where the householder grazed a small flock of Jacobs' sheep. Access to the land was via a narrow lane separated from the side of the house by a strip of lawn and a hedge.

Both house and sheep were sold. The sheep pasture was retained.

A scheme was devised to convert the three dilapidated farm buildings which stood in the pasture into valuable detached dwellings, each sitting discretely in large gardens. Had planning consent been obtained the value of the land would have risen, quadrupling the value of the inheritance.

The highways authority advised against the development because of the restricted access and particularly poor sight lines at the junction between the road and lane. Planning consent was withheld.

Had the proposed development been intelligently reviewed prior to selling the house, widened access and improved sight lines could have been drawn out and reserved as an easement without reducing the value of the house. Because it was not, the side garden and hedge became a 'ransom strip'. The new owner of the house could either prevent the development by refusing to release any rights over the land or alternatively could demand a disproportionately high price for accommodating the proposed development.

> The surveyors advising before, during and after the house sale did not make their clients aware of the impact on the development potential of the farmland that selling the house without providing for access across its side garden would have.
>
> Arguably these surveyors acted negligently and could be liable in damages for the lost development opportunity. The claim would, however, be to some extent speculative and has not yet been pursued.

Easements are a form of servitude[22] and therefore stop short of being rights of ownership. That is, an easement should not prevent the owner's use of the land. Anything that gives exclusive rights of access or occupation probably cannot be an easement.

Some easements are very much like covenants. For example a building could be built up to the boundary of a site, with windows placed in the wall on the site boundary. These windows could provide both daylighting and ventilation. Subsequent development on the adjoining land could block the windows, preventing their continued use. An easement of light or air provides an enduring protection to the function of the windows. This effectively requires open zones to be maintained over the adjoining land so that air and light can reach the windows. Such easements do not go further to, for example, provide a right to enjoy views from the windows. Developments can be built up around the windows as close as is consistent with maintaining the functions protected by the easements.

From a review of decided cases it is hard to establish the principles underlying the definition of an easement or to say exactly what is required for one to exist. The Court of Appeal has indicated the minimum conditions that must be satisfied as follows:[23]

There must be a dominant tenement and a servient tenement. Note that it is the 'tenement' (i.e. the title) that is affected, not the land in itself. Thus a tenant may have an easement against his landlord, even though the land is the same. However, an easement is extinguished if the dominant and servient tenements come into the same ownership.

The easement must benefit the dominant tenement. That is, it must benefit the land – not merely the owner for the time being.

The easement must be granted by a person or body who is legally competent to grant it ('lie in grant').

Some examples of rights that have so far been recognised as easements include rights of:

- access;
- light;

- water;
- storage;
- air; and
- support.

Easements come into existence in a number of ways:

- by grant: that is, an explicit creation of the easement by the owner of the servient property;
- by reservation: that is, where the buyer and seller of a piece of land agree that the seller should retain some limited right over the land being sold;
- by implication: where a court decides that an easement must be implied into a transfer of title, otherwise it would be ineffective (this applies in particular to rights of access);
- by prescription: where a long-established custom is seen as a right (e.g. rights of way).

A prescriptive easement cannot be gained for the 'illegal' use of land. For example the use of land for a purpose which is contrary to the Town and Country Planning Act, after the service of an enforcement notice or the commencement of proceedings seeking injunctive relief, cannot create a prescriptive easement. However, the use of land for a purpose which required planning permission but where such permission had not been obtained could create a prescriptive easement if enforcement action is not taken by the planning authority.[24]

Covenants

Covenants may be regarded as a modern form of easement. They are agreements between land owners to do, or refrain from doing, something.

For example, a lease may include covenants for repair by landlords or tenants or both. Covenants typically oblige the covenantor to refrain from doing something, like blocking a shared drain, or to carry out some specific action, like painting a house.

Covenants arise from agreements between parties, often in the form of a deed.[25] A covenant is distinct from an ordinary contractual agreement in that it attaches to the title to a property. Technically it is a property right or servitude which runs with the land and binds successors in title.

If Bert the builder builds a row of houses and sells them to Joe, Jim and Jerry, he can require each to contract not to block the shared drains.

If Joe sells his house to Susan, the obligation to maintain the drains may not be passed to Susan either at all or in a way which can be enforced by her neighbours. There is no contract between Susan and Bert. Under privity of contract, Jim and

Jerry could not sue Susan because they are not parties to the contract under which she bought the house.

If the obligation to maintain the drains is in the form of a covenant, Jim, Jerry and Joe have rights over each others' land, and those rights attach to the land not to the person. This means that when Susan buys Joe's house she does not have to extract a new agreement from Jim and Jerry. In this a covenant is similar in effect to an easement.

Licence

A licence to use property, as distinct from easements and covenants, is not a property right, and can be revoked at any time subject to contractual considerations. It differs from a lease as follows:

- Unlike a lease, which is an interest in land, a licence cannot be enforced against the landlord's successors in title.[26]
- A lessee has a greater protection from eviction than a licensee.
- A lease can be associated with covenants that are binding on successive owners. This is impossible with a licence.

Apart from exceptional cases, a person who pays regular rent for the exclusive use of a room, building or land has a lease.[27] Other than these exceptions, any person who is not a lessee must be a lodger, i.e. someone who receives some sort of services (perhaps cleaning or meals), or who is provided accommodation with their job.

When the feasibility of a proposed development is considered, it is important to find out not only whether the property to be developed is occupied but the basis on which occupancy is held. Ordinarily, if the occupant is a licensee or lodger unencumbered vacant possession is easier to obtain than if the occupant has a lease. However, the courts have, on occasion, treated a licence as being as enduring as a lease.[28]

In summary, although a licence is not a property right, in some circumstances it can be enforced against third parties as if it were.

A refurbishment in London was accepted as complying with the Building Regulations in respect of means of escape in case of fire because, in part, of the availability of a stair in an adjoining building. The ownership of the adjoining building changed and the agreement to allow shared use of the stair was ended. The local authority refused to allow the upper storeys to be put into use on the grounds that their use would cause the development to contravene the Building Regulations.

The arrangement to allow the stair to be shared was a personal agreement between owners which ended on the change of ownership. No easement had been established. The agreement had not been formalised as a covenant or licence. The use of the stair had not commenced.

The fire engineer devised an alternative scheme, which he thought met current guidance sufficiently to permit approval under the Building Act. The local building inspector did not agree. The developer was left with the choice of appealing the local authority's decision, reducing the scale of the development or finding an alternative.

Interestingly, he explored a novel approach. This was to complete that part of the work which the local authority would approve and get them to certify its compliance. Thereafter he submitted the remainder of the development along with the revised fire engineering design to an approved inspector, having already established that the approved inspector would accept the revised fire engineering design and approve the proposals. This approach has some difficulties but appeared not to be prohibited by the relevant legislation as long as certain procedures were carefully followed.

Design

Although in this book the familiar division of building projects into sequential work stages is adopted, it should not be forgotten that the prevention of defects through design involves a comprehensive approach.

Design considerations which are important to the development of conceptual design but which do not have to be confronted fully until detail design is commenced, are often postponed while the focus is on major design strategies. A lack of completeness when making strategic design decisions can turn what would be minor matters, if included in the strategic thinking, into discordant detail-design problems.

Increasingly, the preparation of production information is removed from the development of designs through the conceptual and outline stages. Large practices are often divided into 'designers' who create ideas but do not see them through – never learning of the detailing problems they create until a failure is caused – and 'technicians' who carry these ideas forward into working drawings – without having the authority to correct aspects of the outline design which impair the development of good detailing and the optimisation of the whole design. These gulfs in the design process may widen when a design concept is issued for development to a design-and-build contractor.

Detailing which is made difficult by an early lack of forethought often increases the risk of failures in the performance of the finished work. This risk is worsened when the detailing of the most difficult areas is studiously avoided by the person drafting the production drawings, thus confirming the maxim that 'the difficulty of the section drawn is in inverse proportion to the draughtsman's skill'.

An example of detailing problems created by a lack of integrated design thinking occurred in some multi-occupancy retail buildings open to the public and containing covered streets fronted by shops.

These were designed on mathematically strict grid systems and contained large public spaces to be used for organised public gatherings, exhibitions and the like.

The covered streets, under some weather conditions, acted as wind tunnels and the public spaces, designed with hard internal surfaces, suffered from strong multiple echoes which made comprehensible pubic address difficult and marred musical performances.

Alternative grid patterns which were acoustically superior without worsening space planning or appearance could have been considered from the outset. This would have assisted sound quality and reduced cost. The principles underlying the understanding and anticipation of the problem were known, having long before been experienced in other large covered spaces such as major railway stations. The acoustic peculiarities caused by reflective surfaces placed with mathematical regularity can be predicted. The avoidance of such problems is straightforward in the early stages of design. If left to be resolved in detailed design there are inevitable compromises, the overall performance falls below what was achievable at the outset and cost is increased.

The mathematical simplicity of the grid system was carried through the space planning, creating commendably clear circulation routes for both people and wind. Entrance doors could mitigate the occasionally high internal wind speeds but the correct placement of door assemblies was compromised by the space planning, which also rendered unachievable the required lobby dimensions to best control air infiltration.

The internal streets were designed to maintain the correct escape widths and were taken into account in the assessment of smoke evacuation. Door assemblies reduce escape widths and access for large objects and may impede air intake required during a fire to replenish that lost through smoke extraction. All this resulted in the need for door assemblies which would – with complete reliability – open on certain fire alarm activations and collapse outward under the pressure of an escaping crowd but close rapidly and hold back the strongest winds. The resultant door installations, due to their complexity, were prone to malfunction and required frequent maintenance.

These problems were addressed only in detailed design and their resolution required compromise, innovation and the application of some previously untried techniques and products.

Forethought during the initial design stages could have allowed flexibility in methods of accommodating the functions of smoke ventilation, emergency escape, access for large objects and wind control. The separation of these functions can lead to greater reliability and reduced cost. Because these problems were not considered timeously, the available design solutions were constrained.

The detailed design resolved the problems as far as was practicable without radical change to the scheme design. The buildings were effectively being repaired before they had been completed, with detailing which sought to mitigate shortfalls in the initial scheme design.

Clients may have sophisticated objectives, combining aspirations about appearance with detailed functional and operational requirements. The optimal design solutions for these requirements involve looking forward toward the detailed design whilst developing concepts and outlines. It often requires the flexibility to move back and forth between concept and detail to remove conflicts. In the best design the conceptual approach generates good detailing and the details reinforce the concept.

Approaches such as design for easy/economical maintenance, the re-usability of components, maximum lifespan and minimum ownership cost can be diametrically opposed to approaches which seek to achieve maintenance-free, fast-turnaround, low-build-cost or limited-life building. These and other considerations – such as breathing or sealed fabric, low energy use and ventilation – can all be taken into account in detailing, but optimum results come from the integration of design from concept to detail so that each complements and reinforces the other.

Objectives such as these involve not only the selection of appropriate components and materials but are also influenced by the choice of site and placement of a building in the landscape, taking advantage of natural features, orientation and massing – all of which control and limit what can be done in detailed design.

Designing for easy maintenance is often misunderstood. The vogue for requiring 'maintenance-free' materials can easily translate into 'non-maintainable' elements, which are impossible to repair once broken and actually present a long-term financial and environmental cost that is rarely factored into briefs. It is more sensible and ecologically sound to combine ease of maintenance with the selection of maintainable building components and materials. Timber lends itself well to this view of maintenance, and in this respect contrasts favourably with pvc-U which, paradoxically, is often sold as a low-maintenance material.

A range of details and specifications that ensure all elements are easily accessed, removable and 'layered' – to take account of differential weathering or wear of different elements – starts as a strategic design decision. This should be outlined early in the design process if it is to be adopted.

An example of the failure to consider these aspects of design occurred in the renovation of a tower block of seaside flats. The tower was over-clad in an insulated render and the windows were replaced with pvc-U double-glazed units, the render being returned at openings to seal to the window frames. The windows were inserted first into the checked reveals. Some of them proved incapable of resisting the rain-laden North Sea winds. Penetrative rainwater found its way through the hollow plastic frames into the walls, where it caused damage to internal finishes.

As is typical of pvc-U windows, effective *in situ* repair/improvement of the windows proved impractical. Window replacement involved either cutting away the new external insulated render or enlarging the window reveal internally.

Figure 2.3: **Not designing for foreseeable future maintenance can turn routine repairs into serious rebuilding work.**

Even had this problem not occurred, pvc-U windows have limited service lives which are often impracticable to extend by site maintenance. Consequently, they will require periodic replacement. Had ease of maintenance been included in the design strategy, the approach to detailing which caused the maintenance problem would have been avoided.

Concept and outline design

> The RIBA Plan of Work identifies outline proposals as Stage C, as follows: *Commence development of strategic brief into full project brief. Preparation of outline proposals and estimate of cost. Review of procurement route.*

The key things to avoid are inadequate assessment of and provision for user needs. The matters which have to be considered vary project-to-project, but problems commonly arise when the following are not addressed and agreed as design progresses from concept into outline proposals:

- durability;
- maintenance cost;
- suitability and appropriateness;
- flexibility/adaptability;
- function;
- appearance;
- heat;
- light;
- sound;
- ventilation;
- view;
- privacy; and
- orientation.

For example, noise nuisance can be addressed in detailed design by building structures to block and absorb sound, but can also be addressed in outline design by such things as the relative placement of spaces and orientation. Similarly, if a building is to be naturally ventilated the appropriate room dimensions have to be considered during outline design. Incorrect layouts, which prevent good natural ventilation, cannot easily be corrected by later detailing.

> A two-storey classroom block was designed as two rows of rooms opening off a central corridor. They were to be naturally ventilated through opening windows on one side only and were slightly over 6 m deep. In summer they overheated and were stuffy.

> The ventilation achieved by opening windows can be calculated, upon certain assumptions. Had such calculations been done, it would have been seen that the depths and heights of these rooms were inappropriate for natural ventilation unless openings were provided on two opposing sides, which, because of the design and need for acoustic privacy, could not be done.
>
> As a result, expensive alterations had to be made and the running costs were increased by the need to mechanically assist summer ventilation.
>
> The school's insurers and the architect's insurers are in touch through their lawyers.

Good conceptual design allows a range of viable approaches to be assessed and narrowed, leading to the identification of optimal choices which can then be developed in outline. As this work progresses, it becomes more and more a team rather than individual exercise. It is important that this team includes both clients and designers.

Progressing matters through planning approvals – particularly where historic structures or development in green belts, national parks and conservation areas are involved – can be problematic. It is not possible to guarantee approval to a proposed planning application, but failure to obtain consent can lead to dispute and non-payment of fees. It is always advisable to make clear whether payment of fees is to be contingent on the outcome of the application. Again, records should be kept.

It is sometimes necessary to revise schemes and to make repeated applications for consent. Requests for payments of additional fees for repeat submissions are often resented. Addressing this contingency in advance can deflect later dispute.

Difficult planning applications may be bedevilled by ill-considered client involvement. Where poorly informed clients meddle with the process, the scope for misunderstanding is worsened and the work for competent professionals can become more difficult and protracted.

Once disputes between client and architect start over planning applications, the architect's fees and competence are often challenged.

> Derek, a developer in Liverpool, wishing to develop offices, bought a piece of land containing two disused listed church buildings and a graveyard. He applied in person to the planning department, who declined approval pending receipt of drawings but were otherwise sympathetic to appropriate development to bring the buildings back into use and preserve much of the existing fabric.
>
> Derek hired a draughtsman and, armed with the single drawn elevation thus obtained, submitted formally for consent. The planning officer demurred,

suggesting a line drawing showing one elevation was insufficient. Undeterred, Derek asked an architect to work this elevation up into a set of floor plans and a couple more elevations. To his disappointment, this got him no further with the planners.

After about two years of proposal and rejection, Derek added another firm of architects to his retinue. These he engaged initially as planning consultants and later as project architects.

These consultants sounded out interested historic-building societies, English Heritage and the planning department. They examined the commercial and conservation aspects of the project and completed a proper submission to the planning authority.

Gaining consent remained difficult. Multiple applications as well as two appeals were made. After much delay, conditional planning consents were granted and allowed to lapse. A total of five planning and listed buildings consents in all were offered. These were subject to Derek's entering into a 'Section 106' agreement[29] and most expired whist Derek dithered over this agreement. A rather more durable conditional approval under the Building Regulations was also obtained.

After five years of negotiation and resubmission, accompanied by several partial redesigns at Derek's request, the consultants sued for unpaid fees and Derek countered, alleging a negligent failure to proceed diligently.

Although the consultants had kept copious records they were incomplete, leaving gaps in the evidence of proper diligence.

The fee dispute was complicated. As planning consultants, they started on hourly fee rates. As project architects, they proposed transferring to standard RIBA terms and conditions with stage payments on percentage fee rates. But Derek neither signed nor wrote to reject the contract of employment sent in these terms. He did, however, pay some invoices submitted on the basis of percentage fee rates.

The architects embarked on a reassuringly profitable reconciliation of their accounts, adjusting retrospectively onto percentage fee scales those fee notes issued previously on (under-recorded) time charges.

It was submitted that this was unreasonable. The architects' entitlement to repeat payments for making more than one planning submission was also disputed.

The first day of the hearing started with a vigorous debate in open court between Derek and his barrister over the way his case was to be presented. Unable to reach agreement he decided to try his hand at advocacy with his barrister on standby, ready to run on as a substitute when Derek ran out of steam. Both judge and barrister frowned on this somewhat untraditional approach and Derek found himself acting as litigant in person without legal counsel, whereupon he proceeded ably to lose every part of his case.

Detailed design, production drawings, specification

The RIBA Plan of Work deals with detailing and production information as follows:

Work Stage D: Detailed proposals – *Complete development of the project brief. Preparation of detailed proposals. Application for full development control approval.*

Work Stage E: Final proposals – *Preparation of final proposals for the Project sufficient for co-ordination of all components and elements of the Project.*

Work Stage F: Production information is now in two parts: F1 – the production information sufficient to obtain tenders and F2 – the balance required under the building contract to complete the information for construction.

Work Stage F1 – *Preparation of production information in sufficient detail to enable a tender or tenders to be obtained. Application for statutory approvals.*

Work Stage F2 – *Preparation of further production information required under the building contract.*

In current practice the technical design for building can be divided into detailing and production information. Terms such as 'working drawings' are deprecated because of the wide range of different meanings they have acquired through variations in custom.

Detail design sets out the principles to be adopted for the construction of each part of the building sufficiently to show compliance with regulations, what materials are to be used and how combined. It embraces both written and drawn information and typically shows standard conditions which, adapted as necessary, repeat throughout the building.

Production information takes the principles set out in detailed design and applies them to each condition to be built. In small simple jobs, distinguishing between detailed design and production information may be artificial. It is rare for all conditions to be drawn and many aspects of building design are traditionally resolved in work as they arise.

Production information should communicate adequately, unambiguously and clearly what is to be built. Properly prepared, it leaves the worker on site with no design decisions to make other than those which may be seen as the application of trade skills – for example, the joiner selecting the number and type of fastenings to fix a painted softwood skirting in place.

The importance of good communication through the production of written and drawn information is illustrated by the following dispute. As is often the case, it was symptomatic of failing relationships and a broader range of problems but it first crystallised around a lack of certainty in the interpretation of the drawings.

An architect produced a design for a new house. On that design he had indicated the position of shower cubicles by drawing a square on the plan.

When, during the contract, the contractor was asked to provide shower trays and fittings of a particular quality, he indicated that the contract did not require him to install shower trays at all. The architect drew his attention to the symbols which he said represented shower trays. The contractor stated that he could not know that the rectangle shown on the plan was intended to be a shower tray and that he had not allowed for them. In view of the quality of the works, this ambiguity over the interpretation of the drawing gave rise to an argument over several thousands of pounds.

The drawings, read in conjunction with the specification, were open to interpretation. There was no cross-referencing between the drawings and the specifications and no notes on the drawings to explain the meaning of the symbols used. It was the architect's contention that he had used a conventional symbol and the builder's contention that this convention was known only to the architect.

Very often the detailed design drawings cover standard conditions but neglect one-off and atypical situations. These are likely to include the points where good design details are most needed.

Detail design is often spread over consultants' general details, manufacturers' workshop or 'shop' drawings and specialist suppliers' or subcontractors' drawings. Where the work is to be split between contracting parties it can result in omitted and incompatible details, often leading to expensive disputes if the scope and detail of what each is to do is not clearly defined at the outset.

The conversion and extension of a historic Hungarian building to form a new hotel gave rise to much debate over drawing practice and terminology.

The first part of the confusion came from specifying each part of the work in one place by reference to Hungarian standards and in another by reference to US standards. On top of this the contract had two languages: certain of the documents were written in English and translated into Hungarian, and vice versa. In case of dispute over the meaning of the translated documents, the Hungarian version was said to take priority in relation to certain of the documents and the English version in relation to other documents. In relation to the drawings and specification, English was stated to take priority. The English used appeared in part based on Canadian usage but much of it had been written by people who did not speak English as a first language.

The contractor was responsible for producing certain drawings and the consultant architect for producing others. In this contract the term 'architect' included engineers, etc. and the practice was set up as a multi-discipline office. Therefore no distinction was made or needed in the contract between consultant architects' and engineers' designs.

The drawings the architect had produced, and was to produce, were shown in two separate schedules which formed part of the contract. The drawings the contractor had to produce were not scheduled.

In various places the contract defined the design work which fell to each party. Amongst these definitions was a clause which stated that the architect was to produce working drawings which were sufficient for the execution of the work. The 'work' was defined as the supply of materials and building the project but not design. Taking these two definitions together it was clear that the architect's drawings should not need any elaboration to allow the building to be built. The architect, however, did not complete the production information and expected the builder, through his specialist subcontractors, to develop the architect's detailed designs by producing what he referred to as 'shop drawings'. 'Shop' and 'engineering' drawings were, under the contract, the contractor's responsibility but the terms were not defined.

The scheduled drawings were listed by topic only – there being no indication of scale, size, work stage, etc. It was therefore possible, from the schedules, to see what the architect was to draw but not how much detail he was to go into.

In the event the architect's drawings went as far as showing the principle on which the detailing was to be done, but did not show all of the details which were to be constructed.

The contractor, in order to progress the work, filled in the gaps in the architect's drawings by producing additional drawings. These drawings were subject to a review procedure by the architect and the employer. These reviews were done by way of inconclusive commentaries which gave the contractor no certainty over what he should do, and the project slipped inexorably into delay and debate.

The process of the review of the contractor's design was carried seamlessly from ambiguous commentary on drawings to condemnation of aspects of what was being built on site. The workers became dejected, to the detriment of speed and quality.

> The result of the uncertainty over the status of drawn design was wasted effort, endless bickering and a complete breakdown of the team spirit. This detracted from the potential of the project and lead inexorably toward very expensive international arbitration.

Where the design of a building is split between contracting parties it is important that the responsibility of each party is set out in clear unambiguous terms. In this case the casual use of expressions like 'working drawings' and 'detailed drawings' gave rise to misunderstanding and dispute.

Designing for workmanship

A designer needs to make reasonable provision for workmanship error and take into account the risk of imperfect work in site conditions.

> This was affirmed in a decided case relating to defective tanking to a basement built into well-drained chalk.[30] The construction was *in situ* concrete and concrete masonry, tanked externally with a bonded sheet waterproofing. Following good practice, a land drain was placed externally but, contrary to best guidance, it was higher than the bottom of the waterproofing. A subcontractor carried out the work to designs provided to him.
>
> The completed basement leaked after heavy rain. Internal water-resisting render was applied and money was withheld from the subcontractor. Law suits ensued.
>
> The design was argued to be faulty for the following reasons:
>
> 1. Clause 3.3 of BS 8102, *Code of Practice for the Protection of Structures Against Water from the Ground*, states that the designer should:
>   (i) Consider the consequence of less than adequate workmanship,
>   (ii) Consider the consequence of leaks, and
>   (iii) Consider the form and feasibility of remedial work.
> 2. Clause 3.1.1 of BS 8102, *Pre-Design Considerations*, recommends that basements should include provision for resisting a pressure equivalent to at least 1m head of water.
> 3. By installing the land drain in the position shown, the designers created a head of water that would bear against the membrane. In these circumstances, any defect would constitute less-than-adequate workmanship, as the consequence of those defects would be flooding through the membrane into the basement.

4. It is not realistic or reasonable to expect a bonded sheet membrane to be applied without any defects at all.
5. The interpretation of the above was that a design team must anticipate that defects will occur in a membrane, and so must design a system in such a way that water pressure is removed before it comes to bear against the membrane. If they are unable to achieve this, it is implied that an alternative form of waterproofing must be used.
6. Furthermore, a bonded sheet membrane is only one element within an overall waterproofing system. The membrane, together with the drainage and the structure, all form part of the system and must be considered together. No one element should be considered in isolation.

The counter argument contained the following:

1. Clause 3.1.1 of BS 8102 says that the membrane alone must be capable of withstanding a head of water of at least 1m without leaking.
2. The installation of the land drain above the floor slab did not induce a water head in excess of 1m, and so the design complied with BS 8102.
3. In the absence of a design fault, the problem has to lie with the installation of the membrane, by default.

Unreserved judgment was given in the subcontractor's favour. Despite the certainty that water must enter though flaws in the tanking, the existence of which must evidence errors in workmanship, the design was blamed for lacking provision for this eventuality and the workmen exonerated. This decision is directly contrary to the findings in some other cases dealing with comparable matters.

Good design addresses the ways in which the work can be done, the circumstances in which it is to be done and seeks to match the tasks it creates for tradespeople to the skills they can reasonably be expected to bring to it. Working in a muddy excavation, in exposed conditions with rolls of relatively delicate material, which has to be kept clean whilst it is stuck to site-formed surfaces, has its difficulties.

The manufacturers of sheet tanking membranes generally claim them to be capable of working as an effective water barrier. Designers have to place some reliance on manufacturers' published guidance when using proprietary products. This does not excuse the reckless abandonment of tried-and-tested design solutions. Traditionally, where tanked construction was desired it was considered wise to combine it with water-retaining concrete or engineering brick and land drainage to relieve water pressure before it builds up against the tanking. New waterproofing systems are available which, from the manufacturers' literature, are capable of maintaining dry basements without reliance on anything but a supporting structure.

As with all aspects of building, designers must decide whether to draw on published guidance derived from long experience or to rely exclusively on manufacturers' claims. In making this decision they must assess whether or not a product's potential can be achieved on the site in question. This will depend on a range of factors, such as: the availability of trade skills and of materials, the working conditions, facilities for storage and supervision. If the designer cannot control for these, it would be prudent to consider fail-safe solutions or to design-in sufficient redundancy to lessen the likelihood that ordinarily poor workmanship will result in failed performance.

Designing for movement

One characteristic of most common building materials is that they move, both in response to directly applied loads and in sympathy with changes in ambient moisture and temperature levels. Designing for this means allowing buildings to be essentially flexible, and accommodating less flexible or brittle materials – such as glass – by suitable provision for differential movements and detailing to prevent this becoming a problem. Whilst seemingly a small issue, taking full account of this when designing fundamentally changes the way one thinks about building, especially in combination with the issue of 'breathability'. In this, much can be learnt from traditional detailing.

The rate of movement of building materials varies. Typically, heat causes expansion and cooling causes contraction. For each material which expands uniformly with temperature rise, the relationship between the change in temperature and change of size is a constant – called the 'coefficient of linear expansion'. Materials do not necessarily expand uniformly with changes in temperature. For example, the dilation of a fibre-cement sheet for a 1 °C temperature rise depends on its initial temperature. Nonetheless, within the temperature ranges ordinarily experienced in buildings, the coefficient of linear expansion provides a useful guide to thermally induced dilations and contractions.

For materials which can absorb water, wetting typically causes expansion and drying contraction. Materials which are impermeable to water tend to be dimensionally stable when wetted. For most common man-made building materials hygral movements are small compared to thermal movements. Wood, and composites containing wood, typically move more on wetting and drying than heating and cooling (provided they are not burnt).

These hygral and thermal movements are reciprocal: if the moisture and temperature are returned to their original values the original sizes are restored. This does not necessarily preclude accumulative movements. Temperature changes, dilations and contractions may occur more rapidly in some materials than others. This, in combination with variations in the restraints to which parts of buildings are subject, can cause accumulative movements.

A cladding system designed to accommodate differential movements between an aluminium frame and metal-faced insulation-cored cladding panels experienced gradual displacement of building components as the gaskets snaked their way along the grooves between shuffling panels.

The panels, being small, elongated less on heating than the relatively long frame sections. The connection between the two was a combination of shelf brackets and clamps, with polymer gaskets inserted tightly into grooves between the panels to complete the weather-sealing. Long continuous gaskets ran horizontally; vertical gaskets were shorter, and discontinuous at each horizontal joint.

When the system heated up and expanded, the panels and vertical gaskets tended to move upwards. When it cooled, the panels and gaskets contracted but did not uniformly return to their original positions. The consequence was a gradual displacement of parts of the system relative to one another. This opened gaps at the butt joints between horizontal and vertical gaskets and, in places, drove the vertical gaskets into the horizontal gaskets, deforming them. Those panels on the elevations which received most sunshine moved progressively out of alignment.

The design was intended, by avoidance of rigid fixings, to allow reciprocal movements without distress. But this lack of rigidity allowed each reciprocal movement to cause slight relative displacements in the panels and gaskets, the accumulation of which over time reduced weather resistance and marred appearance.

Restrained materials will dilate or contract less than free materials. The restraint of naturally occurring dimensional changes causes a build-up of stress within the restrained material. This creates a propensity to fail, which needs to be anticipated and limited if cracking is to be prevented.

A material such as wood may shrink on heating, as heat may dry the wood and thus cause contraction. Concretes expand on heating, unless sufficiently hot for the heat to drive water out of the cement matrix so as to alter its 'phase'.[31] Bearing in mind such exceptions, within normal limits the effect of changes in the ambient temperature due to fluctuations in the weather is to cause swelling on heating and shrinkage on cooling.

Good detailing accommodates the normal range of reciprocal movements in the specified materials.

Designing for a healthy environment

The existence or otherwise of 'sick-building syndrome' is a matter of debate and, while informed opinion is divided, it has been popularised as a result of the trend towards artificially-ventilated, hermetically-sealed building, in which detailing typically minimises ventilation losses through the fabric. Reducing uncontrolled ventilation lessens the building's ability to 'breathe' and 'perspire'.

Ventilation through the building fabric is likely to be lessened further by continued revisions to the Building Regulations, to require ever-higher levels of energy efficiency in buildings. The Building Regulations 2000, in Part L1, stipulate a robust approach to minimising uncontrolled ventilation losses from houses and, in Part L2, impose a more stringent approach for other buildings. Whether or not this will cause ill health to the occupants, it certainly may harm the building fabric if done without enough thought – as illustrated by the developing problems of interstitial condensation, which grew in pace with the introduction of energy-control measures during the last century.

The traditional open fire in poorly insulated buildings, whilst inefficient, had advantages. As the fire was built up it drew air through the room and expelled expiated air along with the smoke through the chimney. Waste heat passed through the uninsulated walls, driving out moisture. The more vigorously the fire burnt, the better the ventilation, the higher the heat flow through the fabric and the more potentially harmful moisture was dispelled.

The replacement of the open hearth with the distribution of heat via hot-water pipes to well-sealed and insulated rooms was accompanied by an increase in condensation damage. The better the rooms were sealed and insulated, the more the condensation risk. Heating was no longer accompanied by ventilation to remove vapour, and the well-insulated building envelope remained cold on its outside whilst heated internally. The result was raised internal vapour pressures, colder parts of the building fabric and the accumulation of condensate in concealed voids within the building envelope. Condensate can eat through lead and corrode steel, as well as encouraged organic decay and potentially harmful environments.

As these injurious side effects of the 20th century's strides into energy-efficient building were recognised, steps were introduced to prevent collateral damage. These followed, rather than preceded, improvements in thermal efficiency: the process was one of failure followed by remedy. Further improvements in energy use, which the EU propose to move on apace, risk a continuation of this process. The rise in asthma in the UK closely shadows the increase in energy-efficient building since the 1970s fuel crisis.

Certain matters are indisputably related to the health of building occupants, such as the need to keep them sufficiently warm in cold climates to prevent hypothermia. Conditions of humidity conducive to mould and fungal growths may also be seen as a health issue, in that released spores may be harmful – particularly to asthmatics and those with weak immune systems.

Exposure to any mould can cause allergenic effects such as skin rash, flu-like symptoms and, on some views, depression. It is not the moulds but the toxins they create which cause the severest risk to health. Typical toxin types such as aspergillus, stachybotrys and trichoderma create extremely toxic mycotoxins.[32] (Known as 'T2 toxins', these have lethal military applications.)

Causal links between building design and health problems such as asthma are not proven, but the following have been implicated:

- the release of mycotoxins from mould and fungi;
- the release of volatile organic compounds (VOCs) from cleaning agents and building materials;
- inadequate ventilation or filtering to reduce concentrations of animal dander, dust mites, gases and fine dust;
- conditions conducive to bacterial growth and circulation.

The creation of healthy internal environments, including the control of relative humidity, is a critical issue in building design. The ambient humidity in a room affects many of the biological, bacterial and physical causes of ill health. It has been argued that controlling this through air-conditioning can increase the problem. Passive control of humidity relies heavily on the porous and hygroscopic nature of certain materials. Surfaces such as timber, plaster and clay will regulate ambient humidity as long as they are not given impervious coatings, such as some conventional paints and varnishes, which obstruct the natural hygroscopicity of these materials.

Some problems associated with air-conditioned buildings have given rise to specific regulation and guidance. For example, outbreaks of legionnaires' disease have resulted in an approved Code of Practice for the control of legionella bacteria in water systems.[33] During its currency, this code, which applies to certain business premises, is enforceable under the Control of Substances Hazardous to Health (COSHH) Regulations and the Health and Safety at Work Act (HSWA) 1974, and has special legal status. It is difficult but necessary for building designers to be aware of all such regulations and codes as they are imposed, revised and withdrawn, if they are to avoid putting their clients at risk.

Product assessment

To asses building products the specifier must consider both the building systems and the materials involved. Field experience is to be preferred over claims based on research and development. Proven engineering principles provide fewer pitfalls than does the application of new techniques and products.

For new materials and products, reliance has to be placed on the reported results of the research and testing which went into the development of the new material or building system. With certain types of products and in certain jurisdictions, reliance on test certificates is compulsory. For example, in Poland it is usual to require a building product to have a 'technical approbation' certificate before it can be put into widespread use. The Polish Building Regulations then require the product to be used entirely as set out in this certificate. The body which tests and issues technical approbations is an official institution.

In contrast, in the UK no certification is required and anyone can lawfully offer their inventions for use in building with no independent endorsement of the underlying science. There is a 'halfway-house' offered by the British Board of Agrément. The Agrément Board can be hired by product manufacturers to test their products. If in the view of the board the product performs as intended, they issue an Agrément Certificate. This is unique amongst test certificates in the UK in that compliance with an Agrément Certificate can evidence conformity with the Building Regulations. It remains a voluntary arrangement, under which the lack of, or non-compliance with, Agrément certification is perfectly lawful.

It follows that well-established products are unlikely to have Agrément Certificates because their use and acceptability has been long proven before the invention of such certification. However, new and novel products are increasingly likely to be submitted to independent testing and certification. It is thus likely that the least reliable products are amongst those promoted by test and certificate.

Properly conducted tests are certified by reference to the parameters covered by the tests and the limits of their validity clearly stated with the results. A clear under-standing of this is essential where reliance is placed on testing to establish the quality of a product. For example, a sealant may, by test, be shown to provide one hour's resistance to fire. To demonstrate this it may have been exposed to fire when placed between two pieces of concrete in a gap of a certain width and to a controlled depth. The sealant may then be sold with a claim that, at the width and depth used in the test, it has a one-hour fire rating. But the test certificate will apply when the sealant is used as a filling in a concrete sandwich only. If used between, say, wood and brick the certificate will not apply but this is rarely apparent to the user from reading the sales literature. Results are valid within the limits of the test carried out, and careful study of the certificates is required if reliance is to be placed on certified test results.

Where testing is carried out in-house as part of the development of new and improved products, the results are rarely made public. Without this it is difficult to make informed decisions when evaluating the assurances given by the product manufacturers.

One method commonly used for assessing materials is the approval of samples. This can vary from examining products in order to select those of preferred appearance, to building trial installations to test the ideas behind the design. An alternative is to visit existing buildings where the material or product being assessed has been used, to see how it is performing and to enquire of the building users whether it gives satisfactory performance. Both of these processes provide good bases for evaluating quality and performance.

To make an evaluation, particularly where unproven combinations of materials are being considered, it is helpful to understand the behaviour of the proposed structure and the properties of materials.[34]

New and salvaged materials

For new materials there are usually written guides on correct use, whether from manufacturers' instructions for proprietary products or from standards, codes of practice and text books for traditional materials. Second-hand materials require the adaptation of these written guides and may not reach the standards specified for new materials.

Using second-hand materials has both advantages and disadvantages. For example, salvaged roofing slate is often reused and its advantage – apart from cost and environmental benefits – is that faults will have been exposed by prolonged weathering. The disadvantage comes from wear at nail holes and the difficulty of adhering to published guidance. Often where second-hand materials are to be used it is necessary to consider the standards which will be required and to identify at an early stage the compromises to be accepted. Specifying 'new' standards where recovered materials are to be used is a recipe for later disappointment and dispute.

[18] *The Shorter Oxford English Dictionary.*
[19] The Law of Property Act (1925).
[20] Section 2 of the Law of Property (Miscellaneous Provisions) Act (1989).
[21] The Land Registration Act (2002).
[22] A servitude is a form of property right that falls short of full ownership, and yet is binding on successors to title in a similar way to ownership.
[23] Re *Ellenborough Park* (1956) Ch. 131.
[24] *Neaverson* v *Peterborough Rural Council* (1902) 1 Ch. 557 and *Hanning* v *Top Deck Travel Group Ltd.* (1994) 68 P& CR 14 (CA).
[25] A legal document intended to bind its signatories to strong legal obligations. A deed has historically been associated with the requirement that it be 'signed, sealed, and delivered'. In recent years what distinguishes a contract by deed from a contract under hand is the wording used and the way it is delivered.
[26] *Thomas* v *Sorrel* (1673): a licence as something that '*properly passes no interest nor alters or transfers property in any thing*'. (But see also Lord Denning in *Errington* v *Errington* (1952) 1 KB 290 and *Binnions and another* v *Evans* (1972) Ch. 359, CA).
[27] See Lord Templeman's speech in *Street* v *Mountford* (1985) 2 WLR 877, in which he defined a lease simply as '*exclusive possession for a time at a rent*'.
[28] *Binnions and another* v *Evans* (1972) Ch. 359, CA.

29 Town and Country Planning Act 1990 Section 106 Agreements secure community infrastructure to meet the needs of residents in new developments and/or to mitigate the impact of new developments upon existing community facilities. To secure this benefit to the community, the applicant is required to enter into a separate agreement regulating development or use of land, with the planning authority, as a condition precedent to receiving planning consent.

30 *Outwing Construction* v *Thomas Weatherald,* 13 September 1999, Case no. 1998 O 011, AC 1027198.

31 In this context 'phase' is used to describe a physically distinct and homogeneous form of a substance characterized by its composition and state and separated by a bounding surface from other forms. If the water removed from the concrete is free, drying does not alter the phase of the cement. If the water removed is released by extracting the water of crystallisation from hydrated cements or otherwise is extracted by decomposing compounds in the concrete, phase changes may be said to occur and heating and cooling may not cause dilations and contractions respectively.

32 The chemical contents of the mould spore are known as metabolites, some of which are mycotoxins that are in effect microbial Volatile Organic Compounds (mVOCs). It is these chemicals which cause health problems.

33 The Approved Code of Practice (ACoP) for the control of legionella bacteria in water systems came into effect on 8 January 2001.

34 See Chapter 5, The characteristics of materials, p. 107.

Errors During Construction

Building procurement

The RIBA Plan of Work deals with building procurement in three stages as follows:

Work Stage G: Tender documentation – *Preparation and collation of tender documentation in sufficient detail to enable a tender or tenders to be obtained for the construction of the Project. [Solely concerned with the documentation required for tenders. Particularly useful with Design and Build or management contracts].*

Work Stage H: Tender action – *Identification and evaluation of potential contractors and/or specialists for the construction of the project. Obtaining and appraising tenders and submission of recommendations to the client.*

Work Stage J: Mobilisation – *Letting the building contract, appointing the contractor. Issuing of Production Information to the contractor. Arranging site hand-over to the contractor.*

Preparation

Knowledge is what you get from reading the contract. Experience is what you get from not reading it. Many disputes arise because one or other of the parties to a written contract assumed, rather than read, its contents.

A well-drafted contract comes from a good understanding of the employer's requirements. Where the use of standard forms is appropriate this has the advantage of neutrality and accumulated experience. Where a bespoke contract is the best option this relies on legal expertise as well as knowledge of construction.

Having settled the form of contract it is then necessary to match the production of information to it. For a well-run project the development of the brief will have anticipated the appropriate contractual arrangements at an early stage so that the production of information can progress accordingly, ensuring the information provided with the tender invitation suits the form of contract envisaged. The following are generally desirable:

- Consistency and compatibility between the terms of each contract used for each member of the project team.
- Where a contract is evidenced in writing by more than one document, the order of priority of the documents should be set out.
- Take care when setting out matters of detail, as if these are in an incomplete form it can lead to dispute and disappointment. For example if a specification says 'the work is to include: a, b, c, d and e', this may be taken to imply it excludes anything else. If, instead of this list, the specification states 'the contractor is to allow for everything necessary for completing the work', it leaves open for future debate what is necessary and, where there are alternatives, what has been allowed for.

Preferred options may be included by combining the lists and general requirements, e.g. 'the contractor is to allow for everything necessary for completing
the work including – inter alia – a, b, c, d and e.'
- Be clear about the distinction between prescriptive and performance specifications
(see p. 77 for an explanation of the two).

Fixed-price contracts

It is a common desire for clients to fix in advance the cost, quality and scope of a
building project.

If complete certainty is required, a simple lump-sum agreement may be appropriate
(see Chapter 1, Traditional/conventional supply-and-build contracts), but most
standard forms are unsuitable as they provide mechanisms for revaluing the
payments due. Before they enter into a building contract, it is wise to ensure
employers fully understand the scope for costs to vary.

Lump-sum contracts require maximum certainty over what is to be done when
building prices are obtained. Builders cannot be expected to price accurately for
tasks which they cannot foresee. As there is always a risk of the unforeseen occurring,
there is always some uncertainty over cost. The contract sets out the basis on which
unforeseen costs will be apportioned between the contracting parties.

The ability to obtain meaningful lump-sum prices depends on the quality of information provided in the tender invitation. Many disputes arise where an attempt is made
to enforce a lump-sum price obtained on insufficient detail.

Where tender information is incomplete, drawings and specifications have to be
prepared and issued during the work to provide the additional necessary information.
On receipt of this information, builders may realise that what is required of them is
not what they envisaged from the tender information – an all-too-common starting
ground for disputes.

Arguments over the interpretation of the production information are common. The
work will be seen as defective by clients or their consultants where it does not
comply with their intention – often as expressed by drawings issued after a lump-
sum price has been obtained. The builders will have made their own interpretation
of the employer's intention from the tender information and will see any further
information issued, which departs from their understanding of the tender information, as variations which should be issued and paid for as such.

Oral and written contracts

Whilst, strictly, an oral agreement is as binding as a written contract, dispute is more
likely and proof more difficult where the paperwork is deficient or non-existent. There
is often merit in the old saw: 'an oral contract is worth the paper it is written on'.

Many builders are far keener to start on site than they are to prepare paperwork. This is frequently true of domestic projects where householders, lacking prior experience in building work and unassisted by qualified professionals, are seduced by the self-assured approach characteristic of many jobbing builders. It is easy to be swept along by builders' general relaxed air of confidence into not worrying over the unknowns of building work. It is, after all, reassuringly routine 'bread and butter work' to builders while they are talking the job in.

Where householders seek the formalities of standard written contracts, they are likely to be assured that 'no one else asks for that' and to be solemnly advised 'that contract stuff makes the job cost more'.

Then the unexpected occurs and causes delays, unforeseen costs and defects – with resulting dissatisfaction and dispute.

Where a contract is prepared without due care, or by people with inadequate training and experience, the resultant documents often do not adequately cover all that has been agreed and, where a dispute occurs, reference has to be made both to the written agreement and that which has been discussed and agreed but not recorded in writing.

In the middle of farm fields, an isolated house, which had been built and altered over a century or more, was extensively modified for its new owner. The owner engaged an individual who took on a role akin to that of general contractor but who described his function as 'project manager' and who had experience but lacked professional qualifications.

The work started based on unminuted discussions and some exchange of correspondence. Initially the documents describing the work comprised the employer's 'wish list' of jobs to be done on the house and his maximum budget.

Because of the need to obtain formal consents from the local authority, the project manager engaged an architect who prepared outline drawings and sporadic specification notes. From these, sufficient consents were obtained for work to commence.

The monies to be spent, several hundred thousand pounds, would have been sufficient to build the accommodation from scratch. In proportion to the envisaged costs the works were relatively modest.

Notwithstanding the project manager's assurances that he would look after the quality, programme and general organisation of the works, the employer was wary of proceeding on too informal a basis and asked if it were not appropriate for a proper contract to be entered into. The project manager acquiesced and engaged a quantity surveyor to draft one. They selected a standard JCT form for contractor's design and prepared both contractor's proposals and employer's requirements which they submitted to the employer for signature.

The proposed contract documents did not refer to the original agreements. The description of the work in the proposed JCT agreement was sufficiently vague to make ambiguity and absence of detail appear a skilled art form which thoroughly obscured the extent of divergence between the original and proposed agreements.

The work progressed poorly, the quality being far below the standard that it was reasonable to expect from the monies being expended. Eventually, when the payments demanded exceeded the original budget although the work was far from finished, the employer sought independent advice. He dismissed the project manager and, by so doing, the various builders and professionals the project manager had engaged.

The project manager brought and won an adjudication for payment of the monies he said were outstanding. The employer appealed to the High Court, disputing the applicability of the JCT form and therefore the adjudicator's jurisdiction. The employer's appeal having been confirmed by the court, much money had been spent but the dispute remained fully unresolved.

Added to the dispute over the quality and cost of the work was an argument over the agreement under which the building work was being carried out. Because much of what had been agreed had been dealt with orally and because the written records of these oral agreements were scant summaries with no detail of the break-down of prices and quality of work, the disputants had to rely extensively on expert evidence. As every aspect of the agreement – as well as most aspects of the quality and correctness of the work – became a matter for debate, the cost of fighting the dispute rapidly exceeded the sums which were in contention.

It was found that the contract contained both express terms (written and oral) as to the scope of the work, and implied terms in respect of quality. Reference to the JCT form was not relevant as it was made after a contract had come into force.

The failure to prepare contract documents and to record agreements in writing is not restricted to domestic work. It is a deceptively easy path to follow. Time pressure to achieve results often leads to a start on site, on a shake of the hand or letter of intent, without full formal records of what has been agreed. Whilst work entered into on such a basis may be completed successfully, it is often later necessary to clarify or vary the terms of the works, with resultant problems.

If a clear agreement is not in place at the outset, or is not properly understood by both parties prior to commencement of the work, the terms of the agreement – i.e. what really was intended by each party – may not be clear. When things go wrong it may require lawyers to sort out matters. The best way of ensuring that lawyers are not needed to resolve construction disputes is to start with a written agreement linked to a set of information which makes clear what is required, how disagreements are to be resolved and, if appropriate, the effect of varying the work.

The relationship between design and construction

The building may be designed before a building contract is let by a professional team or after it is let by the building contractor. The popularity of the design-and-build arrangement comes from two factors:

1. the tendency for this approach to maximise the contractor's liability for all aspects of a project whilst minimising the employer's liabilities;
2. the apparent reduction in design costs.

(It is not clear that design costs are reduced but they may become so intermingled with construction costs that they become difficult to identify. As contractors usually manage design through subcontracting they will ordinarily add their overheads and profit to the design costs. It is therefore possible that employers will pay more for design than they would if they engaged the designers directly.)

Design-and-build contracts are most suitable where the clients:

- know before the contract is let exactly what they want;
- do not expect to vary their requirements during the contract period;
- want the total cost to be fixed as early as possible;
- want liability for faults to lie in one place.

This is not be confused with the 'build-then-design' school of contracting, where a general contractor takes on a design-and-build contract and starts on site as soon as approvals are obtained, without preparing production information. This leaves the trades, subcontractors and suppliers to devise details as work progresses. Because of the lack of independent professional supervision in design-and-build contracts this is both common and a cause of poor-quality building.

Work on site

RIBA Plan of Work identifies the construction phase of a project as follows:

Work Stage K: Construction to Practical Completion – *Administration of the building contract up to and including Practical Completion. Provision to the contractor of further information as and when reasonably required.*

Supervision and site management

Regardless of the procurement process, once on site errors in design can be compounded and good design undermined by faulty materials, poor supervision and bad workmanship. Communication, teamwork and forethought are the best tools for minimising construction errors and for catching design errors before they are built in.

Continuity is helpful. Workers who are together under the same foreman on job after job develop collective skills that are rarely matched by assembling new teams for each project. Continuity for building workers is conducive to learning-on-the-job in a way that was once traditional. This is a long-proven way to impart and develop trade skills, which helps the development of leadership and mutual understanding. Such continuity is now rare, placing much greater emphasis on management skills, formal qualifications and independent supervision.

Where self-employed and subcontract labour is hired in, management and supervision becomes divorced from those actually doing the work and relies more on inspection than constant monitoring. There may, at any one time, be many building activities – some of them off the building site – and it is rare for site management to be so well staffed that the main contractor can supervise all activities. Consequently, supervision is often delegated to subcontractors for their own work and the main contractor's 'supervision' reduced to follow-up action when the employer or their representative complains of faults. This not only lets defects be built in but allows a flawed way of working to continue unchecked until resultant problems force attention to be paid to it. Reliance on subcontractors' supervision does not replace the need for overall supervision although, properly used, it may lessen the reliance on the general contractor's site management.

Good supervision entails controlling the interfaces between trades and also between designers and workers. Subcontractors may be little informed of the work outside their 'package' and are unlikely to have the authority or knowledge to supervise the work of others, even where such supervision is central to the success of their own work.

It is important that those who supervise and inspect have a good practical knowledge of the work involved. Ensuring a combination of suitable skills and relevant experience on site is the best way of optimising a project's chances of untroubled success. It is always necessary to bear in mind the limits of available practical knowledge, so as to anticipate where ideas may need to be tested before full implementation.

> In a remedial contract for an elevated road which roofed part of a shopping centre, it was stipulated that the general contractor should keep on site, at all times, a supervisor who was familiar with the type of work involved. The contractor sent Nigel who, with quiet determination, essayed the role of resident supervisor.

Each difficulty encountered revealed a new aspect of Nigel's unfamiliarity with the specified waterproofing and paving products until his lack of prior experience of them was open knowledge.

The designers' unfamiliarity with this combination of materials was equally profound and equally slowly revealed. Eventually, all realised that combining the specified paving with the specified waterproofing was truly novel.

The architect's request for a better practised supervisor lost its strength, for how could a supervisor have knowledge through experience of something which contains novelty? The contractor confidently asserted that Nigel was by then the only supervisor fully familiar with this type of work.

In view of the designers' inexperience it was particularly prudent of them to seek expertise in supervision, but the experience required of a supervisor needs to be carefully defined. A supervisor informed by fighting disasters on this job was not perhaps what was intended.

Co-ordination, clarity, communication

Good communication is of prime importance. Drawings and specifications serve various functions. They may:

- initiate funding;
- be used to obtain permissions;
- define contractual obligations; and
- explain to the site operatives what is to be built.

For the last of these, clarity and completeness is fundamental.

An analysis of some 200 building defects investigations carried out by Knowles Construction Technology has revealed some common features in much defective and disputed work. One is the tendency for drawn details to describe standard conditions but not the permutations which occur in real buildings.

For example, a new building with cavity masonry walls incorporating steel posts was built from designs prepared by a consultant architect and engineer. The drawings showed the damp-proof courses in the cavity wall and where the steelwork interrupted both masonry and cavity. They did not show the junction between these conditions, and the building leaked at some of these junctions. It was argued to be due to bad workmanship but the builder had contracted to build what was drawn, not to elaborate the drawn details in work to resolve un-designed junctions.

British Standard guidance is for three-dimensional drawings to be provided for complex details in damp-proofing. In contrast, drawing office practice tends to avoid drawing those parts of a building where detailing is most complex. The result is for the most difficult details to be unconsidered until encountered on site. Then they are liable to be subject to the rushed application of uncoordinated mixtures of random 'try-it-and-see' solutions or stoppages whilst concerned site operatives challenge those managing the project to instruct in proper detail how the work is to be performed.

Tolerances and practicality

Casual reliance on written standards and authorities can create problems. Reference to generic specifications, codes of practice and national standards can import a host of terms some of which may prove to be inconsistent one with another. Often these go unremarked until a problem arises.

For each building activity there needs to be proper regard for what is practicable. Each part of a construction brings its own scope for error and deviation from nominally correct alignments and positions – some aspects requiring greater accuracy than others. For example, aluminium glazing frames, to function correctly, generally need to be more accurately positioned than does a structural frame. Where the aluminium is attached to a steel structure the inaccuracies in structural alignments will carry through into the aluminium unless those erecting the aluminium have independent reference points from which to work on site and sufficient adjustment in the connections between the two elements to correct for deviations in the steel.

Unless adjustments are made progressively at connections, deviations – whether permitted or not – will accumulate. Each deviation may be tolerable but their cumulative effect may be damaging, using up designed provision for live movements to accommodate constructional inaccuracies instead. For example, the mechanisms used to connect curtain walling to a building structure generally incorporate simple provisions for differential movements, such as slotted fixing holes. Ideally the fixings will be placed centrally in fixing holes, allowing subsequent differential movements in both directions. Examining such connections often reveals inaccurate work. Where the fastenings are installed so as to be consistently offset towards one end of the slots this may overcome the immediate effects of inaccurate building but reduce provision for subsequent reciprocal differential displacements.

The probable accumulative effect of the permitted tolerances can be calculated statistically using the root sum of squares. Adding together each permitted maximum deviation gives a theoretically possible resultant deviation, which is unlikely to occur unless there is systematic error during fabrication/erection. Ordinarily permitted deviations in each element of construction will randomly reinforce and cancel, so that the resultant accumulative deviations can be predicted as probabilities only.

Where it is probable that accumulative deviations will cause critical parts of the completed works to deviate from their required positions by more than is acceptable, this can be dealt with by working to higher-than-normal tolerances or by incorporating site adjustments in the method of erection. This latter is often preferred because of the impracticability of achieving very fine tolerances.

The use of site adjustments can break the accumulation of tolerances at suitable connections. To do this requires working to accurate benchmarks rather than setting out each subsequent part of the construction from that which precedes it.

The structural steelwork for an office in the Channel Islands was specified by reference to the 4th edition of the National Structural Steelwork Specification, BS 5950 Part 2 and the steel-framing plans. The work was designed by consultant engineers and architects under contract with the employer. The steelwork contractor was required to prepare fabrication drawings, calculations and general arrangement drawings.

The office contained central atria surrounded by steel columns which supported steel beams at each floor level. Secondary steelwork to carry the cladding to the main atrium was bracketed to these steel beams. The accuracy of alignment of the atrium cladding support steelwork was held to be inadequate, and correcting it necessitated altering the steelwork supporting it after it had been installed on site. Provision for such alteration was not incorporated in the steelwork – either in design or in fabrication.

From a site survey, the project engineers found part of the installed steelwork to be out of tolerance. The steelwork contractor maintained his work was within permitted tolerances.

In accordance with the National Structural Steelwork Specification, unless otherwise specified limited deviations in the position of each piece of steel are permitted. BS 5950 Part 2 also stipulates limited permitted deviations in the placement of each piece of steel, which are not in all places the same as the deviations permitted under the National Structural Steelwork Specification.

In accordance with the NSSS and BS, the permitted deviation in the position of each part of a steel frame may accumulate to give a resultant deviation which is larger that each individual permitted deviation. However, NSSS and BS differ in their considerations of the accumulation of permitted deviations.

The steelwork contractor put forward an argument based on the maximum additive accumulation of deviations permitted under the NSSS in rebuttal of the assertion that his work was out of tolerance.

As well as a general requirement to comply with the NSSS and BS there was a stipulation that the permissible deviations for cladding support steelwork were to be to the cladding installer's/manufacturer's requirements. A horizontal channel and angle, attached to the steel beam at each floor level, served as cladding support steelwork and therefore this stipulation would apply to them.

The accumulation of tolerances was not addressed fully in the project specification or in the terms imported by reference to the BS and NSSS. However, a commentary on the NSSS gave some consideration to this.[35]

The commentary draws attention to the need to provide for and observe tolerances in design (of relevant parts), fabrication and erection, as follows:

Successful steelwork fabrication and erection contracts depend upon the design being a practical one and also on the following items which are covered in the NSSS:

- *the preparation of detail drawings or equivalent electronic data which are appropriate to the purpose of the structure and which take account of the need for tolerances,*
- *the fabrication and assembly being carried out to a consistently high standard within recognised tolerances.*[36]

Particular reference is made to the need for the authors of fabrication drawings to understand and show the necessary provisions for tolerances:

The art and science of good detailing practice for fabrication drawings is, in many ways, encompassed in 3.4.4. The NSSS expects that the draughtsman has a full knowledge of the permitted tolerances. His job includes showing the packings and clearances required so that the component can be erected without modifications having to be made at site.[37]

The argued justification for the deviations in the finished positions of the atrium perimeter steelwork was the accumulation of tolerances permitted in the NSSS. This is contrary to good practice as set out in the commentary, which states that the steelwork contractor should detail components to prevent the accumulation of permitted tolerances rendering the completed work unacceptable.

An assembly may incorporate the permitted deviation in either direction . . . If each element in an assembly is made to a tolerance of the same "sign" (+ve or −ve), then the final assembly may be out of tolerance. To guard against this, the Steelwork Contractor must detail his components to avoid an accumulation of deviations that would make the final assembly unacceptable.[38]

Drawings should provide for fabrication tolerance by providing for necessary adjustments:

It is not difficult to show that if the cumulative effect of the fabrication and material deviations coupled with erection deviations are considered, some members may be outside the deviation "envelope" required for fitting other components directly to the steel. This is why, in the preparation of drawings, the fabrication deviations have to be recognised and provision made for adjustment where necessary to comply with the permissible erection deviations.[39]

The commentary addresses cumulative tolerances by way of example as follows:

The straightforward view is that permitted deviations are additive, and in terms of maximum possible values that view is sound, but with an overall requirement that the sum of the discrete values shall not be greater than the permitted deviations for the total structure. Ignoring any inaccuracy arising from measurement error or from errors in locating the nearest position point on the reference survey for the Site, consider this simple illustration of adding deviations from five sources:

- *±5 mm from setting the base level of the bottom of the column shaft (measured above the baseplate) (see 11.4.1(2) in DD ENV 1090–1),*
- *±2 mm from a variation in cutting the column length (see 7.2.5 in NSSS),*
- *±2 mm from positioning holes in the column (see 7.3.2 in NSSS),*
- *±3 mm from positioning of fittings at the end of the beam (see 7.3.1 in NSSS),*
- *±2 mm from positioning holes in the end plate on the beam (see 7.3.2 in NSSS).*

Straightforward addition would lead to the conclusion that the reference point on the top surface at the end of the beam could be ±5 mm, ±2 mm, ±2 mm, ±3 mm, ±2 mm = ±14 mm out of position. However, in this case the NSSS sets a limit of ±10 mm for the deviation of a floor beam from its specified level at the supporting column. It is worth noting that the NSSS does not set a value for the base of the column itself (hence the value from DD ENV 1090–1 was cited above) as the level of the base itself is rarely a concern whereas the floor beam levels are. Hence, it seems that some additional controls may be needed, but whilst cumulative tolerances might all be additive, this would not be expected. Statistically the procedure to predict the expected variation from several independent sources would be to calculate the "root-sum-of squares" [RSS]. In this case it would give a value of ±6.8 mm, well within the permitted deviation of ±10 mm. What this means is that, if each of the individual limits were representative of ±2Σ values (as suggested by BS 5606), then there should be less than a 5% chance that the position of the top of the beam would be outside of ±6.8 mm (with less than 0.3% chance that it would be outside of the "permitted" value of ±10 mm or ±3Σ, and less than a 1 in 1500 chance that it would be outside of the "additive" value of ±14 mm or ±4Σ).

Hence, whilst there is a chance that several individual sources of variation may be additive, the chance of them all conspiring in one direction makes this an unlikely outcome – unless one of two other factors is present:

- *There is a systematic bias in some part of the process.*
- *The sources of variation are not independent.*[40]

Following the above example and applying the RSS to the atrium perimeter columns, the expected maximum deviation due to the accumulation of the deviations permitted in the NSSS were shown to be less than the deviations which had been found by site survey. Additionally, measuring the position of columns at each floor level showed the deviations were inconsistent both in direction and in size. The fact that the arithmetic addition of permitted deviations could generate figures which were as large as the deviations found was academic as it was not the cause of the large deviations found. There was further argument over the definition of *'structural steelwork'* and of *'cladding support steelwork'*. The rules with respect to permitted tolerances were written in different terms for cladding and for structure.

Figure 3.1: **The accumulation of permissible tolerances can cause unaccept-able dimensional inaccuracies.**

Drawn details

The practice of resolving complex details in work on site is traditional and has merit but involves a form of open co-operation between designers and builders which can be inhibited by the fear of claims. Collaboration over the development of details in work can muddy the issue of responsibility if the result is flawed. Building contracts try to give certainty over responsibilities, which can discourage *ad hoc* co-operation on site or turn it into a basis for claims and potential dispute. Flexibility and partnership between designer and builder, which so benefits the effective site resolution of detailing, is unfortunately not readily compatible with some commonly used building contracts, particularly the traditional lump-sum or fixed-price variants.

Some recent contracts based on the 'partnering' approach to building work have good intent and could improve on the recent past, but they are too new for their effectiveness to be confirmed adequately from experience.

The Association of Consultant Architects (ACA) contract form is perhaps a good choice of standard contract where the design consultants wish to retain flexibility to develop some details as work progresses, particularly where it is envisaged that this be done on site collaboratively with the builders.

An important lesson learnt from a study of dispute resolution is that the designers' intention should be explicit and compatible with the form of building contract.

If it is the designer's intention that working details be resolved on site, this should be made clear and the contractual mechanisms for dealing with this should be conducive to the co-operative approach and often collaborative effort that this engenders.

If, however, the parties intend that the building should be built in accordance with pre-drawn details, the drawings must be adequate for this purpose and completed in good time.

Specifications

In all cases a consistent approach to specification is desirable, both for compatibility with the contractual arrangements and for good communications. There are, in practice, two types of specification: prescriptive and performance.

A performance specification sets out what is to be achieved, but leaves the completion of the design to the builder. A prescriptive specification tells the builder precisely what to do. For example, a partition may be specified to be *'a plasterboard and stud construction to provide a 1 hour fire rating and 48 db sound attenuation, to receive an emulsion finish'*. This illustrates a performance specification, leaving the detail of the design to be completed but setting out the important criteria which are to be met. A fully prescriptive specification would have given the type and size of the studs, thicknesses and types of plasterboard, methods of fixing and jointing, etc. to the point that no choices were left to the builder.

Where the two types are combined, allowing equal or similar materials to be substituted for those specified, the document may function either as a prescriptive or as a performance specification, depending on the wording used and on the mechanism adopted to allow the contractor to substitute alternatives to prescribed materials.

Both in maintaining control of the work as it progresses, to minimise the risk of faulty work, and in understanding where blame lies should the work be defective it is important for the process to be clear.

Precautionary measures during construction

There is no point in getting the design right if the builders ignore what is drawn. It is difficult to ensure that site operatives work from drawn information, but they can be encouraged to do so by making the drawings manageable. It is awkward working from A0-size drawing sheets on a windswept, wet site; a folder of A2 drawings is not so difficult to handle. On the other hand an A0 reflected ceiling plan will probably be used late enough in the building process that it can be pinned to a dry, sheltered surface in sight of the area of work. Considering the circumstances in which the drawing will have to be used is a good guide to the format that will best assist those who have to use them. If it is convenient to use a drawing, the likelihood of its being followed is improved.

Revising drawings creates a major site management task. Once a drawing has been put into use on site, ensuring that it is discarded when a later revision is issued is difficult. The ease with which drawings can be copied and proliferated makes it difficult to be certain that all outdated copies have been withdrawn from circulation. With computer-generated drawings, keeping control of the updating process is made easier in all respects – except for the recovery of prints which have been distributed to the workers on site.

Problems can also be caused by using drawings for the wrong purpose.

> In a major commercial development, partitions were installed to an architect's drawing, which had been modified by the electrical engineer to show the lighting layout. The architect had later revised his drawing, modifying some aspects of the partitions. This did not affect the work that the electrical engineer had shown, so he did not revise his drawings.
>
> To the operatives on site a drawing was a drawing and, as the partitions were shown on the electrical engineer's drawing, they built them to this drawing. The drawings had been properly issued under instruction under the contract, and the contractor had to put right this error at his own cost.

A failure to ensure co-ordination of drawings, as they are produced during the progress of the works, is a major source of construction problems. Drawings may be produced by consultants, suppliers or subcontractors, all working independently. But even where they work closely together problems can arise.

A mechanical engineer and an electrical engineer, who sat facing each other in the same office, each designed part of the services for a minor commercial development. The mechanical engineer produced drawings for mechanical ventilation and sprinklers. The electrical engineer produced a lighting layout.

The architectural technician working on the job noted the conflict between various elements of mechanical and electrical design when laying out the ceiling grid. As a result, these conflicts were eliminated on the drawing board.

However, the mechanical engineer created a conflict in his design between upright sprinkler heads above the ceiling and the ventilation ductwork. Because different subcontractors were dealing with each part of this work, he showed the sprinklers on one drawing and the mechanical ventilation on another.

On site it was found that some of the sprinkler heads sat inside the ductwork. As the latter had progressed in advance of the sprinkler installation, and as the sprinklers had to go within close limits to their design positions, the built ductwork had to be altered.

The ductwork had, however, been redrawn by the subcontractor from the consultant engineer's indicative drawings, with the result there was then an argument over who was responsible for the design error. As the mechanical subcontractors were nominated, had entered separate collateral warranties and had subcontracted parts of their works, very wide-ranging discussions over contractual liabilities followed.

Traditional building work generally involves many changes of trade to complete a single item. Designing to minimise the overlapping of trade activities during construction is beneficial both in terms of the overall costs of the project and also in reducing opportunities for the compounding of errors.

The programming of work can have a significant effect on its successful outcome. For example, due to the presence of residual construction water, *in situ* concrete and masonry take a considerable time to reach their 'equilibrium' moisture content. That is, the moisture content which is in balance with the moisture contents of the air and adjoining materials in the completed building. With modern, cost-led building practice, it is normally impracticable to allow sufficient time for complete drying out before buildings are occupied. It is important to allow for this and to prevent unnecessary wetting of the materials during building. In this respect the sequencing of work can be significant.

A building in Wales, which had exposed hardwood finishes, suffered damage when an *in situ* concrete floor was laid.

A large amount of water was released into the internal air as the floor dried. The carefully conditioned Welsh oak swelled and some of it ripped free from its supports. Other parts distorted but held in place. This specially ordered oak was on two years' delivery, leading to difficulty in replacing that which had been damaged.

The relative humidity immediately after the floor was laid approached 100%, an increase of nearly 60% over the preceding conditions. The joinery subcontractor blamed the failure on the water produced by the concrete flooring. The flooring subcontractor stated that he was doing what he contracted to do at the time required by the main contractor. The main contractor withheld payments from both subcontractors.

In the subsequent disputes, the adjudicators decided everyone was to blame for failing to work in an appropriate sequence, but apportioned slightly more blame to the main contractor than to the subcontractors.

Work exposed during construction but which will be covered in the finished building should be protected from the weather. For example, the tops of walls should be protected from rain at all times during construction. This is especially important where walling materials would readily absorb water.

For floors and flat roofs full protection from rain might be impracticable, but precautions should be taken to avoid unnecessary wetting, e.g. by avoiding standing water. This is particularly necessary where the construction is likely to be exposed for a long time.

In central Europe, a building, which was late with consequent pressure to work at full speed, had a flat roof with fibre insulation placed between a vapour barrier and roofing felt. The work continued through showers. Some wet insulation was built in.

After one summer, the roof suffered ponding, which revealed depressions in its surface. Record photographs showed this ponding did not exist when the roof was handed over.

The depressions were found to be soft. Exploratory openings were cut in the roof. The insulation was found to have lost cohesion.

Laboratory examination showed the still-wet insulation to be reduced largely to loose fibre with commensurate loss of compressive strength, allowing it to depress locally. The theory put forward by the laboratory was that the hot summer sun combined with the trapped water had simulated the effect of steaming the insulation. It was known to the laboratory that this type of insulation lost cohesion if repeatedly steamed.

When using wet roof screeds which have to dry inwards after the roof finish is complete, or where they would be dried outwards only by limited ventilation to the exterior, care should be taken to prevent the ingress of excess water. Adequate ventilation should be provided during both the construction and drying-out periods.

Gaps around services through walls and ceilings should be sealed in good time to prevent moisture-laden air entering cold voids. The spread of moisture by air movement is likely to be very much more rapid than by diffusion. Appropriately placed draught-proofing – continuous, and with corners and junctions properly joined – can significantly reduce the risk of interstitial condensation.

Ventilation to relieve condensation risk is easily impaired by other aspects of construction. Aspects that might need particular attention include ensuring that trickle vents, such as those to roof voids, are provided as specified and have not been rendered ineffective by obstructions or by late changes in the design details, e.g. by roof insulation blocking the ventilation openings or by structures interrupting cross-ventilation paths.

Construction information

Precautions taken by a designer can be negated by lack of site supervision and by poor communication between designer and supervisor.

In arriving at a finished design, a good designer will consider the process of construction. The difficulty is that although the design may have been developed to accommodate a sensible and practical method of construction the information the designer provides may not show to the builder the considerations which lie behind this.

In the EU, designers are directed to consider the process of construction so as to ensure they allow for safe methods of working, or otherwise to identify the risks which are inherent in designs.[41] This risk-assessment procedure should focus designers' minds on the process of construction, as well as on what the finished product should be.

There is customarily a division between designer and contractor, in which the contractor takes full responsibility for the method of work. Where designers have properly considered the method of work in developing a design, they will have accommodated the processes involved so as to facilitate good site practice. If this information is not conveyed to the contractor, the contractor may adopt methods of work which were not envisaged by the designer and which are not compatible with design intentions. This can be overcome by good communication and close co-operation between designer and builder.

Best practice undoubtedly involves a two-way flow of information between designer and builder. Thus, if the builder identifies a problem in achieving what the designer has proposed this can be put back to the designer so that the two can discuss alternative solutions to ensure that the design allows materials to be used in appropriate conditions, consistent with the need to apply appropriate skills and care to the construction process.

The designer who invents concepts in an office, isolated from the reality of work on a building site, will have far greater difficulty in developing designs which facilitate good site practice and hence relatively defect-free work than will a designer who learns from experience the processes involved in transferring a concept drawn on paper into built reality on site.

Site checks

Inspections need to be tailored to the type of work and to be varied as dictated by experience. From an analysis of the defects investigated by Knowles Construction Technology, the following may provide some guidance on where inspection may most usefully be focused:

- Pay particular regard to interfaces between different trades.
- Ensure appropriate stores are available and used for materials that are to be delivered to site before they are to be used.
- Ensure adequate protection from inclement weather during vulnerable operations. This is especially necessary in positions where subsequent drying-out may be impaired, such as roof insulation laid above a vapour barrier and beneath an impermeable roof finish.
- Check the working conditions are conducive to maintaining good standards of workmanship. In particular, good lighting and access to the area of work affects both the quality of work and of inspection. Working conditions conducive to good workmanship are also conducive to a safe and healthy working environment. In the UK, this is a matter which designers and contractors are required to consider under the Construction (Design and Management) Regulations and other related law.
- Check routinely that delivered materials are as specified.

Membranes and sheet materials are particularly vulnerable to isolated damage, which can easily go unnoticed prior to being concealed. The importance of checking depends upon their function. For example, waterproof, damp-proof and vapour-control layers must be correctly positioned, cover the whole area to be protected, and be fully lapped and/or sealed at joints. Special attention should be paid to ensure that following trades do not damage the membranes without repair. Where gaps are cut through – e.g. for services – the holes should be appropriately sealed.

Where prefabricated components are to be dry-assembled on site, early checks to confirm that appropriate methods are used can be more effective in achieving good overall results than inspections on completion. With, for example, sheet insulation damage continuity, correct jointing and full cover to the area to be insulated should be checked. Small gaps between sheets may seem minor to unsupervised site labour, but can significantly mar performance.

Self-finished and vulnerable prefabricated materials should be fixed as late as other requirements allow and checked for damage immediately before they are covered.

It is advisable to have schedules of final checks for each part of the construction process, but regarding such schedules as exhaustive is hazardous as it can lead to missing unforeseen faults. The items are common sense and should be based on an understanding of how each part of the construction is supposed to work, what is likely to go wrong and, most importantly, an appreciation of the probable severity of the consequence of any error being left unattended.

For example, for the prevention of condensation risk in buildings, the following are typical of the checks that should be made:

- Has any insulation moved out of position?
- Are pipework and water tanks fully lagged?
- Are any ventilation airways blocked?
- Has dry insulation become damp (impairing its performance)?
- Are seals intact on hatches, and service penetrations?
- Are vapour checks imperforate and correctly terminated?
- Is there appropriate provision for the safe drainage of condensate run-off?

[35] *Commentary on the National Structural Steelwork Specification* by Richard Stainsby DIC, CEng, FIStructE, and Roger Pope MA, MSc, DPhil, CEng, FIMechE, FIStructE, MCIArb.

[36] *Philosophy of the National Structural Steelwork Specification*, p. 4.

[37] *Commentary on the National Structural Steelwork Specification*, 3.4 – 'Fabrication Information For Components', p. 44.

[38] *Commentary on the National Structural Steelwork Specification*, 4.7 – 'Assembly', p. 51.

[39] *Commentary on Section 9* [of the National Structural Steelwork Specification], 'Workmanship – Accuracy of Erected Steelwork'.

[40] *Commentary on the National Structural Steelwork Specification*, 118 – 'Cumulative Tolerances'.

[41] Temporary and Mobile Work Sites Directive.

Errors After Construction

4

> The final construction stage of a project is referred to in the RIBA Plan of Work as follows:
>
> Work Stage L: After Practical completion – *Administration of the building contract After Practical Completion. Making final inspections and settling the final account. [Clearly separated from the construction phase]*.

Completion

In standard forms of building contract, completion is a varied and qualified concept which embraces *'sectional'*, *'practical'*, *'substantial'*, *'works'*, *'defects'* and *'legal'* completion. Each form can have an effect on responsibilities for defects and on the correct procedures for dealing with them.[42]

Sectional (or phased) completion is an option which may be selected in certain contracts. Its meaning and effect will be that given to it in the contract. Typically it is similar to practical completion but restricted to a part of the works only.

Practical completion is a term used in JCT contracts. It corresponds to terms such as *'substantial'* completion in other contracts. Its meaning is not defined by the JCT. It is discussed more fully below.

Works completion is the end of the construction phase, when the physical work is completed. This may or may not coincide with practical completion, and is a matter of fact rather than a term defined in the contract.

Defects completion occurs at the end of the defects liability or maintenance period when the listed defects have been made good.

Legal completion occurs when the paperwork is done and the final account paid. In legal terms the contract has been performed on both sides.

Practical completion

A point may be reached where the work is for all practical purposes sufficiently complete to be put into use but is not necessarily fully complete in all respects. This is acknowledged in many standard forms of contract. It is referred to in the JCT family of contracts as 'practical completion' and defined as coming into existence either when certified by the person so authorised or, in certain stated circumstances, as a consequence which flows from the taking over a part or parts of the works. In other standard forms it is referred to by other names and commences either by certification or as a result of certain events. However it is described, it has the effect of splitting completion of the building work into two stages.

The definition of 'practical completion' is often debated. Early versions of the JCT contracts defined practical completion by reference to the architect's certifying when the works were *'practically completed'*, an expression that has subsequently been dropped from the standard form.[43] Whilst the meaning of 'practically completed' can readily be construed in plain English, 'practical completion' has no clear meaning in ordinary usage. Since dropping the term 'practically completed', the JCT no longer define the meaning of 'practical completion'.

Most independent authoritative guidance is based on the consequences of certification and the provisions under the contract to deal with these consequences. From this it has been argued that, in respect of JCT contracts, a Practical Completion Certificate may safely be issued where there is some outstanding work but not if there are any patent defects. Other guidance offers that minor defects are not grounds for withholding certification of practical completion. Some argue that putting the work into use or the employer's taking possession is overriding evidence that practical completion has been achieved.

Any certificate of completion can alter the rights of the contracting parties with respect to defects. In view of this, certification while there are patent defects can cause difficulty. The practice, for example, of certifying practical completion but attaching to the certificate a schedule of outstanding and defective work may not stand up to legal scrutiny. Unless the contract allows for the issue of qualified completion certificates, such certificates may be invalid or the attached schedules of no effect.

Following legal precedents it is clear that the courts have had difficulty with the meaning of practical completion but a review of case law has led to the following definition: *'practical completion occurs when the works are at such a stage that they are capable of being used by the employer for the purpose for which are apparently required, such that liquidated damages (if the works were to be, or are, in delay) are no longer justifiable'*.[44]

Where a contract is subject to independent supervision, the supervisor's certification of completion can evidence the discharge by the contractor of their obligations in respect of those matters covered by the certificate. This may restrict the employer's rights to require the correction of defective works and leave open no recourse but to require the supervisor to pay for the correction of defects where negligent certification has shielded the contractor from liability.

Defects liability/maintenance period

Many standard forms of contract provide for a period, after the work is practically complete, during which the contractor has a right to come back to correct defects in their work. The JCT forms generally refer to this as the 'defects liability period'. Other forms of contract use alternative terminology.

Under UK law, the period may be set at any length which suits the contracting parties. It would, however, be peculiar to seek to extend this period beyond the cut-off for liability set by the Statute of Limitations (see Chapter 12).

The scope and nature of the defects which are to be dealt with under this provision may similarly be set by agreement and stated in the contract. After this period, contractors have no automatic right to return to correct their errors. This does not alter contractors' liability for their defective work but it allows the employer the option of bringing in others to carry out repairs and to countercharge the contractor for the costs so incurred.

Often, practical or substantial completion is certified for work which contains patent defects or which is incomplete. The pressure to meet preset dates and allow occupation encourages rash actions. The subsequent correction of defects can be frustrated by difficulties over access and disputes over cost and liabilities.

Under most standard forms, such as those provided by the JCT, defects that were patent prior to practical completion do not fall under the rules of the contract attaching to defects occurring after practical completion and before final completion.

Where the employer does not own the building during the defects liability period the matter is complicated. Employers' rights to require the defects to be corrected arises out of their interest in the building. Contractors' rights to correct defects arises out of their contract with the employer. The employer, if no longer the owner, may have no right either to require the contractor to correct defects or to provide them with access for this purpose.

Employers' rights to require defects to be corrected by the contractor are a modification of their common-law right in respect of breach of contract. Instead of the contractor compensating the employer by the payment of damages during the defects liability period (to be assessed on the basis of the losses incurred due to the defective work), defects are to be dealt with by specific performance. If a contractor defaults in their duty to correct defective work, the remedy still lies in damages.

If the employer has sold the building without retaining any liability for its performance, they will suffer no loss as a result of any deficiencies in it. It follows that, although their right to pursue a claim for damages for a breach of contract by the contractor would be undiminished, the damages they could claim would not necessarily be the cost of correcting the defects in the contractor's work and may very well be purely nominal.

It further follows that the provision for a defects liability period should be carefully considered where the employer under the building contract will not be the owner and occupier of the completed building during the defects liability period.

This may be dealt with by way of collateral warranties and through appropriate terms in contracts of sale, leasing agreements, etc. Providing any transfer of the property, occupancy agreements, etc. contain suitable provisions to allow access by the contractor to correct defects, the provisions of the building contract will remain capable of implementation.

The use of collateral warranties may provide a useful alternative whereby the contractor's residual rights and responsibilities can be transferred to the purchaser of the building.

Operating and maintenance manuals

In the UK, the Construction (Design and Management) Regulations require that all construction work to which they apply is accompanied by the production of a health and safety file, which has to be completed and made available on completion of the project. This file is likely to contain, amongst other things, everything that might, prior to these regulations, have been included in operating and maintenance manuals.

The health and safety file should contain the necessary information to ensure that anybody who carries out alterations, repairs, redecoration, cleaning or the like will have details of any relevant risks or potential problems. It is a collation of information provided by all members of the project team, which is necessary to ensure the health and safety of those carrying out construction and cleaning work in or on the structure.

It is the building owner's obligation to ensure that the health and safety file is kept available for inspection by any person who may need information to ensure that they can carry out their function safety.

Typically the contents of the file include:

- record drawings, together with the details of the design criteria;
- general details of the construction methods and materials used;
- details of the equipment and maintenance facilities;
- maintenance procedures;
- requirements and procedures for repairing and cleaning;
- the operational manuals for all specialist plant and equipment;
- details of location and nature of utilities and services.

The maintenance manual needs to explain the correct way to use a building where, and to the extent that, incorrect use would cause damage.

Inaccurate and missing information in maintenance manuals and health and safety files can be a direct cause of defective work. Liability for the consequences of deficiencies in drawings in health and safety files is not always straightforward.

An engineer's drawing, included in the health and safety file, failed to show that block infill panels in a gable wall were load-bearing. Removal of the block panel during demolition resulted in collapse, causing four deaths. A prosecution was brought under health and safety legislation.

It was found that:

- The original building owner was negligent in failing to supervise the original construction.
- The subcontractor's immediate employer had a duty to provide a safe system of work, but could not reasonably have been aware of the problems that led to the collapse.
- The subcontractor's employer, the main contractor, was entitled to rely on the structural engineer's advice.
- The structural engineer was not liable.

Improper use, abuse, inadequate maintenance

Where buildings are let to occupants who have no interest in them or responsibility for their upkeep it is difficult to ensure they are given proper routine care. A lack of maintenance can lead to underperformance, for which designers and builders may be blamed.

This can involve the most ordinary errors in use. For example, a failure to properly shut a loft access trap can allow large quantities of water vapour to escape into a loft space. This can encourage potentially damaging condensation in the roof structure and reduce heating efficiency, with resultant complaints of inadequacy in the design of the heating installation and long-term damage to materials in the roof.

Equally, not using, or unintentionally blocking, the designed provisions to prevent damage and failure can cause problems. Again, this may range from very simple situations to sophisticated built-in building management systems. For example, trickle ventilators can reduce condensation on cold surfaces such as windows, and blocking these ventilators can increase condensation. Other factors may come into play: for example, putting heavy curtains or internal blinds over a window will further reduce the window's surface temperature and increase condensation on the glass. The concentrated accumulation of condensate can cause rapid deterioration to painted wooden surfaces and the rapid loss of paint may then lead to unjustified complaints of poor workmanship on the part of the painter.

In preparing a building which is likely to be put into use for short-term, multiple occupancy, or which will be subject to multiple sub-letting, the project team's potential liabilities to third parties can be daunting. It is probably not feasible to make a building foolproof, and investigation into purported defects should pay due regard to the possibility that failure may arise from misuse.

In the case of owner-occupiers, there is no conflict concerning responsibility for using the building in accordance with the design intent. In landlord/tenant situations, agreements should define the respective responsibilities of the parties for maintaining the various parts of the building.

These include the responsibilities for running and maintenance costs of the plant provided with the building. Occupiers should be given sufficient information to enable them to run the system in the manner intended by the designer.

Even the way a building is furnished can affect its performance. For example, large items of furniture, if placed directly against external walls, can trap pockets of still air behind them causing surface condensation and mould growth on the walls and furniture.

The implications of changing standards

Best practice of 100 years ago, if followed now, would produce what by modern thinking would be sub-standard building. With accelerating revision of regulatory controls, even a building constructed precisely to last year's mandatory standards is unlikely to comply with today's regulations. Accordingly, construction technology has to continually adapt to keep pace with rising expectation and ever-more-demanding rules and regulations.

The substitution of innovation for proven techniques carries with it concomitant risks, and meeting rising performance criteria can undermine once reliable detailing. For example, placing insulation under a lead roof can upgrade thermal resistance to meet new standards and, with equal efficacy, decimate durability.[45] The novel is rarely as safe and trouble-free as the tried and tested.

> The design of trafficked decks – that is, building roofs which carry vehicular traffic – has required continual innovation. Initially these were typically based on bridge design, with which they had much in common. Both require a base which is capable of spanning between supports and a wearing surface which can take both weather and wheel loads.
>
> Trafficked decks became popular in buildings such as shopping centres, in which the separation of goods traffic from private traffic and pedestrian movement is desirable. Bridge-deck design concerned itself with waterproofing only insofar as this was necessary to protect the structure from water damage. When the 'bridge' becomes a roof to a habitable space, the limits of bridge-deck detailing rapidly become apparent, particularly in association with the performance of

articulated joints and perimeter detailing. Upgrading some aspects of what was already tried bridge technology in the light of what had been learnt from modern flat roofing was all that was necessary to develop waterproof flat roofs which could carry heavy goods vehicles.

This worked until the widening scope of regulatory control made the incorporation of some thermal insulation mandatory. Through a process of trial and failure, design modifications were developed which gave the roofing adapted from bridge-deck techniques a further lease of life.

Soon it was necessary to look to knowledge gained in flat roofs rather than to draw further on bridge-deck technology. Upgrading the wearing qualities of flat roofing so that it can carry heavy traffic brings with it a new set of problems but also tried techniques to manage the consequences of building-up thermal resistance.

Each significant enhancement to the mandatory provisions for thermal performance provoked new difficulties, generating investigation, dispute and corrective works until innovations in design overcame the detrimental side effects of improved thermal resistance. The process is ongoing. Each improvement in one aspect of the performance of a roof has potentially deleterious side effects. Lessons are learnt from the problems encountered on site. This feeds back into the design process but, on the way, money is wasted in correcting faults and disputing responsibility.

The 1997 EU Amsterdam Treaty (OJ 97/C 340/01), as interpreted and developing under the guidance of the International Council for Building and the International Council for Research and Innovation in Building and Construction (CIB),[46] is changing some of the standards required of buildings. Much of this is consistent with the direction being taken in revisions to the UK Building Regulations. Issues such as sustainability, equality of access and fire safety are subject to monitoring in completed buildings to obtain an indication of 'real' performance and as a basis for setting targets.

The following illustrate the way in which changes in building standards are being co-ordinated across the EU:

Equality of Opportunity for Every Person in Society: To combat discrimination and remove physical restrictions on participation in society by the year 2010, every new building shall be fully and independently accessible with regard to mobility, usability, communications and information.

Fire Protection in Buildings: To provide a high level of protection and improvement of the quality of the environment by the year 2010, every new building shall be designed, constructed and managed so as to ensure the least adverse environmental impact in the event of fire.

Indoor Climate/Air Quality in Buildings: To provide a high level of human health protection, by the year 2010, radon activity (including Rn-222, Rn-220 and RnD) in every new building shall, on average, fall within the range of 10–40 Bq/m^3, but shall at no time exceed 60 Bq/m^3.

Historically, changes in required building standards have not been applied retrospectively to established buildings until they are subject to alterations. This principle is not consistent with the above environmental objectives. Changes relating to asbestos and access for the disabled have, for example, been imposed in the UK on existing buildings irrespective of whether or not any changes are being made. A brand new building could comply with all relevant legislation one day and offend against a new regulation the next. For this reason designers and builders have to have an eye to impending as well as current rules.

[42] See Viscount Dilhorne in *Jarvis and Sons* v *Westminster Corp.* (1968) 118 New LJ 590 (at first instance); (1969) 1 WLR 1448 (CA); (1970) 1 WLR 637 (HL).

[43] See, for example, the Joint Contracts Tribunal Standard Form of Building Contract for use With Quantities, private edition 1963, July 1977 revision, clause 15 (1).

[44] Thomas Thompson, 'Practical Completion in Building Contracts: a Legal Definition?', *Construction Law Journal,* No. 6 (2004).

[45] See Chapter 5, Traditional/modern forms of construction with metals.

[46] CIB is the acronym of the abbreviated French (former) name: 'Conseil International du Bâtiment' (in English: International Council for Building). In the course of 1998, the abbreviation was kept but the full name changed to the International Council For Research And Innovation In Building And Construction.

Symptom and Cause

The incidence of different types of defects

In the most general sense, a satisfactory building is one which is where it is needed, fits appropriately into its surroundings, and provides adequate space and facilities protected from adverse weather and other undesirable external conditions. Since this protection cannot readily be achieved with short-lived structures, buildings typically outlast many other modern products, and, if built so that they can be adapted to changing requirements and easily repaired, can give satisfactory service for a long time.

Much can be learnt from the condition of the existing building stock about what mostly causes dissatisfaction after completion.

Existing buildings in Britain number about 25 million. Most are dwellings, which in 2000 numbered about 23 million – well over 90 per cent of the total, but it is estimated that in terms of floor area, domestic and non-domestic buildings are roughly equal.[47]

At the beginning of the 20th century there was, in Britain, one dwelling for every 2.6 persons – slightly above the size of today's dwindling average household. Population growth is now slow overall, and current demand for building arises largely from changes in household composition and inter-regional migration. The annual rate at which new dwellings were being completed in 2000 had fallen to well under 200,000, compared with more than double that figure in the mid 1960s.

Consequently, for English houses as a whole recent official figures indicate that more than one fifth are over 80 years old, and around half are 50 years old.[48] There are no comparable statistics for non-residential buildings.

In spite of their age, most existing buildings are still fit for continued use. Government statistics for dwellings officially designate as unfit less than 5 per cent of the total (i.e. 885,000 unfit dwellings). The most common reason for unfitness is disrepair (46%), followed by facilities for the preparation and cooking of food and dampness. Externally, faults occur most commonly in roof features and rainwater goods (34%), exterior wall finish (26%) and windows (25%). Internally, faults are most common in ceilings (22%). This is an increase in the number of houses which are in disrepair when compared to the previous year's survey.

Incidence and type of faults is given as follows:

- no faults: 31%;
- interior faults only: 6%;
- exterior faults only: 35%;
- both interior and exterior faults: 28%.

Other official publications[49] give some indication of the maintenance required. For housing, in terms of maintenance cost, external walls accounted for 13 per cent

Chapter 5

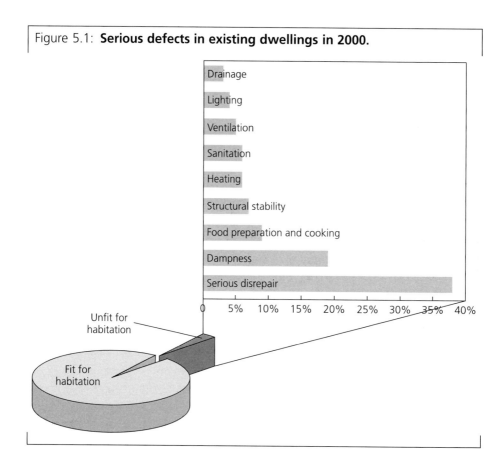

Figure 5.1: **Serious defects in existing dwellings in 2000.**

and windows and doors for 14 per cent. In about six per cent of dwellings, rising damp had affected internal walls and partitions.[50]

Comparable statistics for mainly non-residential properties can be found in the database managed by the Building Research Establishment (BRE) for the Construction Quality Forum. (Fig. 5.2).

From this it will be seen that defects in external elements comprise over half of the total, and that, with adequate maintenance and the upgrading of services and installations, most buildings could probably last a very long time.

This is confirmed by other figures published by the BRE for faults in new-build housing.[51] External walls and roofs each account for about 20 per cent of total faults, doors and windows for up to 18 per cent – a total average for the external building envelope from surveys in 1980 and 1990 of some 58 per cent. The biggest elements of internal works are: services, separating walls, partitions, upper

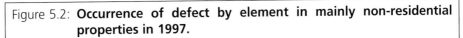

Figure 5.2: **Occurrence of defect by element in mainly non-residential properties in 1997.**

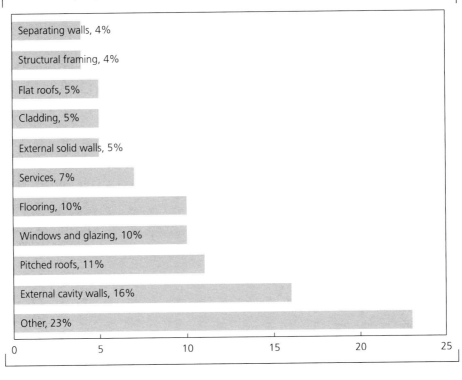

floors and ceilings. Substructure, ground floors and damp-proof membranes together make up less than three per cent. External works add up to about two per cent and miscellaneous defects account for the roughly ten per cent remaining (see Fig. 5.3).

These figures are set out in greater detail in the BRE series on building elements, which is based on several decades of defects investigations. The volume on walls, windows and doors indicates that, of the defects investigations carried out in the 1980s by the BRE, over half were into dwellings. The distribution among building types is shown in the chart in Fig. 5.4.

These proportions have altered since, but dwellings still predominate.

Each volume in the BRE series breaks the figures down to reveal principal characteristics and causes of defects in each element. Advice is given on how to avoid defects, as well as on inspection and diagnosis.

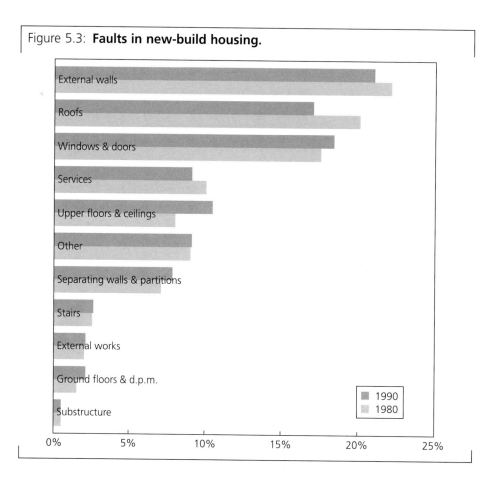

Figure 5.3: **Faults in new-build housing.**

For some elements, statistics are analysed in detail to show where responsibility for defects mainly lies. The overall split is estimated at approximately ten per cent to materials, 45 per cent to site work, and 45 per cent to design and specification With other elements some faults are described as due to shared or other causes, and a distinction is made between 'rehab' and new build.

Failings in design and specification are generally worse in rehab, where they reach a maximum of over 63 per cent in separating walls. By contrast, in new-build the failing ranges from 46.6 per cent with gas services to a minimum of 20.8 per cent with partitions.

From a review of 200 claims in the USA, causes of defects there have been broadly categorised showing that ambiguities, divergences, deficiencies, inaccuracies and typographical errors in specifications, drawings, schedules and the like accounted

Figure 5.4: **Distribution of defects by building type.**

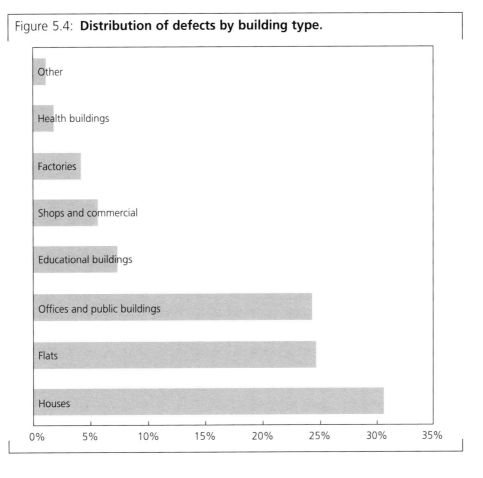

for just over half of all claims – making poor preparation of documents the biggest single factor in causing defects disputes (Fig. 5.5).[52]

Substructure

BRE Elements: Foundations, Basements and External Works states that most foundation difficulties arise from weak and compressible soils and exceptionally heavy loads. Trouble may be caused by either the imposed load or independent movement of the ground.

Approximately half of all housing substructure faults relate to cracking and settlement, one third to defective damp-proof courses and one sixth to durability of masonry below damp-proof courses. In cellars and basements, about half the faults observed related to dampness, and structural faults were few. Although its significance is uncertain, settlement is thought to affect about five per cent of all

Chapter 5

Figure 5.5: **Distribution of defects claims by cause from a survey of 200 US engineering claims.**

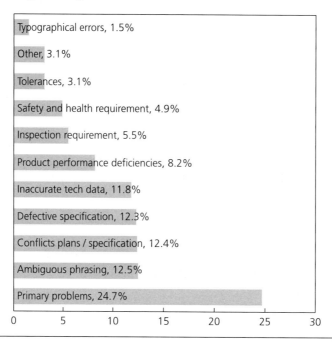

houses. Insurers of new houses report that problems associated with ground and foundations predominate in the first ten years.

External works

In external works, about half of all faults were in boundary and other free-standing walls, and half in pavings and drains. Drainage faults included damaged pipework and leakages, some leading to foundation settlement and some associated with pipes incorrectly carried through external walls.

Walls

Rain penetration was the most common defect investigated in external walls, at around 40 per cent of wall defects looked at by the BRE between 1987–89 and 1992–95.[53] Entrapped water accounted for less than three per cent, and rising damp for less than two per cent; cracking was found in nearly 18 per cent and detachment in 10.5 per cent. Condensation was found in approximately one case out of ten. Nearly two thirds of all faults recorded in house walls were in new cavity construction. Many faults occurred at junctions with other elements.

Sound transmission and fire prevention are more significant in separating walls. Durability and satisfactory performance in terms of weathertightness, etc. was found to be significantly worse in new-build than in rehab dwellings.

Roofs

The BRE's records show that about a quarter of all failures investigated up to around 1970 were for roofs and roofing, and that this had increased to about one third in the 1980s. Flat roof defects outnumbered pitched by more than two to one, and finishes were slightly more significant than structure. Roofing faults can lead to serious problems; Construction Quality Forum (CQF) figures indicate that a high proportion of them result in litigation. Recently, changes in insulation requirements have resulted in numerous faults relating to lack of ventilation, cold bridging, and failures to observe regulations. The BRE indicates a worsening situation with roofs.

Floors

The BRE believes avoidable defects occur too often. A high proportion of enquiries received by their advisory service concerns floors. BRE data suggests that about 30 per cent of all housing faults relate to floors – about two thirds of them to faults shared with other elements.

Figure 5.6: **Faults in flooring in new housing.**

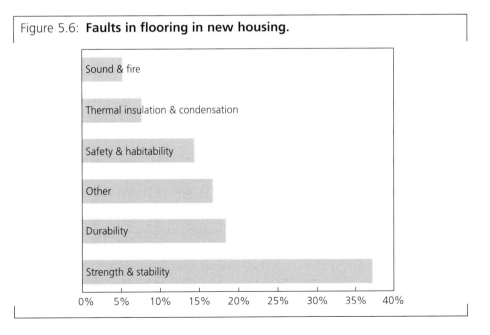

Recent figures indicate that about three quarters of floor defects relate to finishes. Especially significant are the consequences of not allowing sufficient time for concrete slabs to dry. Increased insulation requirements are causing ventilation and cold-bridging problems – especially in ground floors. Upper floors in housing are predominantly suspended timber, and although many faults occur most are minor (Fig 5.6).

Services

The BRE claim that most building services perform well, but that avoidable defects often occur. Their housing data gives no clear indication of how these are distributed among water, gas, electrical and other services. As has been noted, CQF data, which relate mainly to non-domestic building, allocate no more than seven per cent of defects to services, a figure which is divided as shown in Fig. 5.7.

Figure 5.7: **Proportion of defects which relate to service installations.**

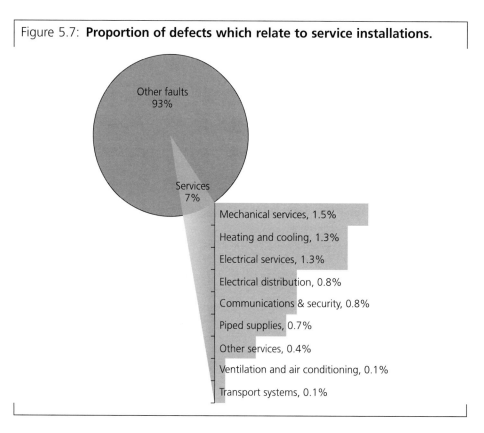

Other faults 93%

Services 7%

Mechanical services, 1.5%

Heating and cooling, 1.3%

Electrical services, 1.3%

Electrical distribution, 0.8%

Communications & security, 0.8%

Piped supplies, 0.7%

Other services, 0.4%

Ventilation and air conditioning, 0.1%

Transport systems, 0.1%

Another recent survey records that house purchasers' complaints concerning unidentified defects in surveyors' reports related mainly to damp – followed by damage, rot and leaks.[54] Most frequently mentioned were roofs. Many complaints related to gas and electricity supplies.

Mechanisms of failure

The basic scientific principles underlying the prevention, diagnosis and cure of building defects have been known, and have not changed, for centuries. See, for example, the works of Lucretius, written about 55 BC:

> *Again, if there were no empty space, everything would be one solid mass; if there were no material objects with the property of filling the space they occupy, all existing space would be utterly void. It is clear, then, that there is an alternation of matter and vacuity, mutually distinct, since the whole is neither completely full nor completely empty. There are therefore solid bodies, causing the distinction between empty space and full. And these, as I have just shown, can be neither decomposed by blows from without nor invaded and unknit from within nor destroyed by any other form of assault. For it seems that a thing without vacuum can be neither knocked to bits nor snapped nor chopped in two by cutting; nor can it let in moisture or seeping cold or piercing fire, the universal agents of destruction. The more vacuum a thing contains within it, the more readily it yields to these assailants. Hence, if the units of matter are solid and without vacuity, as I have shown, they must be everlasting.*[55]

In essence, Lucretius holds that the more a material contains voids, the more susceptible it is to damage by imposed loads, moisture and temperature extremes. The only agents of destruction which he does not appear to consider in this extract are chemical and biological.

Physical faults in buildings, considered in terms of building physics and materials science, most commonly arise from one of the following:

- interactions with materials from the atmosphere, occupants, etc.;
- overloading the building or parts thereof;
- thermally induced changes; and
- biological organisms.

These may give rise to:

- alterations in the characteristics of the materials from which the building is made. This may critically alter their properties, i.e. strength, permeability, etc.;
- alterations in the stress distribution in the building, causing anything from minor cracking to collapse;

- dimensional and weight changes;
- changes in appearance.

Alterations in the characteristics of the materials from which the building is made may result from:

- fire;
- interaction with other materials;
- biological organisms; and
- solar radiation.

Structural alterations may result from:

- applied loads including those from ground movements;
- fire; and
- climatic conditions.

Dimensional and weight changes may arise from:

- applied loads;
- interaction with other materials; and
- change of temperature.

Changes in appearance may arise from:

- wear;
- fire;
- interaction with materials;
- change of temperature; and
- solar radiation.

The above categories are a useful structure for analysing the most complex-seeming failure mechanisms and for preparing evidence to assist an advocate in a dispute where the evidence is likely to be subject to hostile scrutiny and challenge. Dealing with the commonest complaints in buildings, a more limited categorisation is often sufficient, as follows:

- the action of water, either by causing visible dampness or through secondary effects such as rot, etc.;
- the action of applied forces generally leading to the appearance of cracks; and
- the effects of dimensional changes in components of the building.

These categories are by no means exclusive. For example, dimensional changes may be caused by moisture or load and may result in cracking. The cracking, in turn, may allow water ingress, the damage thus involving a sometimes complex interaction of mechanisms. Effective diagnosis involves tracing the path from the visible symptoms, through each stage, to the initial cause.

Basic causes of defects

Ultimately, defects in materials may be regarded as arising in poor design or workmanship. It is arguable that a material itself cannot be faulty, only incorrectly used. For example, using green, rotting or damaged timber for floor joists will result in faults in the floor after construction. Neither a competent designer nor a skilled worker would select such timber where dimensional stability and durability were required; it is incompetent action that causes the building defect.

Paradoxically, the careful selection of flawless timber may give rise to an allegation of faulty materials.

> Some 25 years ago, the following problem was encountered in a new terraced housing development in Milton Keynes:
>
> The floors had been designed so that the living room floor joists were at their maximum spans. The contractor, a cautious and conscientious man, carefully selected knot-free timber for the longer spans. On completion, these floors were disturbingly mobile. People crossing their living room floors excited resonant oscillations, causing furniture at the edges of the rooms to hop gently towards them.
>
> The floors were moving safely within their elastic limit and were acceptably level under dead load. However, the knotty joists, which were so carefully selected out, would, if left in, have randomly stiffened as well as potentially weakened the floor.

In the above example, the joists had been carefully selected to be the 'best of their respective kinds'. The structural design, as an exercise in applied mathematics, was correct and accorded with published guidance. The floors were not 'fit for purpose' because footfall caused unacceptably large resonant oscillations.

The materials were blamed for the fault, in that they were insufficiently stiff to provide stability, although considered solely in terms of the quality of the material the living room floor joists were consistently the best of the structural timbers used in the building!

Defects often arise because the designer does not consider how materials will behave during construction and during the life of the building.

It is fundamental to good building practice that the design takes into account the process of construction. Concrete, for example, is unlikely to be built as a monolithic mass. Each part of a concrete structure will be limited to that which can be built in a single working day. If the inevitability of day joints is considered in the design, their effects on strength can be controlled. It is less certain that their effect on the watertightness of the concrete can be controlled, but good design – which takes into account construction techniques – can greatly reduce the risk of impaired performance.

Good communication between designers and building workers helps to resolve problems. Some designers' lack of practical knowledge is all too apparent to site staff when they are asked to work from ill-conceived drawn details. This encourages building workers to pay scant regard to detailed designs and to implement their own ideas of how to build, working round what they see as bad designs rather than discussing them with the designers. This is particularly common in design-and-build contracts where the builder stands to gain no contractual advantage from drawing attention to design defects.

During an investigation of a dispute between a Dutch contractor and manufacturer over a new partly built factory, the project engineer's drawings were studied.

Part of the ground-bearing concrete floor slab had been carried down to form a lift pit. The drawings showed asphalt tanking to the outside of the pit walls and floor.

Had the work been built to the drawing, it would no doubt have performed adequately.

The problem was that the asphalt would have had to be applied to the concrete after the concrete had been formed. As it was to be applied to the outside of the concrete, this would have involved sending in a team of miners to tunnel under the lift pit with picks in one hand and buckets of steaming asphalt in the other. As this seemed somewhat unlikely, the site agent was asked to explain what he had built.

His immediate and firm answer was that he had built precisely what was drawn. With proper acknowledgement of the admiration due to the mining skills of the asphalters, the impracticability of building what was drawn was spelled out to the site agent. He immediately changed his story and claimed he had recognised he could not build what was drawn and had obtained revised instructions from the engineer, which were, of course, fully recorded, he said, in his site instruction book. Invited to show the revised instruction, he spent some ten to fifteen minutes thumbing through a handwritten journal without success.

It was impracticable to build the detail as drawn. The lift pit had not been tanked. The contractor was in breach of contract but, at the source of the problem, was the failure of the designer to consider how what he had drawn was to be built.

Figure 5.8: **If the design doesn't permit building in a logical sequence it is not likely to be followed.**

As well as the worsening of communication caused by the often shifted sands of truth on a building site, the above problem illustrates the potential pitfalls of isolating the designer from site work. This can militate against both a good understanding of what is buildable and close co-operation between designers and site workers.

Figure 5.9: **'Map' cracking to render which was specified to current British practice, but which was poorly applied on a site which lacked both trade supervision and competent professional inspection during the work. The cracks have been inappropriately repaired in a hard epoxy mortar.**

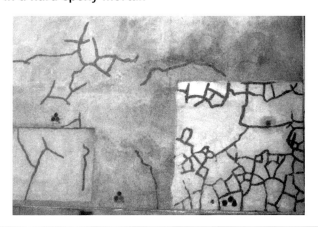

The best design is of no value if workmanship is inadequate. Good design assists workers but it does not prevent errors on site. Site supervision and inspection can catch bad work but it cannot create good work. Skilled tradesmen cannot safely be replaced by unskilled workers no matter how good the inspection and supervision.

The dimensional stability of materials

Equally important in understanding the process of building is for designers to understand the behaviour of the materials they specify, not only during construction but throughout the life of the building.

Ceramics, for example, tend to expand gradually throughout their life. Conversely, cementitious materials tend to contract irreversibly after their initial cure. These movements are small but the forces involved may, if the movement is restrained, be substantial. There is nothing to stop glazed clay tiles providing a satisfactory finish to concrete walls if the differential movements caused by the characteristics of the materials are allowed for in the design. There have nevertheless been many failures of tiling to concrete buildings.

Many problems are caused by a failure to recognise that building materials are not dimensionally stable. In particular their response to temperature changes and, in some cases, to changes in moisture content, can cause movement damage or stress failure.

If we ignore, for the moment, the drying effects of heating, it can be assumed that the components of a building will tend to expand on heating and to contract on cooling. These dilations and contractions are reciprocal movements: a material which has expanded on heating will return to its original dimensions when it cools to its original temperature.

Within limits, for many commonly used materials the rate of thermal expansion is uniform and can be expressed as a characteristic of the material: the coefficient of linear expansion. That is, for a given material, there is a constant relationship between change in temperature and change in size. At temperature extremes this rule tends not to hold. For some materials, the temperature range over which the relationship between size and temperature is constant is small: asbestos cement sheets for example. The coefficient of linear expansion nonetheless allows useful predictions to be made of orders of magnitude of thermal movements within normal UK environments.

Where these reciprocal movements are restrained, this will cause a build-up of stresses in the materials. Depending upon the range of temperatures to which they are subject and on the strength of the materials, this may create internal stresses which the materials cannot withstand and result in their being displaced or damaged.

With most inorganic materials used in building, the amount of movement caused by changes in temperature, once the materials are cured or set, is very much greater than the amount of movement caused by changes in moisture content. Organic materials, such as timber, may not respond in so uniform a way and may react more to changes in moisture than changes in temperature.

When timber takes up moisture it swells preferentially in one direction. This moisture-induced movement is typically large by comparison with the movements caused by heating and cooling. However, heating air without adding water vapour causes a drop in relative humidity. This will tend to result in the timber drying so as to bring its moisture content into equilibrium with the air around it. Thus, heating the building can cause relatively large hygral movements in the timber components within it.

It is normal practice in modern building to incorporate movement control in construction so as to relieve the stresses which would otherwise be caused by restrained movements. The purpose of movement control joints is not simply to accommodate the movements within materials but also to control the otherwise adverse effects anticipated from differential movements between dissimilar materials. It is, for example, common practice to form a movement joint between a timber floor and a masonry wall, allowing both materials to move independently of each other.

Allowance can be made for differential movement by either allowing for small movements at every joint or for large movements at regular intervals. In timber flooring, for example, this principle can be applied by leaving all board joints slightly open or by forming movement control joints at intervals, so dividing the floor into bays.

A lack of consideration of the dimensional instability of materials and the differences in their characteristics is an error that underlies many problems encountered in buildings. Traditional detailing provided for this by covering junctions at which differential movements would express themselves as cracks. The 'modern movement' departed from this tradition, regarding decorative mouldings as non-functional, outmoded affectations. Losing sight of the need to either control or mask the effects of differential movements typically results in visible cracking. Even where this is otherwise non-damaging, it may be condemned as deterioration due to faults in work rather than accepted as the natural and inevitable consequence of aging.

The characteristics of materials

Solids which share common characteristics can conveniently be reviewed in broad classes: cement-based materials, ceramics, metals, polymers and timber. A combination of two or more of these materials to produce a new material, whose properties would not be attainable by conventional means, is called a composite. Examples of composites include steel-reinforced concrete and fibre-reinforced plastics.

Materials commonly referred to as plastics, sealants and mastics fall within the class of polymers. The other group of organic materials which are of great significance in building are those based on cellulose fibre – such as wood – which are usefully considered as a separate category from man-made polymeric materials.

As a rule, rigid plastics in buildings have high rates of thermally induced dilations and low rates of hygral movements. Their abilities to deform plastically and elastically are varied. Their resistance to water in its liquid phase is usually high. Permeability to water vapour is varied and often higher than that of metals. They are vulnerable to chemical attack and may alter their behaviour with temperature changes.

Metals characteristically have large coefficients of thermal expansion, although less than that of many plastics. They are impermeable to water in all naturally occurring phases and are good conductors of heat and electricity. With few exceptions, they are susceptible to corrosion.

Traditional ceramics are made by applying heat to naturally occurring forms of earth (sands and clays). Modern ceramics include more complex and precise processes, often with man-made ingredients. In relation to traditional building materials, ceramics can be said to encompass both glass and brick. Traditional glass is a translucent, lustrous, hard and brittle material made by fusing soda or potash (or both) with other ingredients which, when solidified from a molten state, do not adopt a regular internal (crystalline) structure. Classically, bricks are formed from a stiff tenacious fine-grained earth, consisting mainly of hydrated aluminosilicates, which is wetted to make it plastic, and then kneaded, moulded, and baked or sun-dried. Ceramics have a wide range of characteristics.

The behaviour of wood depends on its growth cycles and species. Because it is a natural organic material, each piece of wood exhibits individual properties. Materials made from processed wood, such as plywood and chipboard, exhibit more uniform properties.

Polymers and plastics

One increasingly common constituent of building components is polymers. These are usually compounds comprising long molecules formed from organic monomers. For example, ethylene is a monomer which may be polymerised into polyethylene (which is more commonly referred to in the UK as 'polythene').

More complex polymers can be formed from mixes of monomers. For example, ethylene + vinyl acetate monomers can be polymerised together to form an ethylene vinyl acetate copolymer (e.g. PVA adhesive).

Rubber is a familiar material based on a naturally occurring polymer (vulcanised latex extracted from the sap of the Hevea tree). However, there are now synthetic rubbers, or elastomers, the percentage differences in whose constituents can lead to major variations in properties.

The term 'rubber' may now be used to mean any of the following:

- synthetic butyl rubbers (made of isobutane – isoprene copolymers);
- synthetic styrene butadiene rubbers (formed by copolymerisation of styrene and butadiene);
- synthetic butadiene rubber (produced by polymerisation of butadiene monomers in organic solvents);
- ethylene propylene rubbers (which are copolymers of ethylene and propylene);
- chloroprene rubbers (which are polymers of chloroprene that are similar in chemical structure to isoprene); and
- polyurethane rubbers (including polyester and polyether varieties containing urethane links).

These elastomers, whilst often referred to as rubber, have sufficiently dissimilar properties that it is imprudent to assume that something which looks like and is called rubber will exhibit the same properties as another 'rubber'. It is likely that all 'rubbers', whether synthetic or natural, will exhibit certain family characteristics such as the ability to deform elastically under load. Their differences are not likely to be readily discernible and sometimes it may be difficult even to recognise the presence of a rubber. For example, Styrene Butadiene Rubber (SBR) may, in aqueous dispersion, be added to concrete to form a polymer-modified concrete. To the naked eye no rubber is present, yet the behaviour of the concrete may be critically affected by the synthetic rubber within it.

The selection of appropriate kinds of, and making appropriate use of, rubber depends on the properties of the elastomers, the objectives to be achieved and the environment in which they are to be used. For example, the addition of a polymer to concrete may improve certain of its physical characteristics while at the same time increasing its susceptibility to chemical attack. The trick is to correctly balance the advantage of polymer modification with the risk of chemical degradation. For some polymer-modified concretes a persistently damp environment may be all that is required for the polymer to degrade.

Organic polymers can be conveniently grouped into families. The list below gives a convenient grouping of polymers commonly used in construction.

Rubber	Natural polymer, used in waterproof membranes, flexible seals, water bars, bridge bearings, electrical installations, etc.
Thermosetting plastics	Synthetic polymers including bakelite and formaldehyde resins
Thermoplastics	Synthetic polymers that can be remoulded in shape by heating, including plasticized polyvinyl chloride (pvc), unplasticised polyvinyl chloride (pvc-U), polyethylene (PE), high density polyethylene (HDPE), ultra-high molecular weight polyethylene (UHMWPE), etc.
Natural resins	Shellac and oleoresins used mainly in coatings and castings

Polymer composites	Polyesters and glass-reinforced plastics, used in laminations and sheets
Polymer emulsions and dispersions	Dispersion of polymers in non-solvents like epoxy resins in water for floor coatings
Seals and sealants	Preformed water bars and joint seals

In addition to organic polymers, which are based on the carbon-carbon bond, some materials based on the silica-silica bond are sometimes considered as polymers:

Inorganic polymer	Formed by silicone chains, used for hydrophobic properties

Polymers are used in admixtures such as floor hardeners, grouts, tile adhesives and joint fillers, industrial flooring, and polymer concrete. They can be formed into water-proofing membranes and sealants, and feature in modern paints and coatings.

Rubbers (or elastomers) occur in a wide range of building products such as fixtures, fittings, piping and hoses. They are also used in civil engineering in roads, railways, bridges and mining. There are a wide variety of elastomers, making their use a matter of appropriate selection to obtain the right properties for each application.

Typical applications include:

- seals and flexible joints;
- coatings to protect vulnerable materials from abrasion or corrosion;
- to protect structures from vibration shock;
- roofing EPDM (Ethylene Propylene Diene Monomer), CSM (a chlorosulfonated polyethylene synthetic rubber such as DuPont's Hypalon) or pvc;
- damp-proof membranes (natural rubbers);
- additives to cementitious materials;
- anti-vibration mountings/mats;
- electrical cable and flex;
- waterproofing membranes for ponds, pools, etc. (butyl rubbers);
- bridge-deck movement-control joints (plain elastomers, laminated rubber and steel, etc.); and
- rubberized wearing surfaces to roads.

Faults involving polymers

The chemical reactions which form polymers are often reversible, and polymers may depolymerise while in use. That is, the polymer chains may shorten or revert to the monomers from which they were made. As the molecular chains shorten, the material may typically lose tensile strength and become more brittle. An example is unplasticised polyvinyl chloride (pvc-U), a thermoplastic. Ultraviolet radiation (exposure to the sun) can excite its molecules at the right frequency to reactivate the polymerisation process. Both depolymerisation and repolymerisation can occur simultaneously, the mix of short and long polymer chains changing until equilibrium is reached. When equilibrium occurs, if the proportion of long molecules is reduced this may be perceived as the pvc-U window frames, rainwater pipes, etc. becoming gradually less resilient – and brittle failure in less than ten years has resulted.

Adding inhibitors (which slow this process) and plasticizers and additives to retard the evaporation of volatile fractions (each of the portions, differing in physical or chemical properties, into which a mixture may be separated (usually by fractal distillation)) can extend the working life of pvc-U when exposed to sunlight. For this reason, good-quality modern pvc-U building products can be expected to last longer than ten years in the sun, and a service life of 30 years or more is often predicted for modern pvc-U. The difficulty faced by specifier and builder alike is that the physical characteristics of new pvc-U do not readily reveal whether it contains a suitable cocktail of inhibitor and additives or not. The probable longevity of the plastic cannot be assessed by unaided human senses, and the user has increasingly to rely on the promises and representations of product manufacturers.

Seeking to confirm the future performance of polymer-based products from past performance is especially difficult. Manufacturers of building products generally buy the chemicals they use on the open market and may seek to buy the same polymer each time at the lowest price. Each of their suppliers may vary their source materials for similar economic reasons. The many stages in manufacture, from the extraction of the raw materials through the synthesis of the monomers and their polymerisation to the forming of the finished products, each contain opportunities for variations to be introduced. These may each appear harmless in isolation and the newly made, finished product may appear unchanged. Nevertheless, seemingly inconsequential changes may combine to make the finished product's longevity vary significantly from batch to batch.

A manufacturer produced an imitation Welsh roofing slate using slate particles bonded together with resin. The manufacturer had the product independently tested by a reputable independent body and published the results. The tests showed his man-made slate to be a serviceable product.

In time failures became apparent. Initial inspection of one poorly performing roof showed many slates to have concave curves, and the tiling to be loose. It was decided to re-roof with the same materials, which the slate manufacturer agreed to provide free of charge.

The remedial work commenced in early summer. The new tiles were checked and appeared to be fine. After the first slope to be renewed was about one quarter tiled, many slates were found to be loose. Initially, poor workmanship was suspected and the nailing was checked. Some nail heads were found to be proud of the slates.

Under the midday sun, the foreman noted that he could bend and straighten new slates. This plasticity was not apparent in the 'dished' slates already laid.

Further study revealed that when the new slates were first heated in the sun they became plastic. This 'second' heating fully cured the resin, so setting the slates in the shape they adopted in the midday sun.

The tiles were fixed as centre-nailed slates. As the slating progressed the load on the lower tiles increased. Under their first exposure to full sun the tiles softened and deformed to settle down onto the slating battens under the load of the slates in the courses above. This allowed the tiles to become loose and made it appear that the nails had not been drive fully home. One they cooled, the tiles set and no longer softened when hot.

For each production run, the manufacturers sourced the products used on the open market, unaware that the resins they bought could exhibit significantly differing characteristics despite each supply having the same generic description. The tiles failed when the resin was sufficiently different to that used in the development and initial testing of the product for it not to be fully cured in the manufacturing process. The result was that many tiles were delivered to building sites as a rigid material only to become plastic when heated, after which they cooled and became rigid.

The manufacturer went out of business rather than face up to the cost of replacing the defective material he had supplied. This was a third-generation resin-bonded man-made slate. The technology was not new. A fundamental error in manufacture was made which was not discernible by any normal site check. It came to light because of the re-roofing work carried out in hot weather under close supervision.

Concretes, mortars, screeds, renders and plasters

Concrete is essentially reconstructed stone. Particles of stone are cemented together with an inorganic paste – in current work, usually ordinary Portland cement. The smaller particles are called 'fines' (commonly sand) and the larger particles 'aggregate' (crushed rock) – although concrete can be made without fines or without coarse aggregate. When made without coarse aggregate – as, say, a render or mortar – it is not normally called concrete, but for the purpose of defects analysis it is useful to understand the similarities between these cementitious materials.

Concrete

The properties of concretes will depend on the raw materials from which they are made, the way they are made and the conditions to which they are exposed, particularly when young.

Concrete is an ancient material and has evolved over millennia. The oldest concrete ever found is in Galilee and is around 9,000 years old. This lime concrete, used for infill, was made of a mixture of burnt limestone, water and stones. Concrete was known in ancient Egypt and was in use in Greece by 500 BC – where, as with much else, it is probable that the Romans copied the idea. They were certainly using and developing concrete technology by around 300 BC.

Roman builders discovered that by mixing the lime with volcanic ash (pozzolano) they could make much stronger concrete, which would even set under water. They also developed very lightweight concrete using pumice as aggregate. Roman attempts to strengthen their concrete by adding rods of bronze were unsuccessful. The bronze expanded in the heat faster than the concrete, resulting in cracking. By the first century AD, concrete was in use all over the Roman Empire. In Britain, the 75 mile long Hadrian's Wall was constructed by pouring concrete over piles of rocks and stones. Once this was set, the next layer was created in the same way.

Portland cement

The modern development of concrete only goes back to 1824, with a UK manufacturing patent for Portland cement. The Victorians developed the technology apace, building lighthouses, stately homes and industrial buildings in this fashionable new material and, in 1854, William Wilkinson, a Newcastle builder, took out a patent for embedding flat iron bars or wire ropes in floors and beams of concrete. Precast concrete came into use as a substitute for stone by 1870. In 1904 the first British Standard for Portland cement was published.

Portland cement is made from quarried limestones and shales. The quarried materials are analysed for the gross elemental composition and then carefully mixed according to the type of Portland cement required (forming the raw 'meal'), fed into a kiln and burnt until the different elements diffuse and the minerals fuse together to form cement clinker. This process may vary, with significant effect on the properties of each cement made. The clinker is cooled in a controlled manner, ground into a fine grey-blue powder and packed into bags.

When the anhydrous cement is mixed with water the cement grains dissolve in the water. The hydration product thus formed acts as glue, sticking the sand and coarse aggregates together.

Cement is a random mixture of different materials (or 'phases'). As these different phases are randomly distributed throughout the cement grain, they are exposed at different points all over the surface of the cement grain. Not all the phases dissolve into the water at the same rate or at the same time, so when water is added to the cement grains little regions of hydration product are formed on their surfaces.

Gradually the hydration regions extend and coalesce to form a complete cover over the whole cement grain – a hydration sphere.

Figure 5.10: 'Map' cracking produced during curing, which becomes visible on light wetting but which is too fine to see with the naked eye when the material is dry.

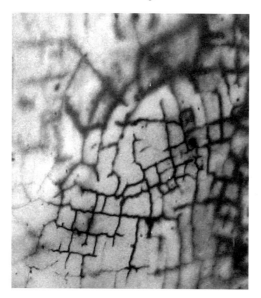

As time continues more material dissolves from the cement grain and is transported by water through the hydration sphere to outer edge of the sphere where the material falls out of solution. It is this envelopment of the sand grains by the hydration sphere which causes the concrete to harden.

A second hydration sphere begins to form as some of the slower phases begin to hydrate, and this expands to fill the space occupied by the first hydration sphere.

At this time the two hydration spheres are different and are known as the outer (first) and inner (second) hydration sphere. This is the reason young concrete gains strength after being mixed with water.

Cement chemists use a peculiar notation. For example, C_2S using standard chemical notation is di-Carbon Sulphide, a nonsensical compound. However, C_2S in cement notation represents $(CaO)_2SiO_2$. Using abbreviated chemical notations such as: $C=CaO$ and $S=SiO_2$, allows the easy manipulation of expressions for complex hydrates.

The different phases contribute different amounts to the short-term and long-term strength of the concrete. The silicate-containing phases contribute most to the overall performance of the concrete. The gain in strength continues as the cement grains dissolve. The cement grains never finish hydrating; the process slows down exponentially but never stops.

This process of curing, whilst initially exothermic and expansive, results in overall shrinkage which is proportionate to the amount of water used. This causes stresses which if well controlled result in harmless micro-cracking, but bad practice can allow significant cracks to develop.

Reinforced concrete

Concrete characteristically exhibits high compressive and low tensile strength. To achieve a more useful balance of tensile and compressive properties concrete is often reinforced with steel, which itself exhibits good tensile strength but is relatively flexible. Burying steel bars within the concrete combines the advantages of both materials: the steel reinforcement bars act as springs, improving the concrete's resistance to cracking under flexural stress, whilst the concrete provides the rigidity the steel otherwise lacks. Steel reinforcement is similarly used in some masonry mortars, renders and screeds. Alternatives to mild steel are increasingly used to improve resistance to weathering.

Faults involving concrete

An appreciation of how concretes decay comes from an understanding of how they are created. From the moment it is cast, the concrete is under attack from nature.

The first wave of assault occurs from the atmosphere. Concrete is highly alkaline – an attribute beneficial in reinforced concrete, where it inhibits the oxidation of steel reinforcement – but carbon dioxide in the air reacts with concrete, reducing its alkalinity.

The action of the carbon dioxide reduces the alkalinity of the concrete by reacting to form carbonates – a process commonly called 'carbonation', the effect of which is to increase the vulnerability of the steel reinforcement bars to oxidation (rusting).[56] When iron (or steel) is oxidised, it expands. For this reason, when steel reinforcement in concrete rusts it presses on the surrounding material, ultimately causing cracking and spalling (see Chapter 7, Example: Corrosion Damage, for further explanation of carbonation).

Ordinary water poses some risk to finished concrete. Cement hydrates are soluble to some degree and can slowly dissolve over time. The amount of water present in the environment of the concrete can lead to changes in the type of hydrates formed – which, in turn, can change the physical dimensions of the concrete, leading to cracking and exposure of anhydrous cement grains deep within its matrix. Exposed grains can then continue to hydrate with renewed vigour.

The amount of water can influence the type of hydrate formed. Depending on the cements present, this can cause complications. Ordinary cements expand briefly as they are wetted and then shrink gradually as they cure. Sulphates and aluminates can modify the hydration process. Some cements – such as anhydrite (anhydrous

Figure 5.11: **Steel beads corroding under cement render, forming a crack in the render along the edge of the bead. The mode of failure is similar to that caused by corrosion of steel reinforcing bars in concrete but, because the bead is close to the surface of the render, the failure is rapid and visible soon after it starts. (The dark areas are the rust stains spreading over the face of the render.)**

calcium sulphate) and anhydrous calcium sulphoaluminate (which hydrates to form ettringite) – expand significantly as they hydrate. This can disrupt the cement matrix and cause cracking. Terms such as 'sulphate attack' and 'concrete cancer' are sometimes used to describe serious deterioration caused by the formation of such expansive hydrates in rigid concrete.

If the cement matrix has holes in it, the crystals may be weakly attached to each other. This reduces strength and assists CO_2 diffusion through the matrix, allowing carbonation at depth.

The alkalinity which maintains the stability of steel reinforcement within concrete can also readily influence the morphology and type of hydrates being formed within the concrete matrix. The potential permutations which may be caused by variations in water and alkalinity during hydration are numerous and can be significant both in initial performance and in durability.

Water readily dissolves many inorganic salts. This can lead to potentially dangerous effects which may destroy the concrete. Aqueous solutions can initiate various problems. For example, groundwater or sewage may be a rich source of sulphates. The effect on concrete of sulphate-rich waters is the (often expansive) formation of different hydrates, which can occur very rapidly – in a matter of hours in some cases. Associated dimensional changes at the surface of the concrete generate cracks, which act as capillaries for the transport of water and sulphates deeper into the concrete.

Figure 5.12: **Floor failure as ettringite formation causes a screed to expand.**

Cracking exposes anhydrous cement grains, allowing the further formation of hydrates – which, in turn, expand and further propagate the crack. This process continues as the concretes disintegrate.

The formation of thaumasite, a crystal with similar properties to that of ettringite, causes high rates of expansion. Ideal conditions for the formation of thaumasite hydrate are:

- wet, sulphate-rich water; in contact with
- calcium-silicate-rich high-alkalinity cement matrix; and
- exposure to cold and vibration.

Salts in water solution form ions. Some ions, in solution, act on concrete in unexpected ways. Sodium ions, for example, migrate from the water into the concrete matrix but do not, as might be expected, spread throughout the concrete matrix. Instead, they congregate at a certain depth within the concrete and this increase in alkali metal ions at depth within the concrete causes the aggregate to react within the concrete – leading to expansion and, typically, to depth cracking.

This is often referred to as an 'alkali–silica' reaction. The consequential decomposition of the concrete is influenced by the type and reactivity of the aggregate used. When a susceptible piece of concrete is exposed, the whole of its surface tends to show expansive cracking. The visible surface cracking may include the 'Isle of Man' three-way crack – a typical indicator of dimensional change within rigid matrices.

Many problems with concrete come from abuse, cost cutting, bad practice and ignorance during construction.

An example of error due to lack of knowledge occurred during the UK post-war construction boom: the inclusion of calcium chloride as an accelerator for concrete, which allowed construction to take place more quickly. Similarly to failure due to loss of alkalinity, the resulting disruption of the matrix was centred on an attack on the steel reinforcement; chloride ions form electrochemical cells within the concrete and, under suitable conditions, the steel reinforcement corrodes causing conical plugs of concrete to spall off the surface.

Problems often arise if finishes are applied to concretes too early, particularly if they are relatively impermeable – for example, floor coverings on concrete ground slabs.

A solid floor is often the slowest part of a building to dry out. For example, the rate of drying of a 50 mm screed is about 1 mm per day. For thicker screeds, screeds which are directly bonded to the slab, or for power floated floors, it can take considerably longer – perhaps a year or more.

Electrical-resistance meters are of limited value when assessing the moisture content of a concrete floor or sand-and-cement screed. The gel bridge method, where measurements are made at depth within the material, provides a quick indication where the meter is correctly calibrated for the cement/sand mix ratio. However, when polymers and other additives are incorporated this can affect conductivity and cause moisture readings based on electrical-resistance measurements to be inaccurate, usually too high.

More accurate measurements of moisture content can be obtained with hygrometric measurements. This method involves measuring the relative humidity of air trapped in contact with the screed or concrete. It is necessary to leave the air trapped for several days in order for equilibrium to be established prior to taking the readings, and is good practice to repeat the readings at, say, four-hour intervals, two or three times until no variation in measurements is seen.

It is the coarse pores in concrete which release water first, because the water in them exerts a higher vapour pressure than that in fine pores. Because the size of the pores controls the vapour pressure that arises in them, it also controls the vapour pressure of a small volume of air entrapped between the concrete surface and hygrometer. The relative humidity of this trapped air is dependent upon the vapour pressure and so measurements of relative humidity of the trapped air, after it has gone into equilibrium with the moisture in the concrete, give a good indication of the remaining amount of potentially harmful water in the concrete or screed. It is customarily accepted that when the relative humidity falls to 75 per cent or less the concrete or screed is sufficiently dry to accept impermeable coverings without a risk of subsequent delamination due to water movement.

This method has on occasion proved difficult when used for measuring concrete screeds in relatively open positions, where drying of the concrete may periodically go into reverse due to fluctuations in atmospheric vapour pressures such as may occur in the early morning when dew is forming.

Lime mortars

Prior to the introduction of ordinary Portland cement, limes were widely used as the cement in mortars, etc. There are two basic types of lime for traditional lime mortars – those that set and harden by reaction with air and those that do so by reaction with water (non-hydraulic and hydraulic limes respectively). Of the latter type there are sub-varieties.

Non-hydraulic limes are made from relatively pure forms of calcium carbonate (e.g. chalk or limestone) burned in a kiln to produce calcium oxide (quicklime). When this is then reacted (slaked) with water it produces calcium hydroxide (hydrated lime). Calcium hydroxide reacts (carbonates) with carbon dioxide in the air to reform calcium carbonate, i.e. the composition of the raw material originally used to make the lime. In a mortar mix it is this setting that binds together particles of sand and bonds it to the masonry units. The setting process is slow, taking several weeks to gain a basic working strength, and many months, or even years, to reach ultimate strength throughout. The setting is dependent on air and not on water.

Hydraulic limes come from naturally occurring deposits of calcium carbonate which include small amounts of other minerals – very often clay or silt. When burned in a kiln, the calcium carbonate forms calcium oxide. The impurities form calcium silicates and aluminates that will chemically react with water to harden regardless of the presence of air. In the manufacturing process just sufficient water is added to the kiln product to hydrate the calcium oxide, forming calcium hydroxide in a dry powder form, but not enough to promote setting of the calcium silicates and aluminates. The material is bagged and stored dry to prevent the commencement of setting by atmospheric moisture.

The composition of raw materials from different sources varies greatly, and variations in the impurities present influence the setting and hardening characteristics of the lime produced. In practice, hydraulic limes are graded according to the rate and ultimate strength of their set and they are described as 'feebly', 'moderately' and 'eminently' hydraulic limes.

Where natural limes were not sufficiently hydraulic, traditional practice included the use of additives (pozzolans) such as brick dust from a kiln or furnace ashes to improve setting and ultimate strength. Mortars made with eminently hydraulic limes and/or pozzolan additives can, in strength and hardness, resemble mixes containing Portland cements. With traditional limes success depends on a good appreciation of the variant used.

Because of the limited independent written authority on the performance of lime-based mixes, care is needed when considering their use. For instance, a lime mortar of comparable compressive strength to a Portland-cement-bound mortar does not necessarily have similar flexural strength, shear strength or durability. The lack of written authority is compounded by lime mortar's poor tolerance to adverse weather and the scarcity of workers who are familiar with its use.

Timber

Wood consists of large numbers of parallel tubes (cells) bonded together to create a strong fibrous structure. Across the grain these cells separate or crush quite easily, making the lateral tensile or compressive strength of timber quite low. Low-density timber such as spruce can be easily marked with a fingernail but, along its grain, has a tensile strength which, weight for weight, can be in the order of four times greater than mild steel.

The parallel cells which follow the direction of the trunk are visible as the wood grain when a board is cut. Some timber may contain cross-grained areas, with the grain not following the edge of the board. This is unavoidable around knots and may be caused deliberately in, for example, quarter-sawn oak boards. Cross-grain is an important factor to be taken into account when assessing strength.

Knots are the remains of branches in the log, are the hardest wood in the tree and always disturb grain direction, causing a reduction in tensile strength.

In cross section a tree trunk consists of a heartwood core, surrounded by sapwood. The whole is encased in bark, under which there is a very thin growth layer called the cambium. The heartwood core begins to form when the tree is around 30 years old, increasing annually in width thereafter.

The chemical structure of all timber species is similar, with approximately 75 per cent composed of cellulose and other sugar molecules, and the remaining 25 per cent a resin-like substance known as lignin, together with small amounts of various toxic chemicals that protect the wood against insects and fungi. Collectively, these chemicals are known as 'extractives' (since they are extraneous to the timber structure and can be extracted with the aid of solvents), and it is their presence which gives distinctive colour to the heartwood of some timber species.

Timbers from different tree species differ in appearance and density. Most of the mechanical properties of different timbers are proportionate to their densities, and a dense timber like oak is generally stronger than a less dense timber such as spruce. The stiffness of different timbers also varies roughly in proportion to their density.

Fast growth in trees produces wide growth rings; slow growth produces narrow rings. The width of these rings affects timber qualities (particularly density) and varies between different species. In softwoods, fast growth tends to reduce density and makes the timber more difficult to machine or work by hand.

For a small group of temperate hardwood species (including oak, ash and elm), density and strength is increased by fast growth. These 'ring porous' hardwoods are identifiable from a distinctive ring of large porous cells visible at the start of each growth ring. These characteristics have some practical implications. For example, fast-growth ash is suited to items which need to be as strong as possible, while slower-grown ash may be better for fine mouldings because it is less dense and easier to machine. With most hardwoods, however, there is little relationship between growth rate and density. Timber technologists group these hardwoods under the heading 'diffuse porous hardwoods'.

Timber is resilient under short-duration loads but tends to permanently distort under sustained loads.

The design strength of timber varies according to its species, grades and, to some extent, origin. Structural grading rules are laid down in BS 4978 (for softwoods) and BS 5756 (for hardwoods). Essentially, they place limits on relevant defects such as knots, slope of grain, wane (the amount by which a plank or roughly squared log falls short of a correctly squared shape; a bevelled edge left on a plank with one face narrower than the other; the imperfect angles of a rough-hewn log) fissures/splits and distortion. For hardwoods, the first two defects are more critical in determining the grade.

Timber may also be categorised by its dilation on wetting. All species of timber exhibit different responses to changes in moisture content.[57]

Faults involving timber

Various insects cause damage to timber, especially in the tropics. In the UK, the range of insect species that attack timber is limited by the cool climate, and consequently fungi are the main agents of biological degradation. Unable to synthesise carbo-hydrates for themselves, fungi look to carbohydrate-rich sources such as wood and spread by microscopic spores (which are everywhere in the environment in summer) These spores need moisture to grow, making timber with a moisture content of over 20 per cent vulnerable to fungal decay. To minimise this risk, timber needs to be properly dried and have details designed to avoid the spread of water from splashing, capillary action or water entrapment. Regular maintenance is essential. A fungal decay problem in a building can often be cured by ensuring that the timber is thoroughly dried and well ventilated, and that all sources of water ingress and condensation are removed. In severe cases, chemical treatments may be needed to control fungi while the structure dries out, but chemicals alone should not be relied upon to cure rot.

Different species of timber have evolved varying degrees of resistance to insect attack and fungal decay. This natural durability is caused by the presence of extractives in the heartwood. It is possible to classify timbers on the basis of heartwood durability, but these groupings are relative and only provide guidance to what will happen in the worst possible conditions. In less hazardous situations, the durability of a timber will be greater than the quoted figures and, in permanently dry conditions, all timbers are at little risk from biological degradation. Providing all the non-durable sapwood is removed, the heartwood of naturally durable timbers such as European oak or

121

European larch is suitable for use in areas likely to be exposed to risk of decay or insect attack, such as external cladding.

Chemical treatment of timber can prolong its life. This is most true for poor-quality timber, badly detailed work or any timber placed where it is at risk from fungal or insect attack. The use of naturally durable timber and designs based on a good understanding of the material can achieve longevity without resort to chemical preservatives. As the biocides present in treatments are hazardous, preservative-treated timber is hazardous waste. As a consequence, the use of preservative-treated wood needs to be carefully considered and justified if due regard is to be given to the requirements of the Construction (Design and Management) Regulations, Regulation 13(2).

Chemical preservatives are applied in various ways, but superficial applications such as painting or spraying are relatively ineffective and should usually be avoided. The most effective application methods involve the use of a pressure vessel to force the preservative deep into the timber (the depth of penetration is dependent upon the permeability of the timber, its moisture content and the length of treatment).

Drying timber

Timber is hygroscopic. When drier than its surroundings it will absorb moisture; when wetter, it will lose moisture. 'The equilibrium moisture content' occurs when the wood's moisture content is in balance with the relative humidity of the surrounding air.

This varies according to climate. In Scotland, timber protected from rain but otherwise exposed to ordinary moist air will eventually attain an equilibrium moisture content of around 16 per cent, whereas in Alaska (a very dry climate) moisture content is as low as five per cent. Changes in moisture content have a significant effect upon the durability, strength, shrinkage and swelling of timber.

Most of the moisture in a freshly felled tree is held as free water within its cell cavities. Removing this free water has no effect on the timber dimensions, but once the moisture content drops to below around 27 per cent all the free water has disappeared and further moisture losses must come from water absorbed by the cell walls. When timber dries below this level (the fibre saturation point), the cell walls begin to dry out and shrinkage occurs. Conversely, if a piece of dry timber becomes wet the cell walls swell until completely saturated. To minimise shrinkage and swelling in service, timber needs to be dried near to the equilibrium moisture content of the environment in which it will be used.

Changes in moisture content alter the mechanical properties of timber. Freshly felled wood is saturated and has only one-third of the strength and stiffness of dry wood. In cases where the timber cannot be uniformly dried – for example, large oak beams – the design should allow for the reduced strengths associated with wet timber (unseasoned structures such as traditional English oak barns tend to become much stronger as they dry out *in situ*).

Hardwoods supplied 'green' are cheaper than fully seasoned material. If the material is thicker than 100 mm, kilning is impracticable. Drying movement is both inevitable and significant and must be considered at the design stage. If the material has a significant slope of grain and the member is not braced, longitudinal distortions can occur. In addition, floor beams drying out under load tend to 'creep'. This is a difficult parameter to quantify, but creep deflection can be two or three times that calculated on an elastic basis.

Because the physical properties of wood are not uniform but tend to vary markedly with direction, the joints of a frame are generally more critical than the members themselves. There are three broad categories of joints:

- traditional, with the members in one plane passing loads from one member to another – primarily in end compression;
- pinned (nails/screws/bolts/connectors), which rely on lapping timbers and making a connection with the fastener in shear; and
- glued (possibly with bolts), using gap-filling epoxy glues to embed a steel rod in a drilled hole.

Green temperate hardwood, with its potential for movement, needs the appropriate traditional jointing such as pegged or dowelled connections which provide for adjustment as the wood moves and shrinks. As the predicted capacity of glued-in bolts is based on dry timber, it is unwise to consider their use with unseasoned material.

An alternative to drying large structural sections is to use glued-laminated structures. Built up from many small pieces of low moisture content timber, they are predictable and uniformly strong.

Treating timber

Woods are often coated with paints, stains or varnish.

Traditional lead-based paints proved very durable, as the lead is a good fungicide. Lead paints are sufficiently permeable to moisture, helping reduce fungal damage by preventing excessive condensation build-up under the paint.

General purpose gloss paints have more limited durability, particularly for outdoor use. The so called, 'microporous' exterior timber coatings should be better able to match the performance of old lead-based systems.

Opaque finishes are more durable than semi-opaque stains. A good modern opaque exterior coating should last about six years before recoating is required. Transparent exterior timber varnishes tend not to last very long.

Preservative treatments are best applied in factories under controlled conditions of temperature and pressure. The penetration of the preservative, which is important to its effectiveness, is more consistent in factory conditions.

Preservatives contain chemicals that can be injurious to health and to other materials. It is wise to check the compatibility of treated timber with the materials with which they will be in contact.

Composite timber products

To increase the versatility of timber, composite materials incorporating woods and glues have been developed. Each such product has its advantages and disadvantages.

To understand the behaviour of composite timber materials it is necessary to consider both the glues and the woods used. For example water and boil proof plywood (wbp) incorporates waterproof glues. These glues are typically highly resistant to the transmission of water vapour. The term 'wbp' does not impart information about the durability of the timber laminates. It follows that wbp may be exceptionally susceptible to condensation damage in, say, an insulated roof. Conversely, plywood made from naturally durable or preservative-treated timbers bound together with vapour-permeable glue may endure better in humid conditions but may damage metals in contact with it. Often terms such as 'wbp' and 'marine' are used to specify plywood without appropriate stipulations in respect of vapour resistance and the incorporation of potentially aggressive natural or added preservatives.

Glued-laminated ('glulam') timber comprises small planks glued together to make large sections of timber. The glue is usually formaldehyde based, requiring dry timber.

Oriented strand board (OSB) comes from forest thinnings. The logs are cut to length, debarked and processed into precise strands averaging 78 mm long and 25 mm wide. The strands are then dried, blended with resin binder and wax, and laid in a precisely oriented fashion to form large continuous mats. To increase strength, the strands are oriented in cross-directional layers and then bonded with moisture-resistant resins under high heat and pressure.

High-density particleboard has been developed as a dimensionally stable substrate for use in flooring.

Metal

The boundary between metallic and non-metallic elements is not firm. Carbon, a non-metal, exhibits many of the characteristics of metals and, along with iron, forms steel. Aluminium is usually regarded as a metal but chemically it is amphoteric, acting in the presence of strongly metallic substances as a non-metal.

Few metals are stable in their pure form. In nature, all but gold and platinum exist in combination with other elements, and once purified for use in building they will tend to revert to the compounds from which they were extracted – that is corrode – unless protected. Some metals (lead for example) form stable oxides which slow down the rate of corrosion. Some do not, and so need to be treated or coated for protection.

Metal alloys

Metals are rarely used in their pure form, but as alloys. For example, steel is an alloy of iron and carbon (containing less than 2 per cent carbon and 1 per cent manganese – and small amounts of silicon, phosphorus, sulphur and oxygen). The physical characteristics of alloys can be controlled by varying their constituents and the process of manufacture: for example, there are more than 3,500 different grades of steel.

Forming alloys provides one way of achieving corrosion resistance.

'Stainless steel' is a name developed, probably by the cutlery industry, for corrosion-resistant steels. The term is peculiar to some English-speaking countries. Similar alloys are available in other countries but the potentially misleading term 'stainless' is less likely to be used. While it has greater resistance to corrosion than other commonly used alloys of iron, it is not corrosion proof nor is it invariably stainless.

All stainless steels contain a minimum of 10.5 per cent chromium. Other alloying elements are added to enhance their structure and properties such as formability, strength and cryogenic toughness. These include nickel, molybdenum, titanium, copper, carbon and nitrogen.

Corrosion attacks the exposed surface of the metal.[58] The rate of corrosion failure depends on the characteristics of the corrosion products. For example, iron corrodes in air and water to form iron oxide. It expands as it oxidises, with the result that the oxide layer (rust) forces itself off the underlying uncorroded metal, exposing fresh iron and so allowing corrosion to continue. By contrast, lead oxidises to form a stable oxide layer which protects the underlying metal, so arresting corrosion at the surface.

Anodising aluminium uses this principle by forming a stable oxide layer on the surface of the aluminium under controlled conditions.[59] 'Stainless' steel is stainless because its heavy ions (chromium, etc.) migrate preferentially to the surface where they form a stable oxide layer inhibiting oxidation of the iron.

For surface oxidation to reliably inhibit corrosion the oxide must be passive (i.e. not react with or influence other materials), tenacious (cling to the underlying metal and not be transferred elsewhere) and self-renewing (if the film is damaged it will normally self-repair).

Even the most durable metals, like lead and stainless steel, cannot be considered indestructible. Their passive state can be broken down under certain conditions and corrosion can result. This is why it is important to select carefully the appropriate grade for a particular application, and to design so that the conditions to which the metal is exposed allow the oxide coat to self-repair.

A Scottish meat-processing plant had stainless-steel-lined partitions. Blood and fat were routinely splattered onto the stainless steel and, at the end of each day, power-hosed off. Above eye level the stainless steel gradually developed 'acne'; the outbreak of brown spots grew inexorably.

Stainless steels – containing chromium, nickel and other alloying elements – resist corrosion mainly because of the passivating[60] influence of a surface layer of chromic oxide. This layer, only about 3×10^{-6} mm thick, retards the diffusion of ions (notably ferrous ions). Oxygen (or an oxidising agent) is needed both to create this passive layer initially and to repair it in service. In the absence of oxygen or other oxidising agents in the environment, stainless steels actively corrode. If the oxide layer breaks down at certain points, pitting corrosion occurs at the anodes. This can be particularly severe if chlorides are present. In this instance, spices, including table salt (sodium chloride), were added to the meat.

The waste splattered on the wall, if not regularly removed, caused two related problems. It sealed the surface, excluding atmospheric oxygen thus inhibiting the 'self-healing' of the passive oxide film and it encouraged bacteriological decay. Bacteriological decay of fats, etc. may produce acids which would attack the surface of the stainless steel.

Regardless of the quality of the stainless steel used, pitting and corrosion is likely to occur under these conditions.

Stainless steel is a relatively new building product. There are several classes of the material: ferritic, martensitic, austenitic and duplex. These names are derived from the crystal structure of the steels, which governs their metallurgical behaviour.

Austenitic stainless steels are resistant to the wide range of rural and industrial atmospheres encountered in the UK, resulting in extensive architectural, structural and street furniture applications. They are non-magnetic.

Ferritic stainless steels are used in more mildly corrosive environments, being often used in trim work and somewhat less demanding applications. They are magnetic.

Martensitic stainless steels have similar corrosion resistance to the ferritic types. They are magnetic and behave much like plain carbon steels.

Duplex stainless steels are alloys designed to have improved localised corrosion resistance, specifically to stress-corrosion cracking, crevice and pitting corrosion. They are used where combinations of higher strength and corrosion resistance are needed.

Stainless steels can also be defined by numeric references – for example: 19–9, i.e. an alloy of 19% chromium, 9% nickel (also referred to as '304' where US terminology is adopted); and 17–12–2.5, i.e. an alloy of 17% chromium, 12% nickel and 2.5% molybdenum (also referred to as '316' in US terminology).

Coatings to metal

As an alternative to surface passivation, coatings can be applied to metals to protect them from corrosion. It is best for this to be done after the metal components have been cut and formed but before they are assembled, to prevent unprotected cut edges and concealed unprotected metal faces. Done badly, applied coatings can worsen durability.

> A building society built a new head office some ten miles inland from the Atlantic coast. The windows were framed in painted aluminium. About a year after the building was occupied, the paint began to wrinkle at the bottom corners of the frames.
>
> The mitred corner joints were cut from painted extrusions. The cut edges were unprotected. Corrosion started under the paint in the bottom corners of the window frames. Passivation due to surface oxidation was impeded by the paint film. Sea salt was deposited on the windows and slowly accumulated on the bottom rails. The concentration of sodium and chloride ions encouraged the breakdown of the frames to start on horizontal ledges. The mitred corners exposed unprotected edges of aluminium. Failure therefore started at the corners of bottom rails and spread under the paint film. The initial signs were what appeared to be localised faults in the paint, requiring no more than cosmetic remedy. At that point, due to the rate of concealed corrosion and the light sections used in the windows, the remaining service life of the aluminium was probably in the order of 5 years.

As an alternative to alloying, the benefit of combining separate metals can be obtained by coating one metal with another. For example, terne coatings – that is, lead with 3–15% tin – can be applied to bright metals such as stainless steel to combine the strength of steel with something of the appearance of lead.

The injudicious combination of metals can cause problems. For example, zinc can be used in close proximity to iron, steel, aluminium and lead without any risk of significant electrolytic corrosion. However, zinc should never be allowed to come into contact with copper or any copper-based alloy – nor should any water from a copper roof be allowed to drain onto a zinc roof, as the rainwater run-off will contain copper sulphates that will eat their way through the zinc. Zinc, in common with most metals used in building, is better not laid in direct contact with timber which contains acids, such as oak or western red cedar. Even the rainwater draining from these woods can stain and sometimes corrode metal.

Chapter 5

Traditional/modern forms of construction with metals

Some well-established traditional materials have changed with the development of modern science. For example most of the zinc produced today is an alloy of zinc, copper and titanium. This alloy is far superior to the old rolled zinc (which was soft when compared to titanium zinc) for the following reasons:

- better tensile strength;
- resistance to creep;
- 30% lower linear expansion rates; and
- superior surface finish.

Other traditional metals have changed little over the centuries, and long-established techniques for their use are still valid. Lead, for example, is subject to very much the same detailing and working techniques as have been used for centuries. It is a very flexible material which can be adapted on site to deal with many situations. It is, however, subject to 'creep' and 'fatigue' if not installed correctly. Each panel should be carefully sized and fixed. Guidance is available in traditional construction textbooks and from the Lead Sheet Association.

New types of building design can require revised detailing. Something as simple as installing thermal insulation can cause well-tried types of construction to fail.

> Insulating ductile and semi-ductile metal roofs led to an outbreak of corrosion failures.
>
> Terne-coated stainless steel was used for roofing a new-build detached house in Surrey. The detailing largely followed that which is traditional for zinc. The stainless steel was supported on close-boarded sarking. The false ceiling below carried a thick layer of mineral wool insulation. There was a polythene vapour check under the insulation. Condensation periodically accumulated on the underside of the stainless steel. On investigation, corrosion pits were found on the underside of the stainless steel while no corrosion was visible on its exposed upper surface.
>
> A similar investigation into a lead roof to a renovated Scottish church found very rapid loss of lead from the underside of the lead sheets. The roofs had been insulated during the renovation work, but otherwise the construction followed proven tradition. Because of the restricted air movement within the roof, oxygen did not have free access to the underside of the lead to maintain its protective patina, allowing it to corrode rapidly where the condensate accumulated.
>
> Both roofs would have been durable but for the condensation caused by upgrading thermal resistance to meet modern expectations, combined with over-reliance on the presumed stability of the metals.

Metals and atmospheric conditions

Installing roofing or cladding during wet weather is fairly common and can be acceptable for some materials as long as the substructures can adequately dry out after installation of any impermeable coverings. Problems are most severe when moisture is trapped behind external finishes.

A common-sense approach, using a basic understanding of physics and the nature of the materials being used, is required. For example, when installing zinc onto under-lays which allow water to adhere to or build up on their surfaces, excess water should be brushed off prior to fixing the zinc panels. If the moisture is not sufficiently removed, underside corrosion will begin, leading to an irreparable breakdown of the zinc. However, a small amount of moisture trapped between the underside of a zinc panel and the topside of the underlay will lead to a build-up of zinc hydroxide but may not cause serious underside corrosion.

Where water entrapment is a foreseeable risk it is possible to plan to control the consequences. For example, providing interstitial ventilation and drainage combats the inherent disadvantage of incorporating impermeable materials into the building envelope. Returning to the example with zinc, newer underlays are available in the form of a structured layer of polyamide monofilaments bonded onto a one-way permeable backing.[61] The zinc panels are installed onto the polyamide structure leaving a 4–5 mm air gap for the water/moisture to run out, so reducing zinc hydroxide formation and impeding the start of damaging underside corrosion.

Many metals are resistant to atmospheric pollutants and stable when in contact with other common building materials. However, overconfidence in the stability of metals is unwise. For example, although stainless steel will not ordinarily readily react with other metals, direct contact with aluminium in a marine environment may result in significant galvanic action.

Similarly, lead, which is known for its high corrosion resistance, can corrode when built into masonry. The first signs appear as a yellow stain leaching from the mortar joint, particularly when lead is used as the material for the damp-proof course. Corrosion is very slow and might have been avoided by coating the lead, which is in contact with the mortar, with bituminous paint. Equally, lead is known not generally to undergo significant bi-metallic corrosion when in contact with other metals. However, in marine environments there is potential for damaging bimetallic corrosion when lead is in contact with aluminium.

Apparently inferior properties of materials can be used to advantage. For example, aluminium's low melting point means that in the event of a serious fire a roof constructed of two skins of aluminium with non-combustible insulation could have a sacrificial function. The roof will melt over the seat of the fire allowing it to vent rapidly through the void, thereby saving the structural frame of the building.

Chapter 5

Ceramics and glass

The word 'ceramic' comes from the Greek word 'Keramos', which means 'potters' earth'. This, in turn, is derived from an older Sanskrit root meaning 'to burn'. In ancient Greece the term was used to mean burnt stuff or earth. Thus the word was used to refer to a product obtained through the action of fire upon earthy materials.

Ceramics can be defined as inorganic, non-metallic materials that are typically produced using clays and other minerals from the earth or chemically processed powders.

The category encompasses manufactured building materials such as bricks, roofing tiles, wall and floor tiles, bathroom fittings and pipes for drainage and sewerage. It also includes products that take advantage of the special properties of ceramics in terms of their resistance to heat and corrosion, such as refractories for the manufacture of such materials as steel and glass.

Ceramics are typically crystalline in nature and are compounds formed between metallic and non-metallic elements such as aluminium and oxygen (aluminium oxide – Al_2O_3), silicon and nitrogen (silicon nitride – Si_3N_4) and silicon and carbon (silicon carbide – SiC). Glass is considered in this book as a subset of ceramics although it has clear differences in that it is amorphous, lacking a long-range crystalline order.

Traditional, or silicate-based, ceramics include the glass and clay products that have historically been used in building. Advanced or 'technical' ceramics – used for applications such as space-shuttle tiles, engine components, artificial bones/teeth, electronic components and cutting tools – greatly extend the range of ceramic materials.

Bricks

Bricks have been used from at least 2300 BC. English brick manufacture was started by the Romans. The use of brick in urban building developed thereafter as a fire-resistant alternative to earlier traditions – a development boosted by the 1666 Great Fire of London – and brick is now common in urban housing. Currently in the UK there are over 1,200 types of brick, made from many different types of clay. The colour and texture of clay bricks are dependent on the manufacturing method and firing characteristics of the clay.

Because masonry construction contains both bricks and mortar there is limited value in considering bricks in isolation. Unrestrained bricks dilate on wetting and heating, and contract on drying and cooling, by predictable, small amounts. These movements are reciprocal. That is, when a brick's moisture content and temperature return to their original state the bricks resume their original dimensions. Thermally induced movements tend to be very much larger than movements caused by changes in moisture content. In addition bricks – like fired clays in general – grow throughout their life, tending very gradually to return to the clay from which they were made.

When built into walls these movements are restrained, creating stresses. Restraint to movement causes much of the fracturing which occurs in brick walls. It is for this reason recommended practice to break large panels of brickwork, jointed in ordinary Portland cement mortar, into smaller panels. The joints used to subdivide brick panels reduce restraint by flexing to accommodate movement. In the absence of adequate movement-control joints brick walls may bow and move outward at corners, thus relieving stress. Such movements are often associated with cracking.

Figure 5.13: **Displacement of bricks at the corner of a house owing to the irreversible expansion of the bricks.**

Dry-bedded damp-proof course acts as slip membrane allowing the outward expansion of brickwork over

Line of damp-proof course

Guidance on movement control in brick masonry relates to carefully engineered walls jointed with ordinary Portland cement mortars. Until the late 1920s, brick walls were typically of thick solid construction jointed with lime mortar. Walls were a brick (215 mm) or more thick. These stout walls were inherently more resistant to bending and flexural stress, and had greater capacity to accommodate dead and applied loads, than the thin brick leaves in modern construction. This type of massive construction, with its substantial restraint to movement, reduced the need for move-ment-control joints below that now recommended for modern thin construction using ordinary Portland cement mortars.

It is sometimes thought that lime mortar is tolerant of movement. This is true but does not mean that movement-control joints can safely be omitted when lime mortar is used.

Historical examples of brickwork with lime mortar and no movement joints are always thick and solid. Great weight imparts restraint and it takes more heat input to raise the temperature of thick walls than thin ones – making thick walls less prone to large thermal movements. The ability of massive masonry construction to limit movement may be more significant than the flexibility imparted by the use of lime mortar.

Tiles

Plain tiles are traditionally $10\frac{1}{2} \times 6\frac{1}{2}$ inches (265 × 165 mm). They perform by overlapping densely up to three tiles deep to achieve a water-shedding layer. Tiling is not necessarily waterproof, being susceptible to wind-driven penetration of rain and, particularly, of light snow. This is why sarking boards were used in best traditional practice – usually replaced in modern practice with under-slating felt.

Plain tiles can be machine or hand made. The former tend to lie flatter, improving weather resistance, but are often weaker than traditional tiles, which tend to bow more but which are less readily damaged. There is, however, much variation, depending on the raw materials used as well as the process of forming the tiles.

Roman tiles, which traditionally were overlapping simple curved tiles, are now available in imitation as interlocking profiles. As with interlocking plain clay tiles this is intended to reduce the number of tiles required and improve resistance to driving rain. Traditional interlocking tiles include various profiles. The pantile's distinctive 'S' profile, which creates a series of ridges and furrows, characteristic of much of mainland Europe, is predominant in the UK in the east and parts of the Southwest. This geographical architectural 'footprint' is a legacy of several centuries of trading, during which pantiles were brought back from Holland and Belgium as ships' ballast.

Traditional roof tiles are free to move slightly relative to each other and to the supporting structure. With tiles which are bonded to a substrate, such as wall or floor tiles, dimensional instabilities and relative movements become key considerations. Clay tiles expand with age, rising temperature and uptake of moisture; the background to which they are attached may not follow suit. A failure to address this type of issue is the main cause of problems with floor and wall tiling.

The finished appearance of tiles may vary from batch to batch, as it is determined by the raw materials and firing process. Obtaining all of the tiles for a job from a single production run may reduce variation in appearance. However, in some firing processes the position of each tile in the stack can cause variation in appearance.

Glass

Glass is often used as a composite in windows which have high thermal resistance. A hermetically sealed double-glazing unit may include trapped inert gases and metallic films. This is an area where state-of-the-art performance is quoted without reference to field experience and longevity.

The energy-saving properties of modern glazing systems rely on their ability to optimise transmission of visible light whilst minimising the transmission of heat. Ceramics, including glass, are poor thermal conductors. Radiant heat is a lower-frequency electromagnetic radiation than visible and ultraviolet light, a phenomenon which permits the greenhouse effect.

The angle of refraction for any sheet of glass depends on the frequency or wavelength of the incident radiation, with the critical angle for visible and ultraviolet light (sunshine) being larger than that for infrared radiation (heat). Light which passes through glass and is absorbed into solid underlying materials tends to be re-radiated at lower frequencies, including more radiant energy in the infrared spectrum (heat). As long as the glazing remains optically clear, energy, in the form of visible and ultraviolet light, may enter whilst part of the re-radiant (heat) energy may be trapped. Putting a thin gold film on the glass (as in low-emissivity or 'low-E' glass) may improve reflectance to heat much more than it reduces light transmission .

To protect this metal film from abrasion and blistering, the filmed side of the glass faces the cavity in a double-glazing unit. If the hermetic seal breaks down, condensate may form, inhibiting light transmission and destabilising the metallic film. The medium-to-long-term performance of low-E double glazing is likely to be inferior to the published (factory performance) figures. This could give rise to complaints of underperformance for any energy-efficient building which relies on the optimised performance of low-E glass in hermetically sealed units.

Hermetically sealed low-E double-glazing units have typical factory performance figures of $1.5\,W/m^2K$ for panes of 4 mm glass spaced 12 mm apart.

By comparison, similar figures for hermetically sealed units without low-E glass are $2.9\,W/m^2K$ for equivalent glass and gap thicknesses. Deterioration may occur unnoticed but, as can be seen from the above figures, this may almost double heat loss through glazing.

Equivalent single-glazed performance is $5.7\,W/m^2K$. Low-E glass is not normally considered for single glazing as, in order to last, its metallic film needs the protection of being on the cavity side of a double-glazed unit. The long-term thermal resistance of double-glazed units will tend to lie between their claimed factory performance figures and that for single glazing.

Symptoms of defects

Where a defect comes to light through the damage it causes, the clues from which an investigation can progress are the reported symptoms: that is, the ways in which the problem manifests itself. A proper diagnosis starts with a careful assessment of what is known.

Initial reports often describe defects in terms which seamlessly confuse observation, hearsay and supposition. Fault and blame are all-too-readily assumed and first-hand accounts of defects are easily influenced by a natural tendency to see what is expected. Unintentionally, many people report as observations supposed symptoms which are consistent with their preconceptions whilst potentially valuable observations, which are inconsistent with expectation, may go unremarked. In contrast to this, proper investigation starts with clarifying first-hand observations, tracing second-hand observations to their source and dismissing assumptions.

An example of the well-meaning misrepresentation of observation occurred in reporting the failure of a screed. The screed failed whilst under temporary protection. As a consequence, the failure occurred unseen.

It was reported that the screed 'erupted' into blisters and that some 40 per cent had failed. It was also reported that it had been extensively and continuously flooded.

Subsequent inspection revealed many isolated, randomly distributed weak areas – some of which contained patches of broken-up, loose material.

Close questioning of eye witnesses revealed that the first and third inspections had each exposed a large 'blister' in the screed. The rest of the screed was not inspected until two more months had passed. The recording of subsequent observation was influenced by these initial inspections to the extent that the flat failed areas found later were assumed to be collapsed 'blisters' and were reported as blisters. This may have been true but it was not what had been seen.

Flooding had occurred but its extent and duration was not known. Some parts of the screed were superficially wet when exposed, but the quantity of water which had reached the screed was not checked.

The symptoms of building defects include changes in the following characteristics of building materials:

- composition (e.g. corrosion);
- condition (e.g. exposure);
- construction (e.g. cracking);
- size or weight (e.g. combustion);
- shape (e.g. bending);
- appearance (e.g. mould growth).

External causes of damage

Whilst some failures occur as a result of inherent deficiencies in the built work, damage is often accelerated or caused by external agents – including the actions of liquids, gases or solids.

The most commonly complained-of problem is water damage. This may manifest itself as discoloration of finishes, rot in timber, corrosion on some metals, lifting and blistering of waterproof films/membranes, disintegration/cracking/softening of some composite materials, dilations of porous materials, mould or fungal growths.

Frost damage

In cold weather, water may be associated with frost damage. When water turns to ice it expands with sufficient force to move or break concrete, masonry, etc. The worst damage tends to occur when the water temperature is oscillating, causing repeated changes between its liquid and solid phases.

The presence of soluble salts can alter the behaviour of water. An aqueous salt solution will typically have a lower freezing point than pure water. The presence of de-icing salts, for example, may both lower the temperature at which freezing occurs and increase the rate of freeze–thaw cycling. The greater the number of freeze–thaw cycles, the greater the risk of damage.

Condensation

Water vapour can penetrate into positions where its ability to cause damage is dependent on temperature fluctuations and the characteristics of the materials used. The diffusion of vapour into voids in the building envelope occurs as a result of ventilation through perforate construction and by diffusion. The rate of diffusion is controlled by the vapour pressure differentials and vapour permeability of the construction.

Condensation occurs when the temperature of a surface falls below the dew point temperature of the adjacent moisture-laden air. It can cause corrosion, rot, damage to decorations and mould growth.

Within rooms, it is often seen where the air is still, ventilation is poor and the thermal resistance of the external walls is lowest. Common locations are:

- corners of rooms, especially corners of external walls;
- behind furniture placed against external walls;
- within built-in furniture on external walls;
- on lintels, reveals and sills;
- floor/external wall junctions especially those containing ring beams;
- on the internal surface of north-facing walls.

Wet patches on ceilings, close to the wall, are often due to condensate running down from within the roof space or to rain penetration. This occurs more often in warm-deck flat roofs where the perimeter wall is, for example, thermally bridged by a window lintel that extends into the roof space. Here, surface condensation may be occurring unseen in a roof void above a false ceiling. This may be regarded as interstitial condensation where the void in which it is occurring is small and inaccessible.

Mould caused by surface condensation, particularly in room corners, first appears as spots or small patches, which can spread to form a furry layer usually grey-green, black or brown in colour. On paint surfaces, it can show as pink or purple.

Hygroscopic effects

Wetting may alter the behaviour of materials after they have dried out. Water that enters building fabrics may contain soluble salts and, as it travels through components of buildings, it may dissolve salts. As the water evaporates it will leave these salts behind. Typically, the deposition of such salt will occur within 3 mm of the surface from which the water evaporates.

Many of these soluble salts will absorb moisture from the atmosphere to such an extent that they will make the parts of the building in which they have accumulated appear damp or dry with fluctuations in relative humidity. Such areas often show a well-defined edge. Typical locations are previously damp chimney breasts and walls.

Rising damp

Rising damp is associated with capillarity and limited accordingly by the characteristics of the materials in which it is rising, by gravity and by atmospheric pressure. Consequently, damp which is more than about 1,500 mm above adjoining ground level is unlikely to be due to rising groundwater.

Because soluble salts are often present in groundwater and in concretes and masonry, rising damp is often revealed by the deposition of salts. Aqueous salt solutions will rise until the water is lost by evaporation. The salts which are left behind crystallize out (effloresce). When this occurs at the surface, the crystal will form a fragile feathery crystalline growth usually white in colour and often forming 'tide' marks. When it occurs below the surface, e.g. behind a paint film or within plaster, the crystals will grow and can lift the paint film or disrupt the plaster.

The presence of efflorescence strongly indicates that water has reached the surface from within the wall and is not condensate. The absence of efflorescence is not proof that the dampness is not due to rising damp, as rising damp may not contain sufficient dissolved salt to cause efflorescence.

Corrosion

Corrosion is the natural degradation of a material due to its dissolution, caused by reactions with the surrounding environment. Corrosion is nature seeking to recombine elements which have been reduced to an unnaturally pure form. Corrosion of metals may be subdivided into uniform, galvanic, pitting, crevice, intergranular, exfoliation, stress and filiform. In addition, stress-corrosion cracking and corrosion fatigue may occur as a result of a combination of applied loads and corrosion.

Uniform corrosion

This is a common form of corrosion, where all areas of the metal corrode at a similar rate. Over a period of time, the exposed metal undergoes oxidation by aggressive ions. The corrosion then propagates at a rate determined by a combination of the corrosive environment and the alloy composition.

Galvanic (bimetallic) corrosion

This type of corrosion occurs when two conducting materials of different chemical composition are joined and exposed to a conducting solution. If the corrosion potential of the two metals is significantly different, and they are in direct contact and immersed in an electrolyte, the more 'noble' metal will become the cathode and the more 'active' will become the anode.[62] A measurable current may flow between the two. The corrosion rate of the anode will be increased and that of the cathode decreased. The increased corrosion of the anode is called 'galvanic corrosion'.

Galvanic corrosion is very damaging because it concentrates on the less-noble metal at the metal–metal junction, where deep attack occurs. At the junction a large corrosion current can pass because the electrical resistance of the short path through the electrolyte is low. Common forms of metal joining, e.g. brazing, welding etc., provide junctions at which galvanic corrosion can develop.

Pitting

Pitting is a form of localised corrosion which occurs when a film-protected metal is almost, but not completely, resistant to corrosion. Pitting may also occur in crevices, in which case it is called 'crevice corrosion'.

Crevice corrosion

Crevice corrosion is an intense form of localised corrosion ranging from small pits to extensive corrosion over the whole surface, and it occurs under the same conditions as pitting. It can occur within narrow crevices that may be formed by:

- the geometry of the structure, e.g. riveted plates, threaded joints etc.;
- contact of metal with non-metallic solids, e.g. plastics, rubber etc.; and
- deposits of sand, dirt or permeable corrosion products on the metal surface.

Attack starts more easily in a narrow crevice than on an unshielded surface. Crevices, such as those found at flange joints or at threaded connections, are thus often the most critical sites for corrosion.

Intergranular corrosion

This type of corrosion consists of localised attack, which may occur if the area around the grain boundaries[63] is less corrosion-resistant than the matrix in the medium in question.

Exfoliation

Exfoliation corrosion is a specific type of selective attack that proceeds along multiple narrow paths, e.g. grain boundaries which run parallel to the surface of a metal. Generation of corrosion products forces the layers apart and causes the metal to swell; flakes may be pushed up and peel off.

Filiform corrosion

This appears as a random non-branching white tunnel of corrosion product, either on the surface of non-protected metal or beneath surface coatings. It is a structurally insensitive form of corrosion which is often more detrimental to appearance than strength.

Stress-corrosion cracking

A material failure may be accelerated by the combined effect of corrosion and mechanical stress. The most common type is transgranular stress-corrosion cracking, SCC, which can occur unexpectedly – resulting in the failure of components. Often a material chosen for its corrosion resistance in a given environment is found to fail at a stress level well below its normal fracture stress. Rarely is there any obvious evidence of an impending failure, and it can occur in components which are externally unstressed.

A typically SCC attack takes the form of thin, branched cracks.

Corrosion fatigue

A material subjected to a cyclic load far below the ultimate tensile stress can fail – a process called 'fatigue'. If the metal is simultaneously exposed to a corrosive environment, the failure can take place at even lower loads and after a shorter time. Contrary to a pure mechanical fatigue, there is no fatigue limit load in corrosion-assisted fatigue.

Although it is often possible to provide adequate protection for metallic parts which are stressed under static conditions, most surface films – including naturally protective oxides – can be more easily broken or disrupted under cyclic loading.

[47] *BRE Building Elements: Building services: Performance, Diagnosis, Maintenance, Repair and the Avoidance of Defects*, 2000, p. 5.

[48] *DETR English House Conditions Survey 2001: building the picture.*

[49] *DOE, English House Condition Survey*, 1993.

[50] *BRE Building Elements: Walls, Windows and Doors: Performance, Diagnosis, Maintenance, Repair and the Avoidance of Defects*, 1998, p. 8.

[51] *BRE Building Elements: Foundations, Basements and External Works: Performance, Diagnosis, Maintenance, Repair and the Avoidance of Defects*, 2002, p. 3.

[52] American Society of Civil Engineers, *Reducing Risk and Liability through Better Specification and Inspection*, 1982.

[53] *BRE Building Elements: Walls, windows and doors: Performance, Diagnosis, Maintenance, Repair and the Avoidance of Defects*, 1998, Introduction.

[54] Consumers' Association, *Which?*, July 2002.

[55] Lucretius, *The Nature of the Universe*, 'Book 1 – Matter and Space', pp. 42–3.

[56] For a more detailed account of carbonation, see Chapter 7, Example: corrosion damage, p. 173.

[57] *BRE Technical Note No. 38, The Movement of Timbers*, May 1969 (revised August 1975).

[58] See the section on corrosion (this chapter).

[59] Anodising is an electro-chemical process which physically alters the surface of the metal to form a particularly structured and dense oxide layer that resists abrasion and thus protects the underlying metal. During the anodising process the oxide layer is at first porous at the molecular level, and at this point it is possible to introduce a coloured dye. The porous layer is then 'sealed' by boiling the part in water (which converts the oxide to a different crystalline form), permanently trapping the dye beneath the surface. The anodised surface is aluminium oxide which exhibits a very high resistance to electric current. Not all aluminium alloys can be easily anodised – cast aluminium (with its high silica content) is particularly difficult.

[60] In this context 'passivating' is the prevention of corrosion by altering the surface layer in order to make it passive or inert.

[61] Polyamide monofilaments are single strands of linear polyamides (a modern development of nylon). They characteristically absorb water and can help to draw water away from the underside of the metal.

[62] In this context, 'noble' refers to a metal which is distinguished from an active metal by its relatively low position in the electrochemical series and correspondingly low chemical reactivity.

[63] The microstructures of rocks, metals, ceramics and other materials are made up of relatively rigid 'grains' separated by a network of 'grain boundaries'.

Diagnosis of Defects

6

Procedures

The efficient and effective investigation and correction of defects is often marred by failure to distinguish symptom and cause, and the over-enthusiastic starting of repairs before completing diagnosis. Adopting a methodical approach is the only practical method of minimising embarrassing failure and abortive cost.

Diagnosis is the essential first step in dealing with defects. Not until the causes and mechanisms of failure are understood can reliable decisions on remedy be made. It requires, in addition to a good insight into the design and fabrication processes, a proper understanding of scientific investigation. Correct diagnosis should provide a proper basis for cure and, where required, the allocation and apportionment of blame. Investigation starts with an objective study of the symptoms and proceeds methodically to look for underlying causes.

The cardinal starting points for all defects investigations are:

- discard preconceptions;
- adopt a systematic approach;
- collect all available data;
- marshal the facts;
- observe the chronology; and
- distinguish opinion from observation.

Where possible, start by collecting as much background information as is available from the project team, building users, etc. on the nature and characteristics of the problem. Contemporaneous written record, however incomplete, is often more reliable than uncorroborated memory.

In this aspect of the work, it is helpful if the investigator is in familiar territory. Someone who has experience of the design and/or construction processes which have led to the defects under investigation may have insights that others lack. A site architect or contract manager who has run similar jobs to the one under investigation will know from experience what sort of records are normally kept and, typically, how complete these will be.

Next, study the design from such drawings and specifications as are available. Bear in mind that maintenance records, copies of correspondence, architect's instructions, site directions, etc. may record alterations not shown on the drawings.

Where proprietary materials are used, obtain all available contemporaneous manufacturers' written guidance. (The Barbour compendium can be of assistance here, as it can provide – from microfiche – 'out-of-date' information on discontinued or altered products, provided only that details of these products were previously published in the compendium.)

In the future, investigation of completed building may increasingly be assisted by the Construction (Design and Management) Regulations 1984. Under these regulations, for buildings in England and Wales built from April 1985 onwards, a health and safety file should be available from the building owner.[64] The regulations do not prescribe the exact form and content of this file but, typically, one which is correctly prepared should contain:

- a brief description of the work carried out;
- a note of residual hazards and how they have been dealt with;
- key structural principles incorporated in the design of the structure, and safe working loads for floors and roofs;
- any hazards associated with materials used;
- information regarding the removal or dismantling of installed plant and equipment;
- health and safety information about the equipment provided for cleaning or maintaining the structure;
- a note of the nature, location and markings of significant services, including fire-fighting services; and
- information and 'as-built' drawings of the structure, its plant and equipment.

From the study of the reported problem, the design and the materials used, assess possible causes in order of probability and devise a progressive programme of investigations accordingly. Systematically eliminate potential causes that do not fit the evidence.

Where site investigation is required, consider non-invasive techniques first.

Where investigation involves invasive or damaging techniques, ensure all interested parties have the opportunity to observe and comment. Invasive and damaging investigations may be best structured as part of a remedial-works programme.

Damage may be caused by more than one fault, making diagnosis difficult. Do not assume that identifying a single fault will completely resolve the problem.

Equipment and techniques

There are no universally accepted lists of correct equipment and techniques for defects investigations. There are, however, some rules that apply generally to scientific investigation and working on buildings:

- For anything more complex than a hammer or screwdriver, carefully read the manufacturer's instructions. Understand the functions and limits of the equipment.
- Test and calibrate new equipment before use. It is advisable to check new equipment by using it in known conditions, where anomalous results can be recognised, before using it on the unknown.
- Regularly check and recalibrate old equipment.
- Practice makes perfect. Restrict the use of specialist equipment to competent operatives with the appropriate skills, physical ability and experience.
- Record observations as and when they are made. Keep the original records.

- The interpretation of test results is a vital part of the investigation procedure. This requires a clear, accurate record of observed fact and a thorough understanding of the investigation techniques used.
- Site investigations should be approached with a proper regard for the safety, both of those doing the investigations and of others who might be affected by the investigators' activities. The planning of a site investigation should include the identification of hazards, assessment of risks and development of safe methods of work.

Unscientific investigation and imprecise reporting is potentially more descriptive of the level of competence of the surveyor than of the condition of the surveyed building.

A Trading Standards office requested the preparation of evidence for the prosecution of a damp-proofing company.

The company under investigation held rising damp and groundwater to be unrelated. From this, they offered a new 'quick fix' for damp walls. They attracted custom by promising to cure damp without inconvenience to occupants. Troublesome damp-proof courses could be ignored as they played no part – an approach which was as attractive as it was unscientific. It was not, however, simply the technical merit of their 'cure' which was being investigated but the adequacy of their surveys and advice to customers.

They operated by carrying out free surveys. With each survey report, they confused the potential customer with a profoundly impenetrable description of the mechanisms of rising damp and the working of their 'cure'. This mystery dressed in scientific clothing aside, their reports followed an all-too-common pattern, being based on the ill-informed use of electrical-resistance moisture meters.

To evaluate their work, their survey of a traditional, solid-wall, brick terraced house was studied. The house was typical of its age and construction. It exhibited the usual limited resistance to damp, suffering minor intermittent problems which varied with the seasons.

Their survey report showed commendable consistency, being as unscientific in the interpretation of the moisture meter readings as it was casual in describing the process of investigation and obscure in explaining cause and remedy:

- no check on the meter's accuracy was reported;
- the calibration of the meter was not given;
- no check for contaminants, such as salts, was recorded; and
- the degree of dampness was over-reported because the meter was calibrated for use in wood but was used to measure moisture in plaster, and the results interpreted as direct moisture content readings.

A check for salt deposits, where moisture readings are interpreted as symptomatic of rising damp, is fundamental. The presence of surface salt deposits makes electrical-resistance moisture meter readings unreliable. Conversely, the absence of such salts reduces the likelihood of rising damp being the cause of the moisture found.

Isolated moisture measurements alone rarely show the cause of the dampness. Collaborative evidence is required and is often readily obtainable by, for example, taking a moisture profile of the suspect wall. Clarity, thoroughness and completeness are good watchwords for reporting defects investigations.

In the presentation of his findings, the company's surveyor made clear his lack of understanding of scientific technique, whilst failing in his objectives of demonstrating the presence of rising damp and the appropriateness of the remedial works he proposed.

Tools for site investigations need to be selected to suit the tasks to be carried out. For example, the examination of tall buildings may involve the use of ladders, access cradles, abseiling equipment, etc. Alternatively, it may be tackled from the ground with high-powered binoculars or the like. A planned approach allows the appropriate selection of tools. It is always prudent to allow for contingencies and to provide for alternative approaches to overcome unforeseen site conditions and eventualities.

Unexpected complications can arise.

A detailed study of cracking in the over-cladding to three refurbished residential tower blocks just north of Glasgow resulted in police intervention. Cracks were being located using a tripod and high-powered monocular lenses from the ground prior to venturing higher. As the cracking was prevalent in the widow reveals, the survey concentrated on the windows. Late one afternoon, the police arrived to investigate a report of a peeping tom. Fortunately the survey had stopped for the day about 10 minutes before they arrived, avoiding the risk of the surveyor being detained at Her Majesty's pleasure pending proof of the relatively innocent intent of the survey.

Embarrassing events are more commonplace where surveys of similar buildings are carried out from suspended cradles, but these are perhaps best left unpublished.

The following pieces of equipment are generally useful:

- screwdrivers;
- hammer;
- wrecking bar;

- camera and whiteboard;
- ladders;
- binoculars;
- magnifying glass;
- feeler gauges;
- level/plumb line;
- Dictaphone;
- battery-powered torch;
- suitable clothing: robust, cheap, washable, good pockets, all-weather;
- mobile phone.

For some tasks the following are worth considering:

- illuminated magnifying lens;
- endoscope;
- digital micrometer and depth gauge;
- small mirror on a telescopic arm;
- ultrasonic leak detector;
- cover meter;
- hand-held ground-penetrating radar;
- hand-held sound-level meter;
- time-lapse or video cameras.

Records

Records may be written, drawn, photographic, dictated or any combination of these. For example, in some cases, notes have been written on the building alongside the defects being investigated, a clearly marked scale placed next to them and the whole photographed so that the notes, the scale and the defects were recorded in a single picture which both documented and explained the defect. In other cases a digital video record containing a spoken narrative made as the parts of the defective construction are progressively exposed has proved effective. Generally, however, the combinations of site-drawn sketches, observations recorded on a Dictaphone, and still photographs are the most convenient approach.

As a rule, where conventional photography is used to record defects, it is far better to take too many photographs than to risk missing something which later is realised to be significant, or losing evidence due to errors which may not be noticed at the time.

For still photography, 35 mm SLR (single lens reflex) cameras, with zoom lenses covering the range from 22 mm to 350 mm, remain a good compromise between quality, convenience and cost for recording detail. Compact digital cameras are excellent for note taking. That is, where photographs are required as exhibits to evidential reports or to explain a built detail, the quality of the 35 mm SLR outweighs the convenience of compact cameras. However, the handiness and immediate results obtainable from small digital cameras have advantages where photography is being used as an aide-mémoire in drafting a report or preparing drawings. As they reduce in price, digital SLR cameras are a good alternative to traditional film cameras and use the same or comparable lenses.

Medium and large format cameras (that is bigger than 35 mm film size) with appropriate lenses are excellent but rarely essential for recording defects on site. They have often been used for recording laboratory tests in controlled conditions.

An autofocus telephoto lens attached to an SLR camera may be used in preference to binoculars to view distant parts of buildings.

Automatic cameras are convenient for most purposes but it is advisable to ensure that the automatic settings can be fully overridden. Manual settings allow difficult photographs to be taken where automatic settings can be confused. Photographing blemishes in light coloured walls can upset autofocus systems, for example. An automatic aperture priority setting is particularly useful for quickly obtaining the best compromise between depth of field and exposure.

Any photograph, however – whether digital or on film – can be made to show what the photographer wishes. Only those who are not skilled in the use of the medium hold the belief that the camera never lies.

On one occasion a project engineer asked a professional photographer, using a 35 mm SLR camera, to record the variation in dampness of no-fines lytag concrete exposed by the removal of an asphalt wearing surface. The damper concrete could be distinguished by eye from the neighbouring drier concrete because it was a slightly darker green. This could be observed clearly only in good sunlight.

The characteristic of the material which the engineer wished to be recorded was briefly explained to the photographer.

Knowing what the engineer wished to see, the photographer produced prints on which the distinction between the degrees of dampness in the concrete was clearer than it had been to the naked eye. The engineer was faced with a choice of prints, each of which gave a different enhanced view of the moisture darkening of the concrete but none of which were identical in the way they emphasised the 'truth'.

Having been asked to accentuate an aspect of what could be seen through the lens, the photographer merely required to know the degree of emphasis that was wanted. On request, her photographs would show what was required, whether or not this mirrored or modified reality.

Data backs are useful in automatically imprinting the date, time or reference number onto the corner of the film. This is often an optional accessory for 35 mm SLR cameras

but is included as standard with some compact cameras. Using the correct software, files created by digital cameras contain information on the date and time that the image was recorded but this information is not automatically displayed on prints created from the digital files.

Video cameras make excellent notebooks. Their output can be fed directly into a computer via simple interconnecting devices into USB ports. With the use of mobile computers, this allows photographic records to be reviewed whilst on site or transferred electronically for study in remote offices.

The use of a chalkboard or white board, which can be wiped clean and written on again after each picture, allows easy labelling so that the photograph can readily be identified. (The lower-quality digital cameras often allow a short, spoken statement to be recorded with each image. This is useful but, where the photograph is to be used in a printed report, a visible label is often preferable.)

Figure 6.1: **Suggested white board for use when photographing building defects. Permanent regular markings to the edges help to give scale to the photograph. Nail holes to allow the board to be pinned in place are often useful.**

A surveyor's sectional ladder is sufficient for many situations. If better access is needed, attendance by a builder or access specialists is usually advisable for health and safety reasons. Aluminium is the preferred material for the ladder owing to its high strength-to-weight ratio.

Ordinary tools such as wrecking bars, screwdrivers, hammers, etc. can be useful for prising open stuck access hatches, lifting manhole covers, sounding hollow surfaces or probing cracks.

A simple hand-held magnifying lens is useful for studying such things as cracks, delamination, etc.

Standardised site inspection sheets can be useful, and sometimes it is beneficial to prepare specific sheets in advance for large investigations. Each sheet should be uniquely numbered and may usefully contain the following information:

- date/time;
- location/project;
- purpose of inspection;
- weather conditions;
- those present;
- equipment used (calibration); and
- observations.

The more care that is taken in site records, the less work there is to do afterwards in converting site notes into reports.

Example: diagnosis of the causes of water damage

The investigation of water damage provides a good example of the techniques appropriate for the diagnosis of building defects generally. It involves a logical structured approach with a sequence of steps to allow possible causes to be analysed.

Causes of dampness may include any of the following, acting separately or in combination:

- rising damp;
- condensation;
- water penetration;
- presence of hygroscopic salts;
- plumbing leaks.

It is not always possible to devise an infallible system for differentiating between alternative causes of dampness and often the matter has to be decided on a balance of probabilities. Confidence in conclusions drawn on a balance of probability must always be limited. Where remedial works are implemented, the long-term efficacy of the repairs will help to demonstrate the validity of the diagnoses made.

The following guidance is based on practical experience from a series of investigations and, while not an infallible guide, illustrates a generally useful approach to building-defects investigations.

Step 1 – Investigate the history of the problem

Enquire of the people who built, maintain or use the building:

- Has it been left unoccupied – if so, for how long and how often?

Figure 6.2: **Initial symptoms of water damage to render which has been carried across the damp-proof membrane to pavement level.**

- Has it been open to the weather or flooded?
- What is the occupancy pattern, e.g. intermittent, continuous, seasonal?
- Is the building heated – if so, what is the pattern of heating, e.g. intermittent, continuous, seasonal?
- What activities are carried out in the building? Have these changed over the building life – if so, how does the timing of this relate to the discovery of dampness?
- What plant, machinery, appliances, etc. are used in the building, and has the pattern of their use changed?
- Is the building ventilated – if so, what is the method of ventilation and how is it controlled? Is there any record of its use?
- Have temperatures and relative humidity been recorded at any time?
- Are there other similar properties – if so, do they suffer similar damage?
- Does the dampness vary with weather, seasonally, etc.?

Step 2 – Investigate the building fabric and structure

It is always useful to obtain drawn details, specifications and schedules showing concealed construction. This allows probable water-ingress paths, condensation risks, etc. to be analysed without invasive investigation.

Where historical information is poor, modelling the problem can be particularly useful. Potential areas of risk can be discovered by examination of the building fabric, taking into account the use of the internal spaces. The probability of interstitial condensation, for example, can be calculated for each area of identified risk.[65]

Every opportunity should be taken to obtain as much relevant information as possible from the occupants.

Chapter 6

Step 3 – Examine the symptoms

Depending on the cause of the water damage, how long it has been happening and which building components are wet, the symptoms are likely to include some of the following:

- decay in timber or cellulose products;
- corrosion of metals;
- excessive moisture movements of materials;
- distortion, and in some cases weakening, of sheet or thin slab materials;
- blistering of impermeable finishes;
- deterioration of decorations and surface finishes;
- mould growth;
- flaking of soft distempers;
- reduction in the gloss of some impervious paints;
- breakdown or loss of adhesion in plasters, lime mortars, etc.;
- distortion of sheet materials, e.g. plasterboard or fibreboard;
- breakdown of adhesives;
- hydration reactions, which may be expansive and disruptive.

Figure 6.3: Blistering/detaching paint to render, starting within a few months of painting and extending gradually thereafter. Examination revealed clean separation of paint and render, and damp in the underlying render.

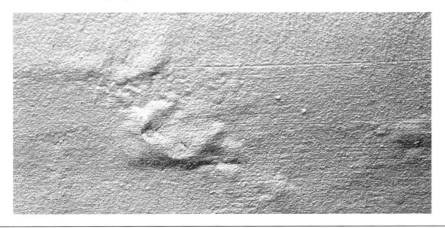

Different causes of water damage can be distinguished from each other by careful observation. For example, surface condensation on a non-absorbent surface will characteristically form droplets. Rising damp will not.

Salts analysis can assist. Chlorides and nitrates are often present in groundwater, and may be present in construction water – they will not be present in uncontaminated condensate. Site tests can be carried out to give an indication of the presence of such salts but laboratory analysis is more accurate.

Step 4 – Site measurements

Measurement can reveal patterns which are not readily apparent to the naked eye. Measuring moisture content on a three-dimensional grid can reveal what is commonly referred to as the 'moisture profile'. This will reflect the way in which the water entered but also will be influenced by whether the construction is becoming wet or drying at the time the measurements are taken.

The method of measurement must take into account the conditions in which they are carried out and the possible scope for error. Accurate measurements of moisture content cannot always be obtained by the use of electrical-resistance moisture meters because the presence of salts increases the electrical conductivity of the water, giving falsely high readings. However, electrical-resistance meters are commonly used without confirmatory checks for the presence of soluble salts. Gravimetric methods[66] carried out on samples taken from the fabric give the most reliable results. The use of chemical-absorption-type moisture meters will give a result in a short space of time and be almost as reliable.

Taking a moisture profile of a damp wall, floor slab, etc. is one of the most reliable ways of differentiating between sources of dampness. For example, in a solid masonry wall:

- Surface condensation will cause more dampness on the surface than at depth.
- Rain penetration will cause a moisture gradient across the wall.
- Active rising damp will cause a moisture gradient from the centre to the faces of the wall.

Step 5 – Elimination

From the preceding steps, the possible causes of any dampness should be listed, tested and reduced by a methodical process of elimination.

The following is a suggested checklist:

- rain ingress through the building fabric, i.e. roofs, walls, windows and doors;
- defects in the rainwater drainage system;
- plumbing leaks;
- rising groundwater – defects in damp-proof courses and membranes;
- area of wall surface affected by hygroscopic elements, e.g. parapets, balconies and porches;

- surface condensation;
- interstitial condensation.

Some of these can readily be eliminated with little or no investigation. For example, if there is no water-carrying pipework, plumbing leaks cannot be the cause of the dampness. Those possible causes that are left can be put in order of probability and methodical processes of examination devised. The possibilities can then be examined sequentially until all that cannot apply are eliminated. The causes can thus be narrowed down, but it is not always possible to come to a single proven cause by this process of elimination.

Example: diagnosis of the causes of organic decay

Organic decay is often promoted by dampness. Like many manifestations of building defects, it is generally a secondary effect of a concealed primary problem. Investigation may require specialist techniques and knowledge.

Generally, organic infestations such as wood-boring insects and fungal decay arise because of deficiencies in the built environment that encourage decay. Investigating the infestation is necessary to a diagnosis of its cause.

Wood-boring insects have often attacked old timbers, the evidence being the flight holes formed as the insects exit the wood. The flight holes do not indicate live infestation requiring treatment. An active infestation will cause fine wood dust or powder to appear in or under flight holes. This is a seasonal event and is best treated when the wood-boring insects are likely to take flight.

Most wood-boring insects will not eat the heartwood of durable hardwoods, preferring the more nutritious sapwood. In old buildings containing oak structures, the sapwood may be riddled with boreholes while the heartwood may be imperforate. It is often a mistake to regard such timbers as defective or to propose treatment.

Water can cause timbers to rot. Removing the water is all that is required to control wet rot. Rotted timbers may be more susceptible to insect attack. For this reason signs of rot and of insect infestation may indicate water activity, making measurements of the moisture content of the rotted and infected timbers a vital part of diagnosis. The surest form of cure is the removal of conditions conducive to decay. Intervention with insecticides and fungicides are not a good alternative to curing dampness where this is the underlying cause of failure.

Recent concern about the toxic effects of some moulds emphasises the need for a considered approach to organic infestation. 'Toxic-mould phobia' has caused some building insurers to exclude cover for the consequences of mould in buildings – leaving designer and builder in the firing line.

Mould

Mould spores cover the planet. They are one of Earth's natural clean-up systems, eating dead or decaying organic matter. Hundreds of thousands of mould types exist, of which some 16 variants have been identified as toxic to humans. All of these have been found in water-damaged buildings.[67]

Initial signs are a musty odour and surface discoloration (black or coloured marks). Mould may be concealed, for which reason investigation may have to start with a check for conditions conducive to mould growth, such as warm, wet, sunless spaces. Ill health may also be a symptom of allergenic or toxic mould (see Chapter 2, Designing for a healthy environment).

Testing for toxic or allergenic moulds by swab and culture analysis will not reveal dead mould or mycotoxins. Effective alternatives include:

- non-viable[68] air and surface sampling;
- viable air and surface sampling tape lifts;
- polymerised chain reaction (PCR); and
- visual assessments.

Where ill health indicates a potential toxicity, the investigation should include checks for allergens and toxins from moulds.

Sampling should be designed to test hypotheses and avoid unnecessary data collection. It may involve special equipment. For example, air-flow (exchange and dilution) dead spots are investigated by releasing a trace gas, SF6, and tracing it throughout the building to identify source, route and dilution. A portable analyser is used to identify dust size and quantity.

Evidence may be required for the pursuit of claims, as well as to assess risk and devise a cure. If mould develops after a flood, it may be the responsibility of the surveyor, builder, etc. who advised on and implemented restoration measures. Mould claims have hit insurers in the USA, where poor or incompetent flood restoration has resulted in allegations of health problems caused by toxic moulds.

Reports

The nature and content of each report will depend on the purpose for which it is being prepared. Technical reports should follow broadly the standard model for scientific and engineering reports, i.e. impersonal and factual. The alternative – that is, a forensic report – may need to be set out in a form suitable to be the evidence-in-chief of an expert witness. The structure and content of each type of report are considered below.

In all cases it is useful to number each paragraph to facilitate reference to parts of the report in discussions. The abstract or summary should be capable of standing alone; for this reason it is customary not to number the paragraphs in the abstract.

Technical reports

There is no prescribed format for reporting but there are widely accepted customs. Impersonal language is used. The first major section introduces the purpose or objectives of the report. The final substantive section concludes the report by answering the questions posed – explicitly or otherwise – in the introduction.

Factual observations, measurements and reference material are kept completely separate from opinion and interpretation, and may be appended to the report rather than included within its body. Alternatively, they may be included in separate sections within the body of the report.

The report may contain any of the following sections, depending on the subject matter:

- Abstract (sometimes called executive summary or summary);
- Table of contents (or index for long documents);
- Acknowledgements;
- Introduction;
- Objectives;
- Theory;
- Method or methodology or procedures;
- Results;
- Discussion or interpretation;
- Conclusion;
- Recommendations;
- References and/or bibliography; and
- Appendices.

If abbreviations or shorthand terminology are employed, a list of the expressions used should be given. Where technical terms which may be obscure to the intended reader are used, these should be explained. Where terms which have more than one meaning are used, their use in the report should be clarified – at least where this is necessary to a proper understanding of the text.

Facts relied upon must be supported by reference to their source, or if assumed this must be stated. Otherwise the reliability of a stated fact must be demonstrated within the text of the report.

Abstract or summary

The abstract is a synopsis or précis of the report. It must be as short as is consistent with giving a complete overview of the essential contents of the report. A good length for an abstract is 300 words.

Introduction

The introduction sets out why and for whom the report is written, what it covers, and what its role is in relation to other work. It should state whether the report extends or supersedes these earlier studies and reports. The scope of the report and the readership for which it is intended should be given.

When describing an investigation, the introduction will usually state explicitly what the investigators set out to find.

Objectives

This is a statement of what the work being reported was expected to achieve, why it was undertaken, and at whose instigation. A good approach is to tabulate the matters to be addressed by the work covered in the report. The conclusions can then refer back to the tabulated matters, dealing with each in turn.

Acknowledgements

If the work of others has been used, this should be stated. If the report is the work of more than one person, the role and contribution of each should be made clear. This may be put before the introduction as a foreword.

Theory

If used, this sets out any proposal or hypothesis which the work intends to test.

Method

It is appropriate to state any matter which has a bearing on the validity and accuracy of the procedures adopted. As a minimum, the way the work was carried out should be described – including the equipment used. Additionally, such details as the accuracy of the equipment and competence/experience of those using it are often worth stating.

Results

This should contain the results of any tests, inspections, examinations, etc. in simple summary without interpretation or elaboration. If the results are copious, they can be appended and summarised here.

Discussion

In this section, a reasoned examination of the results is given. Prior to this, the author's opinion should not be given. This is the 'bridge' linking the reported facts to the author's reported opinions in the following section. The discussion should show the reasoning behind any conclusions and recommendations given in the report. The results may be interpreted, compared with other published findings and assessed for potential shortcomings. Any speculation about the proper interpretation of the results should be in this section.

Conclusion

The conclusion gives the overall findings of the study. The conclusions should be statements that are the evident logical outcome of the rest of the work.

Recommendations

The recommendations should demonstrably arise logically from the results, as interpreted and considered in the discussion section.

References and bibliography

The purpose of citing references is to allow the reader to check that the conclusions drawn follow from the sources cited. There should be sufficient detail to allow the reader to follow up the references. For books give the authors, year, edition (if more than one), publisher's name and publisher's location. For articles in journals give the authors, year, name of publication, volume and page numbers.

For references published on the web the same basic principle applies as it does to citing printed works: the citation must be sufficient to allow the reader to follow up the reference. If possible, give a URL that will take the reader directly to the document cited; giving the URL for a 'home' or 'welcome' page is generally not helpful. Give the names of the authors and the publication date where known.

The bibliography is the set of publications that the authors referred to in a general sense in writing the report, which will not usually be cited explicitly in the text. References, on the other hand, are given in support of some specific assertion and are always mentioned explicitly in the text, normally after the statement the author wants to support. A common method is to give the authors and year in the text – e.g: (Bloggs, 1999) – and the full details at the end of the report, or in a footnote.

In scientific writing, any statement that is not one of plain fact or measurement must be justified, or reference made to a supporting publication.

Appendices

The appendices are where the author will usually place any material that is not directly relevant to the report, and they will be read only by a small number of people.

Visual material

Provide numbered captions to all charts, graphs, etc.

Allow that coloured illustrations may be reproduced in black and white. Choose colours for critical information with this in mind. Black-and-white photocopies of colour photography may lose much information, and when faxed the results are very poor.

Forensic reports

Where a matter is in dispute a report may be required to address the issues in dispute in terms of liability and responsibility as well as cause and effect. Where the dispute is subject to legal proceedings the report may be termed 'forensic'. Usually such reports will be called for as expert evidence. The expert witness, and associated report writing, is dealt with in Chapter 11.

Report writing may start as a technical assessment, with the intention – if the findings would support a claim – of later developing it into a forensic report. With this in mind, methodically reporting each stage of an investigation can serve two purposes: it follows good scientific principles for a technical study and can form the basis for compelling written evidence in a dispute. Although video recording has the merit of keeping a continuous record, still photography and drawn records are more commonly used.

There is no set form for recording forensic evidence in building disputes, but Fig. 6.6 illustrates an approach which has been effective in large investigations where iterative sampling is appropriate. In this case a series of point inspections was made on each component of the building which was under investigation. A uniform technique for reporting each investigation was adopted and each inspection was set out in a separate report. These reports were collated chronologically and formed an appendix to an interpretative report. Purpose-designed forms were prepared for use during the inspections, to help the inspection team maintain a uniform report style (see Fig. 6.4).

Figure 6.4: **Example of site inspection sheets prepared as part of a forensic report.**

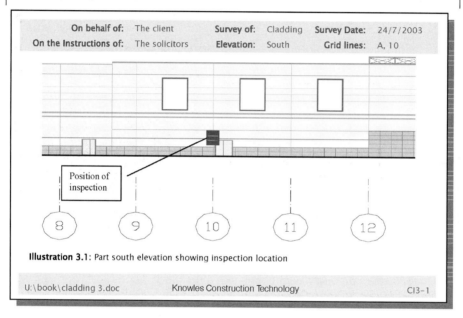

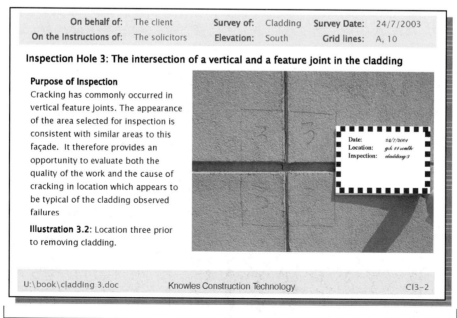

Figure 6.4: **Continued.**

| On behalf of: | The client | Survey of: | Cladding | Survey Date: | 24/7/2003 |
| On the Instructions of: | The solicitors | Elevation: | South | Grid lines: | A, 10 |

Condition Prior to Opening Up

The vertical crack in the groove between the polystyrene boards passes through the horizontal groove. The finish to the edges of feature joints is particularly uneven and lumpy.

Inspection

Sections of cladding were cut out around the intersection of the feature joints. This showed that the Cladding was placed over profiled metal sheets.

Illustration 3.3: Closer view of crack at intersection of vertical and horizontal feature joints

U:\book\cladding 3.doc   Knowles Construction Technology   Cl3-3

| On behalf of: | The client | Survey of: | Cladding | Survey Date: | 24/7/2003 |
| On the Instructions of: | The solicitors | Elevation: | South | Grid lines: | A, 10 |

This is contrary to the System manufacturer's Specifications, Section 118, sub-section 1.04 System Description, C. Design Requirements where the substrates listed as acceptable exclude profiled metal sheets.

"*Acceptable Substrates for the System:*

a. Unglazed brick, cement plaster, concrete, or masonry.

b. Exterior grade gypsum sheathing

c. Silicone treated gypsum core sheathing surfaced with inorganic fibreglass mats

Illustration 3.4: Cladding removed to the sides of the feature joints.

U:\book\cladding 3.doc   Knowles Construction Technology   Cl3-4

Chapter 6

Figure 6.4: **Continued.**

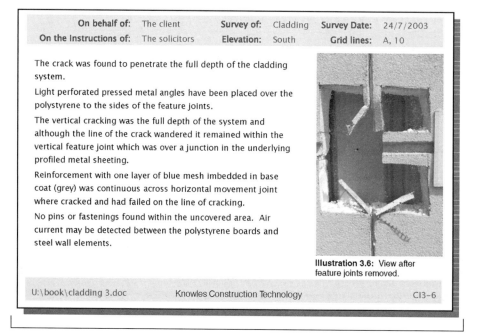

| On behalf of: | The client | Survey of: | Cladding | Survey Date: | 24/7/2003 |
| On the instructions of: | The solicitors | Elevation: | South | Grid lines: | A, 10 |

d. Exterior fibre reinforced cement and calcium silicate boards.

e. Exterior grade Plywood, nominal 13 mm, minimum 4 ply.

f. Exposure 1 rated Oriented Strand Board (OSB), nominal 13 mm

g. Galvanized expanded metal lath 1.4 or 1.8 kg/m² installed over a solid substrate."

Similarly, the applicable national standard does not include steel walls as an accepted carrying structure. Compliance with this standard is mandatory.

Illustration 3.5: Closer view of bottom edge of inspection hole.

U:\book\cladding 3.doc   Knowles Construction Technology   CI3–5

| On behalf of: | The client | Survey of: | Cladding | Survey Date: | 24/7/2003 |
| On the instructions of: | The solicitors | Elevation: | South | Grid lines: | A, 10 |

The crack was found to penetrate the full depth of the cladding system.

Light perforated pressed metal angles have been placed over the polystyrene to the sides of the feature joints.

The vertical cracking was the full depth of the system and although the line of the crack wandered it remained within the vertical feature joint which was over a junction in the underlying profiled metal sheeting.

Reinforcement with one layer of blue mesh imbedded in base coat (grey) was continuous across horizontal movement joint where cracked and had failed on the line of cracking.

No pins or fastenings found within the uncovered area. Air current may be detected between the polystyrene boards and steel wall elements.

Illustration 3.6: View after feature joints removed.

U:\book\cladding 3.doc   Knowles Construction Technology   CI3–6

Figure 6.4: **Continued.**

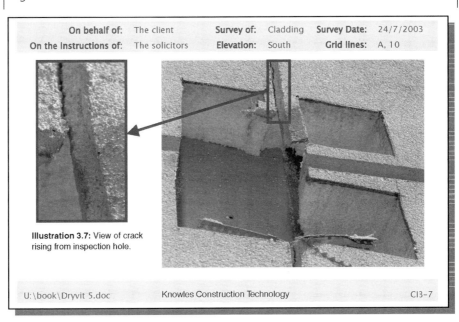

| On behalf of: | The client | Survey of: | Cladding | Survey Date: | 24/7/2003 |
| On the instructions of: | The solicitors | Elevation: | South | Grid lines: | A, 10 |

Illustration 3.7: View of crack rising from inspection hole.

U:\book\Dryvit 5.doc   Knowles Construction Technology   CI3–7

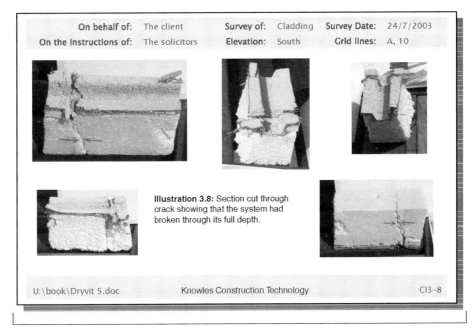

| On behalf of: | The client | Survey of: | Cladding | Survey Date: | 24/7/2003 |
| On the instructions of: | The solicitors | Elevation: | South | Grid lines: | A, 10 |

Illustration 3.8: Section cut through crack showing that the system had broken through its full depth.

U:\book\Dryvit 5.doc   Knowles Construction Technology   CI3–8

Figure 6.4: **Continued.**

| On behalf of: | The client | Survey of: | Cladding | Survey Date: | 24/7/2003 |
| On the Instructions of: | The solicitors | Elevation: | South | Grid lines: | A, 10 |

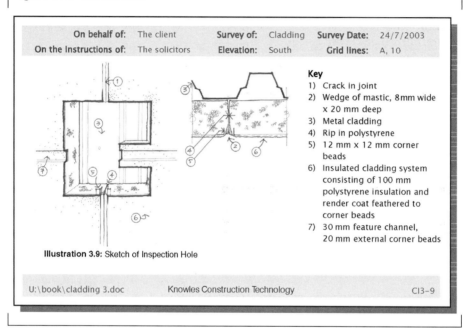

Key
1) Crack in joint
2) Wedge of mastic, 8 mm wide x 20 mm deep
3) Metal cladding
4) Rip in polystyrene
5) 12 mm x 12 mm corner beads
6) Insulated cladding system consisting of 100 mm polystyrene insulation and render coat feathered to corner beads
7) 30 mm feature channel, 20 mm external corner beads

Illustration 3.9: Sketch of Inspection Hole

U:\book\cladding 3.doc   Knowles Construction Technology   CI3–9

Defects schedules

An excellent summary form for reporting cases where there are multiple defects is to draw up schedules, which can be extended to deal with remedy, liability, cost, etc. as appropriate in each case (see Fig. 6.5).

Often the expert appointed for each side will find it useful to prepare such schedules, even where not instructed so to do. They are useful to explain the issues to client and lawyer and often a valuable aid during 'without-prejudice' experts meetings.

Schedules can form part of the stated case put before the court and be a joint exercise between the lawyers and experts (see Fig. 6.6).

Figure 6.5: **Example of a defects schedule.**

Item	Location	Defect	Damage	Remedy
1	All areas of flat roof	Vapour control layer omitted in design, allowing water vapour to rise into the roof and to accumulate under the roof membrane as condensate.	The fibrous insulation is becoming waterlogged and loosing cohesion. This is reducing the thermal resistance of the roof and its capacity to carry foot traffic.	Strip off all flat roofs to expose the metal deck. Install vapour-control layer and re-form roof over, using new materials as necessary.

Figure 6.6: **Extract from a Defects Schedule Used as Part of a Statement of Case.**

Item	Location	Breach	Particulars of Breach
Missing vertical movement-control joints to the external brickwork leaf. Vertical movement-control joints should have been installed within 6 metres of all corners of the Blocks.	All external brickwork.	Poor Design constituting a breach of:	1. In failing to design and/or detail and/or specify the incorporation of movement-control joints in the brickwork at the locations specified herein, the builder failed to comply with the requirements of clauses 20.2.3.2 and 20.3.1 of BS 5628, Part 3 1985 and thereby failed to design the Works:
		(i) Clause 2.1 of the Conditions, and/or;	(i) in accordance with clause 3.4.5.4 of the Architect's Requirements and/or;
		(ii) Clause 2.5.1 of the Conditions, and/or;	(ii) in accordance with clause 5.2.1 of the Requirements as to Detailed Design and/or;
		(iii) Clause 6.1.2 of the Conditions and/or;	(iii) with the skill and care of a reasonably competent architect;
		(iv) the implied terms set out in paragraph 9(iv) and (v) of the statement of claim.	2. Further or alternatively in failing to design and/or detail and/or specify movement-control joints for the masonry, the builder caused the brickwork to crack thereby allowing moisture to penetrate to the inner leaf of the flats causing damp and mould therein in the manner set out in column 6 herein, and thereby failed to design and/or construct the Works:
			(i) in accordance with clause C8 of the Regulations as required by, inter alia, clause 3.4.1 of the Architect's Requirements, and/or;
			(ii) so as to ensure that the same and in particular the cavity walls therein were fit for their purpose, and/or;
			(iii) so as to ensure that, upon completion, the flats were fit for human habitation.

Consequence of Defect	Claimant's case on Causation	Remedial Work	Remedial Work Cost
The brickwork cracks as a result of its failure to cope with thermal and hygral movement within the masonry and between the masonry and the reinforced concrete structure.	Had this defect existed in isolation it could have been remedied by locally cutting the affected brickwork, replacing cracked bricks and forming vertical movement joints to control the movement in all elevations.	(i) Strap brickwork as set out more fully in paragraph 22 of the Introduction to sections I & II to the Schedule.	(i) £2,750,952 for strapping as set out in paragraph 23 of the Introduction to sections I & II to the Schedule, and;
Cracks within the brickwork exacerbate water penetration and limit the resistance of the brickwork to wind-driven rain. This increases the amount of water penetration when considered in combination with the defects identified in parts B and/or C above and/or items D4–D9 below.	However, since it is also necessary to stabilise the brickwork as a result of the defect identified in Section III below and to minimise any future movement in the cracks, a more appropriate remedial scheme is:	(ii) The Over-cladding Scheme	(ii) £5,510,763 for the Over-cladding Scheme as particularised in paragraphs 21.1–21.3 of the Introduction to section I & II of the Schedule.
All such defects cause and/or contribute to water penetration, damp and mould in the flats.	(i) to strap all cracks to reduce further movement in the existing cracks and to discourage the occurrence of future cracking, and hence minimise the amount of water which can penetrate, and;		
Typical examples of the most likely route of water penetration caused by these defects are set out in the column headed *"Claimant's case on causation"* in the relevant parts of Section I.	(ii) to over-clad and thereby reduce the fluctuations in the temperature of the bricks by installing a layer of insulation within the over-cladding, thereby reducing the amount of movement and cracking in the brickwork when installed in combination with the strapping set out above.		

Scott schedules

Named in the 1920s after His Honour George Scott QC, these are often required by the official referees[69] and generally provide a good format for setting out matters for negotiation and discussion.

One party tabulates, item by item, the detail of their case and the other comments on it in equal detail. These schedules should not contain broad allegations or unsupported blunt denials. For this reason it is generally better for them to be prepared by experts.

In extensive disputes, the parties may nominate representative items from the schedule for trial to reduce time otherwise spent in court.

Although there is an established form to Scott schedules their size and content may vary. Some deal exclusively with defects, some with costs and some with both. Some contain the terminology used by lawyers; others are confined to the technical language of building experts. It does not matter as long as each schedule is appropriate to the purpose for which it is required.

Often, the first column contains the item number. It is usually appropriate for the next column to be a factual statement of the item, the wording for which may be taken from the pleadings or statement of case. If the description in the second column is taken from the statement of claim, a subsequent column may contain the related statement of defence (see Fig. 6.7).

Figure 6.7: **Scott schedule.**

No.	Statement of case	Alleged defect	Reply to allegation	Proposed remedial work	Defendant's reply
1	The design is deficient in that it does not provide for the control of interstitial condensation in the roof.	Vapour-control layer omitted in design allowing water vapour to rise into the roof and to accumulate under the roof membrane as condensate.	It is agreed that the design did not provide a vapour-control membrane. Due to the low internal relative humidity and high vapour resistance of the metal deck no vapour check is required to control interstitial condensation.	Strip off all roofing to expose the metal deck. Install vapour-control layer and re-form roof over using new materials as necessary.	No work is necessary as the roof as designed is performing correctly.

Figure 6.8: **Extract from a schedule prepared under court directions.**

Item	Description of breach	Defendant's response	Claimant's valuation of work/repair	Defendant's valuation of work/repair	Judge's comments
15	In breach of the agreement to abate from the tender sum the value of the works to the room over the garage, the Defendant has failed to remove this value from its valuations of work completed.	These works and the associated costs were not included in the contract.	£14,840	£0.00	

Such schedules may go on to deal with cost, or separate Scott schedules dealing with cost may be prepared (see Fig. 6.8).

[64] Similar rules exist in Scotland and Ireland, but the dates of implementation vary. Under the Temporary and Mobile Worksites Directive, comparable rules should exist throughout the EU.

[65] BS EN ISO 13788 provides a method for this.

[66] Sometimes referred to as the 'wet/dry' or 'oven dry' method: a sample of the material is weighed, oven dried and weighed again. Provided the composition or 'phase' of the material is preserved, the reduction in weight gives a good indication of the weight of free water present in the sample prior to drying. This can be expressed as a percentage of the dry weight of the sample as a moisture-content reading.

[67] See Chapter 7, Remedies for organic infestations, p. 188 for a more detailed explanation of how mould spores develop.

[68] In this context 'viable' refers to the ability to live; having spores which are able to germinate.

[69] That part of the judiciary which presides over the Technology and Construction Court, which tries major construction cases in England and Wales.

Remedial Works

Is remedial work necessary or practicable?

To predict the effectiveness of any action to correct defects it is necessary to take account of the intended use of the building and to obtain a comprehensive understanding of the causes of the defects and of the resultant damage.

Where faults exist, the wisdom of intervention will depend on various factors, such as the balance between the detrimental side-effects of remedial work and the consequences of delaying or avoiding repair. Germane considerations vary but, in habitable building, the following are common concerns:

- Do the defects jeopardise structural integrity or are they a manifestation of structural decay?
- Will they permit water ingress and, if so, will the water cause damage?
- Do they mar appearance or otherwise interfere with the perceived quality of the building and, if so, will the value of the building be lowered?

A thorough investigation should lead to a prognosis which addresses such questions as:

- Are there benign faults, which will not cause damage or impair performance?
- Are there malignant faults, which will destabilise, compromise or otherwise degrade the building?
- Is the visible damage a manifestation of ongoing progressive failure or decay?
- Is appearance compromised?
- Is there a loss of amenity, performance or value?
- Is the integrity of any part of the building impaired?

The visible manifestations of defects are often symptoms of underlying failure. Treating the symptom and not the cause often provides no more than short-term relief. Eliminating every defect will correct the building's performance, but can be unnecessary. Tackling the mechanism of failure, so as to break the chain of events which is causing damage or annoyance, can provide an effective remedy without necessarily removing the originating defects. The available remedies for cracking and corrosion damage in reinforced concrete illustrate this point.

Example: cracking

The general principles for assessing the need for repair from a study of the symptoms are well illustrated by the example of cracking, which can appear alarming to occupants without being symptomatic of impending collapse. To ensure a proportionate remedy, it is necessary to distinguish cracking which may impair stability, or which may be a manifestation of structural failure, from other types of crack.

BRE Digest 251 classifies visible cracking in walls in terms of crack width, but warns that this should not be the only factor considered. Cracks up to 5 mm wide can usually be repaired by filling. Above this, more extensive repair may be necessary.

Numerous cracks, or cracks over 25 mm wide, may cause instability. An intelligent approach to assessing the implications of visible cracking requires an understanding of the function of the building components which are cracked and of how they came to be subject to loads they could not withstand, so causing them to fail.

A close examination of the cracks can provide clues. Their shapes and positions can indicate whether the cracks:

- are relieving tensile or compressive stresses;
- are accommodating rotational, linear or reciprocal movements;
- correspond to lines of weakness or probable lines of stress concentration;
- reflect other manifestations of failure.

It is necessary to consider – in addition to the widths, depths and distribution of cracks – the nature of the cracked materials and whether or not the cracks:

- follow the junctions between materials, or fracture monolithic materials;
- extend through the full thickness, or extend to the edges, of the cracked building components;
- are continuous or intermittent;
- follow a discernible pattern (perhaps relating to features such as corners, openings, etc.).

Even small differential movements within a foundation can disturb walls, floors and roofs. Depending on the nature of the foundation movement and the characteristics of the overlying construction, this may distort or crack various parts of the building.

Cracks induced into rigid superstructures by unstable foundations are likely to be few and isolated, and to link weak points such as openings in walls. A similar pattern of cracking may, however, occur in solidly founded walls. For example, the stresses built up by restrained thermal movements in brickwork can fracture a brick wall in a similar pattern to that caused by certain foundation movements.

Fractures caused by foundation movements often have certain distinguishing features. They include cracks which:

- taper with height;
- pass through the damp-proof course;
- are likely to pass through the full thickness of walls, even where these are in cavity construction.[70]

Dry lining can be more tolerant to movement than masonry, and may conceal narrow cracking in block- and brickwork. When it fails, the lining panels are likely to split at joints rather than directly over the cracking, so confusing the evidence of structural failure.

Horizontal cracks in masonry close to the ground, often at the level of the damp-proof course, may indicate differential ground movement disturbing the foundations.

Equally they may be caused by greater thermally induced movements in the masonry above ground than occurs in masonry at and below ground level. When expanding, the bricks may slide on the damp-proof course, which may act as a slip membrane, particularly if it has been dry bedded. This may cause horizontal cracking on the line of the damp-proof course and minor displacement of bricks at corners.

Where pointing has been carried across the edge of a flexible damp-proof course, the mortar may gradually break away to expose the edge of the membrane. This often has the appearance of serious cracking but is not structurally significant.

Where the walls contain openings or other features, these may influence the positions of the cracks. If the cracks are close to roof level this may indicate roof movement, which may be associated with ground movement.

Figure 7.1: **Part of a horizontal crack running the full length of a brick wall; diverted to follow an arched window head and door sill.**

Vertical cracks in masonry often result from excessive, restrained movements but they may also indicate disturbed foundations. Whatever the cause, they often link openings or form at lintel bearings or the junctions between phases of building.

Sloping or stepped cracks at the end of walls are an indicator of foundation failure, particularly where the vertical parts of the crack are wider than the horizontal. Generally, subsidence cracks tend to be diagonal and to taper from wider to narrower – starting high on a wall, or at a door or window, and propagating downwards at an angle.

Figure 7.2: **One of a series of vertical cracks in rendered masonry. Each crack runs through circular window openings. Usually circular openings are less likely to induce cracking than openings with square corners, which latter characteristically generate high stress concentrations. The wall cracked due to insufficient provision for movement. There were no other features to influence the wall's strength and the wall formed 'natural vertical movement' joints at regular intervals centred on each window.**

Tapering cracks indicate distortion. If caused by settlement (sagging), they tend to be widest around damp-proof-course level. If caused by heave (hogging), the cracks will tend to widen with height.

Foundation movements which cause cracking are likely to disturb line and level, so checking that walls are plumb and floors level can provide useful clues. However, it should not be assumed that the walls were truly vertical and the floors truly flat when built – for this reason, small deviations in line and level do not necessarily indicate movement, and should be considered collectively with other evidence.

Defects in the substructure may reveal themselves in gaps under ground-floor skirtings; sticking doors; cracked pavings, ducts and walls; and movement in general.

Confidence in deductions made from a study of cracks is improved if corroborated by other evidence. Distortion in frames, displaced masonry, bulging or out-of-plumb walls, sloping floors, cracked lintels, or sticking doors and windows are all possible indicators of structural distress. Where cracks pass through the full thickness of a wall, or coincide in both leaves of a cavity wall, this strongly indicates foundation damage.

Figure 7.3: **Vertical crack in brick cavity wall owing to differential movements in the piled foundations. Similar cracking could be found in the inner leaf of the cavity.**

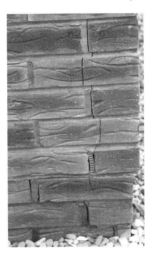

The study of the manifestations of defects should lead to an assessment of:

* their structural significance;
* whether deterioration has ceased, is continuing or worsening;
* the probable causes of the damage, and whether they are indicative of underlying failure.

Figure 7.4: **Horizontal crack in outer brick leaf of cavity wall continues internally through plastered door reveal, indicating that the cause is probably an underlying fault in the foundations.**

 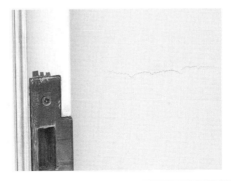

Figure 7.5: **To establish the significance of cracks in render some areas were cut away. In this case the visible cracks in the render reflected underlying cracks in the blockwork, indicating that the wall as a whole was failing – not merely the render.**

To make this preliminary assessment, and to establish the direction of subsequent more detailed investigations, the following should be noted:

- the positions, shape and extent of cracks;
- obvious movements (where these can be distinguished from built-in inaccuracies) such as displaced masonry, bulges and distortions, floor slopes, etc.;
- deviations in level (usefully checked at damp-proof-course level, along a floor edge or other continuous horizontal feature);
- damage to rainwater goods, drains, sewers, water pipes and the like;
- evidence of alterations to trees or other vegetation (recent landscaping works, infilling etc.);
- general topography of the area;
- any history of damage; and
- any information of similar problems in adjacent or nearby property.

This preliminary assessment should provide sufficient data to comment on the significance of the damage, and its possible causes and future effect. If ground movement is indicated, a more detailed investigation will be necessary.

The profiles of cracks merit particular consideration.

Crack severity can be classified by consequence, as follows:

- affecting only appearance;
- compromising the integrity of the building fabric (e.g. weather resistance);

- reducing serviceability (e.g. water supply, drainage);
- impairing stability.

Some of the most difficult decisions are associated with impaired stability. These arise when a building is in an advanced state of deterioration and the choice falls between repair or demolition. *BRE Digest 25, Assessment of Damage in Low-Rise Building* provides some useful guidance.

Once initiated, cracks often extend until the stresses causing them have been fully relieved, and simply filling them can prove ineffectual. Cracks, once formed, often relieve stress by acting as movement joints, for which reason rigid repairs may result in recurrent cracking. Flexible sealants are difficult to apply correctly in narrow joints, and tend to perform poorly if incorrectly applied – again leading to recurrent cracking.

In interpreting the evidence it should be borne in mind that foundation movements can be seasonal, so altering crack profiles throughout the year, and that dilations and contractions can alter the characteristics of cracks initiated by structural distress.

The reappearance of repaired cracks and growth of existing cracks may not indicate renewed failure but merely inappropriate repair.

Example: corrosion damage

Reinforcement corrosion is perhaps the single most common defect in concrete structures erected during the 1960s and 1970s. Its main cause is thin cover to the reinforcement and, to a lesser extent, poor quality concrete. This most often occurs in combination with carbonation of the concrete.

Steel does not corrode when embedded in highly alkaline concrete, despite high moisture levels in the concrete, because a passive film forms on the steel and remains intact as long as the surrounding concrete retains an alkalinity (pH value) of 12.5 or more.

The pH of concrete is significantly influenced by the hydration of its cement – one of the by-products of which is calcium hydroxide, which provides the alkalinity. A reserve of calcium hydroxide serves as a buffer to prevent the pH from dropping. Calcium hydroxide may be removed by free water passing through the concrete and is chemically altered by reaction with carbon dioxide, a process called 'carbonation'.

Atmospheric carbon dioxide penetrates the concrete through its capillary pores. The rate of carbonation depends upon environmental conditions, the quality of the concrete and its molecular porosity: the higher the porosity, the higher the rate of carbonation.

The rate of carbonation with time is not linear; it is related to the square root of time, i.e. $D = KT^{-2}$, where:

D = depth of carbonation;
K = carbonation coefficient; and
T = time of exposure to carbon dioxide.

Carbonation is not deleterious to concrete – on the contrary, its effect is to locally increase the strength. It is its indirect effect on embedded steel which is of concern.

In dry conditions the depth of carbonation typically exceeds that in comparable concrete which is exposed to periodic wetting and drying. This is because the pore structure of the latter concrete is effectively blocked for much of the time, thus reducing the rate of CO_2 ingress.

Figure 7.6: **Carbonation of concrete: a process which causes deterioration of the concrete due to the action of atmospheric carbon dioxide. Carbonation results from the chemical reaction of the lime in concrete with CO_2 from the air to form $CaCO_3$. This reduces the alkalinity of the concrete.**

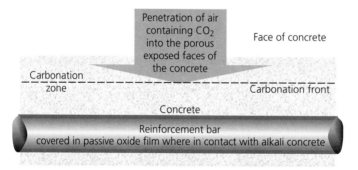

When the depth of carbonation reaches the reinforcing steel, the natural alkalinity of the concrete is sufficiently reduced to allow the steel to corrode if both water and oxygen are present. This initiates an electrochemical mechanism involving the formation of a 'corrosion cell' with an anode, a cathode and a current flowing between them. Electrons flow through the steel from the anode to the cathode and the circuit is completed via the electrolyte, which is formed by an aqueous solution of ions in the concrete. The consequence of this current flow is the release of metal ions at the anode, i.e. a loss of material from the reinforcement.

Insoluble iron oxide (rust) forms on the surface of the reinforcement. As the steel rusts it expands to up to five times its original volume, pressing into the concrete. The resultant pressure forces the concrete cover to crack and spall. The rate of corrosion is controlled by the rate of oxygen transfer to the cathode in the presence of moisture.

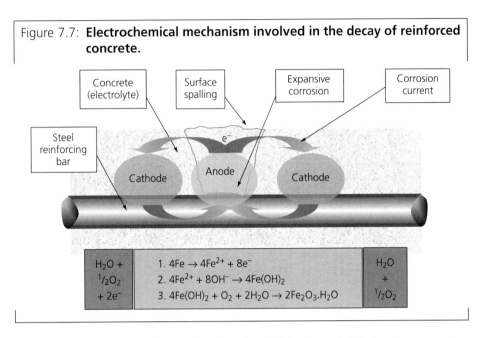

Figure 7.7: **Electrochemical mechanism involved in the decay of reinforced concrete.**

Even if concrete is not carbonated or showing visible signs of deterioration, corrosion may still occur if it contains sufficient chlorides. It is for this reason that failure of reinforcement may occur without any visual sign of cracking or spalling. The overall risk of reinforcement corrosion caused by chlorides is associated with the depth of reinforcement and the depth of carbonation. (Carbonation releases combined chlorides to form free chloride ions, thus increasing the likelihood of corrosion.) It is important, therefore, in selecting a remedy to distinguish the damage caused by chlorides from that caused by carbonation alone.

Free chloride ions within the pore structure of the concrete interfere with the passive protective film formed naturally on reinforcing steel. Chloride ions exist in two forms in concrete, namely: 'free' chloride ions, mainly found in the capillary pore water, and 'combined' chloride ions, which result from the reaction between chloride and the cement hydration process. If chloride is introduced at mixing, for example as calcium chloride, approximately 90 per cent may form harmless compounds, leaving only 10 per cent as free chloride ions. If, on the other hand, sea water or de-icing salts penetrate the surface of the concrete, the ratio of free to combined chloride may be 50:50. It is the presence of free chlorides which is most deleterious.

Chloride-induced corrosion results in localised breakdown of the passive film rather than the widespread deterioration that occurs with carbonation. The result is rapid corrosion of the metal at the anode, leading to the formation of a 'pit' in the bar surface and significant loss in cross-sectional area. Occasionally a bar may be completely eaten through.

A simple approach to repair, where the concrete has been found to be faulty in terms of the cover provided to the steel before corrosion has started, would be to apply an anti-carbonation coating. That is, a film over the exposed face of the concrete which prevents the ingress of carbon dioxide but allows the outward diffusion of water vapour. If the durability of the coating is sufficient, this will, in theory at least, extend the service life of the concrete without requiring the correction of the faults in its construction.

Where damage is advanced by the time repair is considered, manifesting itself as spalling and corrosion, patch repair may seem appropriate. Cutting out the failing concrete, neutralising the rusting surfaces and making good in new concrete will remedy the damage. It may, however, leave an active mechanism of failure in place – the repaired steel now acting as the cathode accelerating the decay of neighbouring areas which appeared previously to be undamaged.

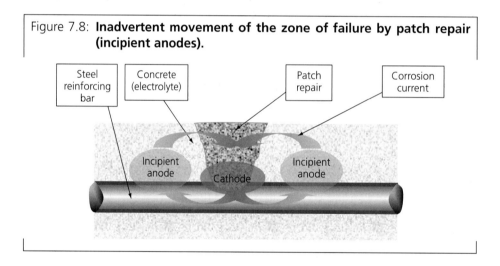

Figure 7.8: **Inadvertent movement of the zone of failure by patch repair (incipient anodes).**

An interesting option is to use the electrochemical nature of the failure mechanism to provide a way of controlling, or even reversing, the rate of failure. Sacrificial anodes can be built into a repair to prevent or limit the risk of incipient anode corrosion. The long-term durability of this method of repair is unproven, but effective performance of five to ten years is claimed by some.

Permanent impressed current installations or cathodic protection, using small current flows of in the order of $10–20\,mA/m^2$, can be combined with computer monitoring to give good damage control. The polarity of the circuit can move negatively-charged, potentially damaging chloride ions away from the steel reinforcement and increase alkalinity close to the steel. In this way, the condition of the structure can improve gradually as the mechanism of failure is put into reverse.

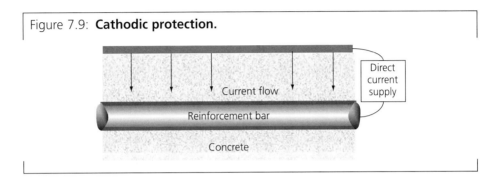

Figure 7.9: **Cathodic protection.**

Remedial works during construction

Where faults become apparent during construction, the need for corrective action often has to be weighed against the consequent delays and costs. Often it is appropriate to look for alternatives which limit the effects of the faults, rather than to pedantically undo defective construction so that everything can be redone correctly.

Many building contracts contain requirements for the investigation of incorrect work. Generally the cost follows the findings. If investigation shows the suspected faults exist, the contractor pays; if not, the employer pays. This may deter the employer or their agent from instructing opening up to look for suspected faults. The result is often that payments are withheld against suspected defects without clear instruction for investigation. Generally, the withholding of payment because of suspected deficiencies in the contractor's work is as unsatisfactory as suing for damages without first establishing a sustainable claim. It is also contrary to the 'innocent until proven guilty' principle, which in civil disputes is reflected in the doctrine that places the burden of proof on the party which asserts something to be a fact. Thus it is for the party which accuses someone of fault to prove that accusation, not for the other party to disprove it.

A more sophisticated approach, given in some standard forms and incorporated in many bespoke contracts, is to make establishing the extent of the defect the contractor's responsibility once its existence has been established. Thus, once the contractor has been found to be at fault, the cost of establishing the scope of the remedial work required lies with them.

Often, blame is allotted prematurely without prior investigation. If, for example, a material cracks, the subcontractor who supplied and fitted that material is routinely the first to be blamed. The blamed subcontractor is then told to resolve the problem. If they research the cause and prove it was not their fault, they are rarely compensated for their efforts. Where the faults do not lie in their work, they are unlikely to have the skills to form a proper diagnosis – resulting in inappropriate repair. For example, when finished work fractures, the visible failure is in the finish – perhaps painted plaster or render, tiles or panels, etc. The fractures may simply reflect under-lying failures, but the finishing contractor – say, the plasterer or decorator – is impli-cated because the manifestation of failure is in their work. No amount of repair to failed plaster over live cracking in the substrate can effect a permanent cure, but it could temporarily disguise the real problem – causing not only abortive costs at the time but further abortive costs in subsequent repairs until the root problem is addressed. It is an excellent way of generating disputes which provide further oppor-tunity to waste time and money.

Proper regard should be given to the terms of contract. Often they will stipulate the procedures to be followed. Standard forms generally deal with the right to withhold money if the builder is responsible, but are less helpful where consultant designers are to blame.

Rising standards

As standards and expectations rise, once-acceptable building stock is perceived as sub-standard. The periodic improvement and renovation of old buildings can keep their performance from falling too far below contemporary expectation, but may itself be a cause of damage.

For example, higher levels of comfort expectations and rising heating costs have led to a reduction of uncontrolled air movements in existing buildings. Cost-effective heating involves the reduction of draughts by, for example, the replacement of open fireplaces with sealed systems and draught-proofing. This elimination of fortuit-ous, if uncontrolled, natural ventilation improves comfort and has energy efficiency benefits but creates condensation risks, with the associated perils of rot and decay.[71]

Simple home improvements, such as laying additional insulation in a loft, can sufficiently alter the thermal regime to cause condensation damage in a previously 'healthy' roof. The retrospective installation of vapour-control layers is rarely fully effective. The introduction of mechanical extract to remove moisture at source is recommended but is wholly dependent on user understanding and co-operation.

It should be remembered that extracted air has to be replaced by incoming air, which in turn needs to be heated. If improvements in thermal resistance and reductions in uncontrolled ventilation are made to save energy, only to make forced ventilation necessary to prevent dampness and decay, the overall benefit is not obvious. The appropriateness of reducing draughts (as with any remedy to a perceived deficiency in a building's performance) has to be judged on an assessment of the balance between expenditure and benefit.

Upgrading old buildings to meet modern performance standards without com-promising their historic character is a particularly difficult area. Ill-conceived improvements can accelerate the deterioration of susceptible concealed materials.

Improving one component in the course of repair can create the need for modifying associated elements. For example, upgrading thermal resistance by introducing modern foamed-plastic insulants can increase thermal movements. Basic roofing felts, which would work on the relatively dimensionally stable old types of roofing boards, are unlikely to tolerate the large reciprocal movements in foamed plastics. For this, modern high-performance roof membranes are required. Similarly, re-laying a defective, traditional stone slate roof in compliance with current Building Regulations requires improved standards of insulation and draught-proofing. This reduces uncontrolled ventilation and may make necessary the introduction of a designed provision to ventilate the underside of the stone and the timbers on the cold side of the insulation.

Identify optimal approach

Before commencing the correction of faulty construction, it is often worth reviewing the options. Sometimes an error can be addressed by altering the way in which a building is used, rather than altering the building itself. In some circumstances faults, if not cured, may give rise to an increased need for maintenance, but this may be more acceptable than the disruption caused by reconstruction to remove defects. In some circumstances a building can be altered so that the defect is no longer active or damaging, whilst leaving the defective items of work alone.

A building-defects problem which gave rise to all these considerations occurred in southern Europe. The external fabric of blocks of flats was allowing water ingress during periods of heavy rain and the masonry was cracking under load. The problem lay in the relationship between the building envelope and the structure.

The alternative of building new accommodation to replace the defective buildings was seriously considered, owing to the anticipated high cost of repair. This proved impracticable due to the limited availability of suitably placed building land.

The buildings were occupied and the cost of temporary re-housing to gain vacant possession was taken into consideration in evaluating remedies. This gave a strong incentive to looking for solutions which could be implemented without decanting the residents. It was decided that over-cladding could be carried out so as to shield the defective parts of the building envelope from sun and rain. By so doing, hygral and thermal movements could be minimised, removing a key cause of masonry cracking. The over-cladding would itself provide a new water-resisting layer, so preventing water ingress in heavy rain.

In addition, the masonry was to be reinforced so as to improve its tensile strength and increase its ability to withstand the forces which had hitherto been causing cracking. None of these remedies removed the original defects. They did, however, sufficiently alter the building that the defects ceased to cause damage.

> The windows leaked in heavy rain, and the further opportunity was taken in over-cladding to incorporate sculptural features around them, so as to divert rainwater run-off away from them. The combination of the drips and mouldings and the increase in the depth of the reveal created by over-cladding reduced the amount of water which reached the windows, reducing rain ingress at windows to a trivial amount. The small quantity of moisture which still gained entry into the window frames was insufficient to penetrate internally and cause noticeable damage to finishes. After rain, the water quickly evaporated harmlessly and the windows, although still defective, were no longer troublesome.
>
> There were also deficiencies in smoke evacuation and means of escape. A scheme was developed to provide alternative emergency escape routes and smoke ventilation, which, if accepted, would have bypassed the need to correct the faults in the existing work.
>
> Whilst this was being considered, the fire brigade provided special cover. This included stationing a fire appliance by the site which, if continued, would have obviated the need for correcting the deficiencies in the fire safety aspects of the buildings. There was no reason in principle why this approach could not have been retained but some improvement to the performance of the building, combined with improvements in the automatic alarm connections to the local fire brigade, was considered a better long-term arrangement.

In the above example, the largest single cost in the corrective works to the buildings was in the over-cladding. A cost-benefit analysis was carried out to see which remedial approach gave the greatest overall advantage. Consideration was given to both capital and maintenance costs during the predicted lifetime of the proposed installation. The analyses were brought together and tabulated in a report from which the client was able to consider the desirable initial level of expenditure against the benefits achieved, including the longevity and durability of the systems.

The analysis compared the benefits of repairing and modifying the failing brick cladding to the concrete frames with benefits of alternatives. The options were divided into three categories:

- reforming the brickwork as necessary to correct the faults in it;
- removing the brickwork and installing an alternative cladding; and
- over-cladding the brickwork.

Over-cladding was further divided into sealed and rain-screen cladding.

The systems brought forward from preliminary assessment to the final study were:

- the repair/renewal of the brickwork;
- the replacement of the brickwork with glass reinforced pre-cast concrete panels;

- the replacement of the brickwork with ceramic tiles on an insulated aluminium framing;
- rain-screen-cladding in proprietary cladding panelling on light metal framing;
- over-cladding in curtain walling; and
- over-cladding with a self finished render on stainless steel lathing.

Suitable examples from each category were assessed against the following criteria: maintenance, longevity, construction considerations, appearance and cost.

Each of the main assessment criterion included specific assessments as follows:

Maintenance:

- cleaning requirements;
- major maintenance intervals;
- any special requirements for maintenance;
- ease of repair.

Longevity:

- routine inspections/repairs required to maintain performance;
- limited life components;
- anticipated (maintained) lifespan.

Construction:

- time on site required to complete the work;
- extent of disruption to occupancy during construction period;
- noise during construction;
- the ease with which the system can be adapted on site to overcome variations in the existing construction, etc.;
- ease of supervision and any special requirements.

Appearance:

- availability of colours, textures, etc.;
- effects of weathering;
- compatibility with original design intent and environment.

Cost:

- Construction cost;
- Maintenance cost;
- Cost of periodic renewal to achieve required life span.

The results are illustrated in fig. 7.10

Cost-benefit analysis

Cost-benefit analysis involves a balanced consideration of projected spend on both capital (initial building) cost and lifetime (projected repair and replacement) costs.

Figure 7.10: **Extract from a cost-benefit analysis report on repair options**

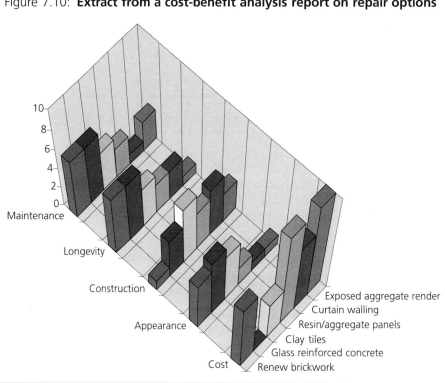

One way of doing this is to calculate anticipated maintenance cost in terms of the equivalent capital cost. For example, if option 'a' has a life to first replacement of 20 years and option 'b' has a life to first maintenance of 60 years, for a 60-year life span option 'a' will have to be replaced twice while option 'b' will not need replacing. If option 'a' costs £100,000 and option 'b' costs £200,000 the capital costs will be:

'a' £100,000
'b' £200,000

Assuming, for simplicity of this example, that no interim maintenance will be required, the lifetime costs for 'b' will be £0 and for 'a' they will be £200,000. The total costs can be tabulated as follows:

Option	Initial cost	At 20 years	At 40 years	Equivalent capital cost
'a'	£100,000	£100,000	£100,000	£300,000
'b'	£200,000	£0	£0	£200,000

It would appear from the above table that option 'b' has the lower lifetime cost. However, this does not allow for inflation and financial growth were the required money to pay for the 60-year cost of each option to be invested in full at the outset. Assuming monetary growth exceeds inflation by an average of 5 per cent a year, in terms of the money which has to be invested at the outset, the above table can be rewritten as follows:

Option	Initial cost	At 20 years	At 40 years	Equivalent capital cost
'a'	£100,000	£37,689	£14,915	£152,604
'b'	£200,000	£0	£0	£200,000

This second table, although based on simplified projections, illustrates how allowing for monetary growth can radically alter the apparent results of comparing the benefits of using short-life with those of using long-life materials.

A full benefit analysis will consider the advantages and disadvantages of each alternative more broadly than in terms of cost alone.

Accommodating faults versus removing causes

Defects do not necessarily cause damage. Usually where a defect is implicated it is part of a mechanism causing damage, and it is often possible to arrest the damage by remedies which do not eliminate the defect. Protecting or isolating the defective parts of a building can sometimes end the damaging effects of the defects and be more economical than correcting them. Approaches worth considering are to:

- isolate occupants/perishable finishes from the defective component of the building;
- remove a cause of damage so that the mechanism of failure is interrupted; or
- change the susceptible finish for a less-susceptible alternative.

Following these principles, there is a range of solutions for under-performing buildings which attempt to get round the effects of a defect rather than to correct them.

For example, placing a corrugated plastic membrane over a slightly damp basement wall with ventilation slots at the top and bottom of the cavities formed between wall and membrane, and then plastering and decorating the internal surface of the membrane, is an established technique for minimising the effects of dampness on decorative finishes and the like without having to remove the underlying causes of dampness.

This approach is viable where all the damage is visible. Where the damage is a symptom or cause of concealed decay, restraining the visible symptoms whilst leaving an active mechanism of failure operating unseen provides short-term relief but risks more severe breakdowns developing without apparent warning.

A similar approach might be to improve land drainage outside a damp cellar wall, so as to divert water and thus reduce the amount which enters the wall. Under some circumstances this can be sufficiently effective to make remedying the underlying problem unnecessary. A leaking cellar which is tanked externally can rarely be repaired by exposing the defective tanking and patching the holes in it. Although, in theory, this would remove the defect and ensure correct performance, it can be prohibitively difficult and expensive. To the extent that options such as locally improving land drainage are cheaper and simpler, they are more worth considering first. This can lower the hydrostatic pressure on the tanking. Without substantial pressure to force the water through the cellar walls, the interior may dry sufficiently to allow the cellar to be used for many purposes.

If the intended use does not require continuously low humidity, such an approach can provide a cost-effective alternative to the correction of defects. However, if the wall contains materials such as steel or timber, which may be damaged by the dampness, the life of the structure may be shortened and the remedy, to this extent, prove unsatisfactory.

If, in the above example, the cellar was to be used for storing papers, adding drainage could not be expected to sufficiently alleviate the problem and more drastic measures would be needed. Complete repair of external tanking requires substantial partial demolition. It may in such circumstances be worth considering options such as building alternative accommodation or re-designating the uses of built spaces.

The presence of a defect does not necessarily require corrective action. Many buildings contain defective work but perform sufficiently well to be regarded as satisfactory. Such defects may safely be left, provided sufficient precaution is taken against the risk of there being concealed damage that may lead to the need for much greater repair later if preventative action is not taken early.

Sometimes, preventing damage requires a change in materials or design so as to accommodate the mechanism of failure while removing its adverse effects. For example, osmotic blistering of finishes to concrete floors has reportedly been cured by replacing a conventional epoxy-resin floor covering with one which 'breathes' a little, so relieving the osmotic pressure.

Correction of defects

The correction of defects must be based on a proper understanding of the causes and mechanisms involved. Taking the apparently obvious approach without a proper understanding of what is involved can exacerbate the problem. For example, drying a building which is infested with mould may accelerate the production of mould spores. Moulds recognise the threat to their existence when subject to drying conditions and will try to propagate before they die by releasing (potentially harmful) spores.

If damage always follows a certain set of events, the cause and hence remedy may seem self evident. The effectiveness of a cure will demonstrate the soundness of the thinking behind it. Sometimes trial repairs may be an effective way of identifying the cause of the problem, but the injudicious application of an inappropriate solution can impede both investigation and remedy. All of the available evidence should be considered before intervening to arrest the failure.

A newly built, two-storey, detached house on the outskirts of London had a roof which comprised a series of tapering ridges and valleys formed in plywood, with a semi-ductile stainless-steel covering. Internally there was a plasterboard false ceiling. A polythene vapour-control layer was laid over the ceiling under a glass-fibre quilt.

Sometimes, after rain, water ran out of the ceiling. It was assumed that the roof leaked but the mechanism by which water got in could not be found. There was no visible fault in the roofing and, usually, heavy rain did not cause leaking; it was more often associated with showers at the end of a warm day.

After investigation with fluorescent dye gels, it was found that water was sucked through joints in the stainless-steel valley linings when cold rain at the end of a warm day caused rapid cooling, thus lowering the pressure within the roof void.

The water which was drawn in was contained between the roofing and vapour-control layer. Gradually it spread through the roof void – periodically condensing on the underside of the plywood, where mould began to grow. During summer, high humidities and dampness built up in the roof void. Periodically, the rapid chilling of the roof, when cold rain followed a hot day, would cause a sudden accumulation of condensate. If sufficient condensate formed it flooded over the lower edges of the vapour-control layer.

As this occurred during rain it was natural to assume the roof was leaking – but no amount of searching could reveal where to patch the roof. The more complex mechanism which was causing the problem was difficult to identify but, without doing so, no effective remedy could be devised.

'A stitch in time . . .'

Small faults can lead to major damage if not attended to in good time. A pinprick in lead lining to a timber gutter can be repaired with solder in few minutes, but if left unattended the pinprick will allow water damage to the timber which might continue unseen until complete reconstruction of the gutter is required.

What is necessary is an understanding of the potential consequence of the fault so that the necessity and urgency of repair can be foreseen.

Some manufacturers and suppliers give specific advice on maintenance. This can often be found in standard forms of warranty, Agrément Certificates and the like, giving useful guidance on the urgency of attending to various foreseeable forms of damage and deterioration. Examples of this can be found in some proprietary cladding and roofing systems, which advise immediate correction of damage to waterproofing layers.

Some building systems are robust, contain redundancy or incorporate fail-safe mechanisms. Much traditional building falls into these categories and is tolerant of neglect. Modern, highly-engineered construction tends to be more vulnerable to deterioration once damaged. Refinements to optimise economy of construction tend to reduce capacity to withstand deterioration due to flaws in the finished work. Delayed maintenance in such circumstances can be a very costly false economy.

Acting before expiration of warranty, limitation periods and anticipated changes in regulations can all be good reasons for pushing on with repairs. Changes in regulated standards are rarely retrospective, but they can apply to remedial works – making it necessary to upgrade buildings, not simply repair them.

It is often easier to press home a compensation claim for the actual costs of corrective works which have been carried out, than for the estimated costs of repair which has not yet been done. With due regard for periods of warranty and limitation periods, getting the work done to in time to facilitate claims for damages can require careful timing.

Remedies for organic infestations

Insect and fungal infestation can be difficult to eradicate. The general principle is to remove the infested materials and the conditions conducive to the infestation. Using insecticides and fungicides can suppress the evidence of the infestation without eradicating it. Sometimes, trying to kill the infestation can temporarily boost unhealthy conditions – making destroying or neutralising moulds problematic.

Mould spores can contain toxic chemicals which may be released when the spore is destroyed or ruptured. Chemical or biocide treatments can rupture or decay spores, releasing toxin-covered sub-micron particles, the inhalation of which can be harmful.

Mould growth is often associated with surface condensation.[72] Damp houses provide good conditions for its development. Mould spores exist in large numbers in the atmosphere and, to germinate, need a nutrient (oxygen), a suitable temperature and moisture. Sources of nutrition are widespread in buildings and ordinary habitable interiors can provide suitable temperature for growth. As oxygen is also always present, mould growth is principally dependent upon the moisture conditions at surfaces and the length of time these conditions persist. Studies have shown that moulds do not necessarily require the presence of water. As a guide, if the average relative humidity within a room stays above 70 per cent for several days, the relative humidity at external wall surfaces will be high enough to support the germination and growth of moulds.

Although the symptoms of mould growth are fairly easily dealt with by either washing with diluted household bleach followed by clean water or the use of a proprietary toxic wash, it is better to remove the causes of the mould growth such as high relative humidity. Care should be taken not to cause the release of toxins and allergens.

Mould produces enzymes to digest its food source. Once established in porous materials these resist cleaning, and applying fungicidal paints may not prevent regrowth if conditions suitable for growth persist. Disinfectants can destroy the mould cell wall, but chemicals held within the cell are released, creating toxic dust. Even long-dead dry mould can cause allergenic or toxic effects.

The surest remedy where mould has been established is to remove porous materials and clean non-permeable surfaces. Suppressing dust is important. In the USA, the control of mould and mycotoxic dust involves techniques similar to those suited to the disposal of asbestos. The following are typical of what is required to safely control mould:

- remove standing water;
- dehumidify persistently damp atmospheres;
- regulate the temperature (prevent uncontrolled evaporation);
- ventilate;
- illuminate with ultraviolet light;
- thoroughly decontaminate evidently mouldy areas;
- suppress the spread and release of spores and mycotoxins into the air;
- negative and positive pressure systems and special filtration may be required to control the spread of contamination.

The elimination of mould problems requires the removal of the conditions causing mould. Flourishing mould where none should be is a symptom of building failure. The rectification of the underlying failure is the most effective long-term measure to control mould growth.

Proprietary anti-fungal paints and wallpaper pastes, which can be used in areas where condensation occurs regularly, are also available.[73]

Until drying-out is complete, humidities which are conducive to mould growth may recur. New buildings contain large amounts of water in concrete, plasters, etc. Old buildings which have been left unoccupied or in a state of disrepair can accumulate large quantities of water in their fabric, and one or two years can elapse before it has all dried out. During this period, moisture can continue to appear on the walls – as slow-drying parts of the fabric gradually release water, and owing to the deposition of surface condensate on the parts of the envelope that have their insulating properties impaired due to absorbed water.

The insulation values of open-cell or fibrous materials will be adversely affected if wetted. Remedial work should include drying materials that are to be re-used. Precautions should be taken to prevent wetting of all new materials introduced into the structure.

The provision of protection against mechanical damage to insulating materials should also be taken into account.

Consideration should be given to removing built-in furniture from an outside wall to allow heat to reach the wall from the room – otherwise water vapour could penetrate to the wall and condense, resulting in mould growth, not only on the wall but also on the contents of the furniture.

Particular attention should be paid to the ventilation of larders, unheated storage spaces and enclosed porches. Water vapour migrates to these areas from adjacent heated spaces where the vapour pressure is higher. Consideration should be given to the heating and insulation of such storage spaces.

The materials used for decoration during a period when the building is drying out should be capable of allowing moisture to evaporate through them without incurring damage. Neither wallpaper nor impervious paints should be used until the structure has dried sufficiently. It is preferable for the moisture contents of walls and floors to be in equilibrium with the relative humidity expected in the rooms after remedial works are complete. Occupants should be advised of the anticipated drying-out periods and be discouraged from applying vapour-impermeable finishes until equilibrium conditions are attained.

It is necessary to take adequate control of heating and ventilation, especially until drying-out is completed. This is particularly difficult to manage in rented premises, where the tenant may not be responsible for maintaining the building fabric and where occupancy patterns may be subject to unforeseeable changes. In such rented property, it might benefit the owner to make a provision for background heating or controlled ventilation or both, so as to ensure that the building is not damaged by prolonged high humidity and the accumulation of condensation.

In dealing with ventilation rates and methods, economic considerations often conflict with that which is desirable for control of fungal growth.

Remedying condensation

Dealing with condensation problems illustrates the way in which building construction and use have to be considered together in devising effective and durable remedies.

Controlling condensation risk requires anticipating occupancy patterns along with a comprehensive consideration of heating, ventilation, vapour resistance and thermal insulation.

In theory, surface condensation can be eliminated by heating the affected surfaces to maintain their temperatures above the dew point. Associated evaporation caused by the heating might necessitate some accompanying ventilation to atmosphere.

A common cause of harmful condensation in existing buildings is lack of adequate heating. This may be due to forced economy or insufficient heating installations. By considering heating, ventilation and insulation together with occupancy patterns, optimal solutions to balance the control of condensation with capital and running cost can be devised.

Ventilation to remove water vapour will expend energy. Avoidable energy loss can be limited by the use of heat exchangers in the path of the exhaust air. Extraction of vapour at the point of production can be a most effective method of controlling condensation risk.

The purpose of this ventilation is to keep the dew point temperature of the air below the inside surface temperature of the building envelope. Powered extract from spaces where activities generate high humidity is often more effective than extract where condensation occurs, if remote from the source of the water vapour. Trickle ventilators local to positions where surface condensate accumulates can reduce the deposition of condensate.

Thermal insulation in the building envelope tends to move the risk from internal surface condensation to interstitial condensation. The position of the thermal insulants, the vapour resistivity of materials used and the environments within and outside the building all influence condensation risk. A repair may appear to cure a problem only to move it somewhere else if thermal resistance, vapour control and ventilation are not kept in balance.

[70] More guidance on this is given in the *BRE Building Elements* series: see, for example, p. 92 of the edition on *Walls windows and doors*.
[71] See Chapter 2, Designing for a healthy environment.
[72] See Chapter 5, Condensation.
[73] See *BRE Digest 139*.

Damage and Remedy

Damages

The remedy for breach of contract is damages. In this context, 'damages' means the compensation payable for a breach of contract, by the person who breaches the contract, to the party injured by the breach. Damages, as a reflection of natural justice, should balance the losses caused by the breach.

Pursuing a claim for damages may be said to be a commercial activity. Money, time and effort are ventured in the hope of financial compensation. Before launching such an enterprise, it is as well to assess both risks and potential benefits.

Sustaining a claim for damages

There are certain generally applicable tests to establish whether or not a sustainable building-defects claim exists. In the first place, there must be a defect or fault in the work which gives rise to a loss. In the second place, the party which caused the defect must owe a duty to the party suffering the loss and must, in causing the defect, have been in breach of that duty.

There are therefore two distinct and related lines of investigation to establish the facts on which a building-defects claim can be established or refuted: one, into the relationships between those involved; the other, into the relationship between defects and loss.

Loss may not flow from a defect

Breach of contract, failure to discharge a duty, or the mere existence of a defect does not, of itself, necessarily give rise to a sustainable claim for damages.

Many poorly built buildings perform their function adequately, despite the faults in their construction. Under such circumstances, a legally valid claim that the construction is defective may not be worth pursuing. If the building works as intended, despite containing some technically incorrect construction, there is arguably no loss.

A claim which succeeds in law but which obtains only nominal damages is of little value. It may be comforting to know that a court of law, arbitral tribunal, etc. supports your view but such endorsements tend to come at high cost. Unless this results in the award of damages which are substantial in relation to the cost of pursuing (or, as the case may be, defending) the claim, it would be better not to be drawn into litigation or arbitration.

> In a design-and-build contract for a factory, warehouse and office complex, a dispute arose over the roofing membranes to the office suite.

Chapter 8

> The contract documents specified the roof membrane separately in two places. In one place it was described by its generic type; elsewhere, the documents named a proprietary roofing product.
>
> The contractor did not use the named proprietary product, although the membrane he chose did conform to the generic description. The employer condemned the work and instructed the replacement of the membrane with that named in the contract. The contractor refused, contending that the completed work was equal to that specified and that his breach of contract occasioned no loss to the employer.
>
> It was common ground that the employer could sue for breach of contract and that, if he did so, he would win. What was uncertain was whether the victory would benefit him. It was contended that no loss would be suffered by leaving the membrane in place and therefore damages would be purely nominal.
>
> The matter was settled, while the lawyers were still arguing, by the failure of the roof. Before the failure of the roof, the consensus of legal opinion was that there was an arguable case but that a substantial claim for damages could not be sustained.

Damages are assessed on the principle that they should put the injured party into the position they would have been in had the breach not occurred. However, if the injured party is suffering no loss because the defective building is working as intended, they risk achieving no more than a pyrrhic victory in court. They may successfully demonstrate a breach of contract but fail to show that this has caused them (significant) loss and, as a consequence, may be awarded no more than nominal damages. Pursuing a claim for damages is a commercial activity involving investment, risk and return. Potential litigants should quantify their loss and estimate the cost of pursuing legal remedy before committing to it.

> A much-quoted example of a breach of contract giving rise to a sustainable claim, but where the damages awarded were for much less than the cost of correcting the defect, is the case of an undersized domestic swimming pool.
>
> For the pool in question, the employer, in the building contract, had specified a certain depth because he liked diving. The pool, as built, was shallower than specified. It was held that it did not conform to the specification but that it was nevertheless deep enough to allow diving. The employer sought to recover the cost of rebuilding the pool so that it conformed to the specification. He wanted no more than to get what he had specified at the agreed price.

Figure 8.1: **The compensation payable for a breach of contract is intended to put the damaged party in the position they would have been in had no breach occurred. Awards may fall short of that principle where the cost of rebuilding to specification is disproportionate to the loss suffered.**

The builder opposed the employer's claim for damages through successive battles in progressively higher courts. The eventual outcome was very much in the builder's favour. In summary the relevant points include:

(a) the built pool deviated from the specification;
(b) both as designed and as built, the pool was deep enough to permit diving, i.e. the deviation from the specified depth of construction did not alter its suitability for its intended purpose;
(c) due to (a) above, the builder was not entitled to the whole of the contract sum as he had not built all that he had contracted to build;
(d) due to (b) above, the employer was not entitled to recover from the builder the cost of rebuilding the pool to the contract specification;
(e) it would be unreasonable to have the pool rebuilt;
(f) the employer was entitled to recover for loss of amenity only.

Although the employer won his argument that the pool was not built as agreed and that he was therefore entitled to damages, he was refused the compensation he sought. The decided case affirmed the principle that the employer need not pay the agreed price for less than the agreed work. It also affirmed that the remedy for breach of contract is in damages for the loss suffered. The problem for the employer was in the ascertainment of that loss. It was successfully argued that the incorrectly built pool could be used for its intended purpose, in view of which he could retain the pool as built without loss. His quantification of loss, based as it was on the cost of rebuilding the pool, was rejected.

Perhaps relevant here is a principle of equity. The cost of correcting the defect would have been more than the original cost of building the pool. The effect of the defect, to the extent that it did not impede use, was, in comparison, minor. In such circumstances, obliging the builder to pay in damages more than he had received for building the pool might be regarded as inequitable. The employer successfully demonstrated that the builder was in breach of his contract, only for this moral victory to be turned into a crushing commercial defeat in the House of Lords.

Importantly, this case has set a precedent. Precedents are, however, changed from time to time and a comparable future case may be distinguished from this, so setting a contrary precedent. In this way legal systems based on precedent continually develop.

In litigation, the act which gives rise to a legal action may be termed the 'cause of accrual of action'. Perpetrators of the cause of accrual of action, where in breach of a duty owed, may be regarded as the culpable party and their delinquent actions may equally be called the 'culpable act'. To bring a successful claim, the claimant must be able to convince a tribunal that:

• the defect was caused by someone **(the culpable party)** doing something that they ought not to have done **(the culpable act)**;

- the culpable party was responsible for fulfilling an obligation to the claimant **(duty)**;
- the culpable act was a substantial failure to discharge this obligation or responsibility **(breach)**;
- the claimant has been harmed by the culpable act and is measurably worse off as a consequence **(loss)**; and
- this loss is a consequence of the culpable act **(causality)**.

Figure 8.2: **To sustain a claim for the cost of rectifying defects under English law, both causal and legal relationships need to be established.**

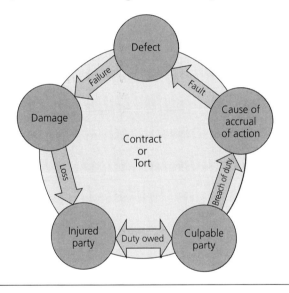

Liability under contract depends on the terms of the contract. Many liabilities may exist which are not expressed in it. These are referred to as 'implied terms'. Broadly speaking, terms may be implied into a contract by statute or if they are necessary to give that contract business efficacy.

Claims may arise outside a contract, in tort. There may therefore be contractual or tortious claims dealing with express or implied terms.

By way of illustration, a fictitious example of a tortious claim follows:

Archie, an architect, in casual conversation with Owen, a homeowner, discusses Owen's intention to upgrade his cellar. Archie advises Owen in general terms that lightly reinforced concrete would restrain the ground under the gable. Archie neglects to tell Owen that to prepare proper detail of this work it is necessary to investigate the ground conditions and the stability and bearing of the wall above.

Owen, knowing Archie is an architect, relies on Archie's advice and acts accordingly. The work is unsuccessful and disturbs the superstructure such that Owen is now faced with a substantial bill to correct the damage caused by this work. Owen sues Archie for professional negligence arguing that:

- Owen relied on Archie's advice (**reliance**);
- at the time Archie advised Owen, Archie was aware that Owen might rely on Archie's advice and that in so doing without further more detailed advice he could damage his building (**foreseeability**);
- in giving Owen this advice, Archie owed Owen a duty (**duty of care**);
- the immanent collapse of Owen's house was due to his following Archie's advice (**causality**);
- preventing collapse necessitated expensive repair (**loss**);
- in failing to give adequate advice, Archie was in breach of his duty of care, (**breach of duty**);
- Archie's behaviour was substantially below the level reasonably to be expected of his profession (**negligence**).

Thus a claim arose despite the fact that Owen had not paid for Archie's advice and no contract existed between them. Had Owen, for example, bought Archie a pint whilst soliciting this advice, the offer and acceptance of the beer in return for the advice might have created a contract between them. The claim would then be in contract; otherwise it was in tort.

Had Archie qualified his advice by a recommendation that he inspect the building and provide more specific proposals (perhaps for a modest fee), Owen's claim would probably be unsound because he would not be able to show that he had relied on Archie's advice. If Archie had also said that to act on the general construction principles he had espoused without inspection would be unwise, Owen's claim would be even less tenable because of the difficulty in proving negligence.

Without such qualification Owen could pursue a claim in tort. He would have to show that Archie acted below the standards reasonably to be expected of a representative body of like qualified professionals. He would also have to show that he relied on Archie's advice and that Archie knew, or ought to have known, that Owen would do so. Finally, Owen would have to demonstrate, in monetary terms, the size of his loss and that this loss flowed from his reliance on Archie's advice.

Researching the cause of and blame for a building defect involves technical and forensic studies.[74] These two areas of investigation can run in parallel or be carried out sequentially. The results of each line of enquiry need to be brought together to

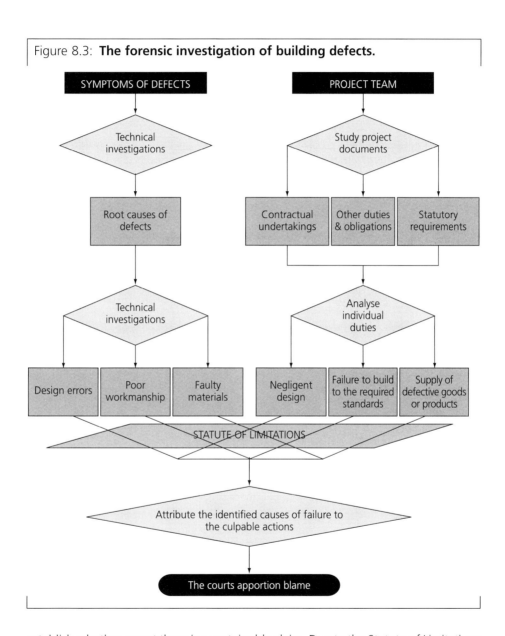

Figure 8.3: **The forensic investigation of building defects.**

establish whether or not there is a sustainable claim. Due to the Statute of Limitations in England and Wales, and other rules elsewhere, there is a limited time to bring a claim for defective work.[75]

The nature and proximity of relationships, the cause of defects and their effects, and the passage of time all have to be considered.

'State-of-the-art' defence

'State-of-the-art' may be defined as the current stage of development of practice or technology, involving the use of the latest techniques or equipment. It often involves the first or early use of materials or techniques before they have been proven by long practice. There is inevitably a risk in being one of the first to use something new. This risk may reduce in time as use reveals the weaknesses inherent in each development. Thus, with practice, the flaws in that which was innovative are discovered. Growing familiarity with each state-of-the-art development provides the knowledge base to improve reliability and avoid error.

Where this knowledge was not available at the time the state-of-the-art development was made, the persons involved cannot subsequently be held to be culpable on the basis of better knowledge provided by hindsight. This applies to negligent liability involving common-law duties of care but is not likely to be accepted as a defence in respect of strict contractual duties. It may not apply in the case of novel designs which the employer is not warned are untried. This was made clear by the judiciary in 1984 in relation to designs for a low-maintenance building:

> For the architects to use untried or relatively untried materials or techniques could not in itself be wrong, as otherwise the construction industry could never make any progress. However, architects venturing into the untried or little tried were wise to warn their clients specifically of what they were doing and to obtain their express approval. When the architects mentioned their intention to tile to the Plaintiffs, anxiety was displayed which made it all the more incumbent on the architects to be careful. The university wanted a low maintenance building and the architects wrote saying the tiles should last the life of the building. Any doubts about the reliability of the tiles should have been resolved by not using them. Although not obliged to follow the recommendations contained in literature on the subject, the architects should certainly have taken the information into account as opposed to disregarding it. They designed the centre without features to protect from the rain; they used fondu No 1 [a proprietary product] without waterproofing additive and failed to bring about necessary changes in design where the staining began. It also would seem that on no occasion did they discover that the subcontractors were not doing their work properly. Consequently, it was to be inferred that the architects did not inspect properly. Accordingly, the architects acted in breach of contract and were negligent in their design for both phases, in their supervision and failure to review the design.[76]

Third party/Section 20 actions

Often, in connection with building defects, reliance on information conveyed by manufacturers is cited as a cause. For example, a material or product may be specified because of the representations made by the manufacturer or supplier about its qualities. The product once bought may be found to be unsuitable and the sales literature to misstate the product's qualities.

Building owners making the claim may have no contract with the product manufacturer. They may nevertheless, either directly or through their design team, have placed reliance on the representations made by the manufacturer.

In multi-party litigation, claims against manufacturers and suppliers may be brought in through what were called 'third-party' actions and are now, by reference to the Civil Procedure Rules 1999, more commonly called 'section or part 20' actions. For example, employers may sue through the building contracts, so claiming against main contractors for the provision of defective products. Contractors may in turn claim it is the fault of subcontractors, who may, in their turn, accuse their suppliers of delivering defective goods – which supplier may, in their turn, blame the manufacturer. Equally, employers may claim that they and their consultants, acting as their agents, listened to the representations made by manufacturers about the qualities of their products and, in reliance thereon, specified what proved to be defective building products or systems. Thus, either through the contractual chain or by separate related claims, all may be joined together in a single legal action.

Such multi-party proceedings are usually protracted and expensive.

However, to the extent that the defendants blame each other rather than deny fault, multi-party proceedings may be to the claimants' advantage. As the defendants seek to pass blame one to another, they implicitly acknowledge that someone is at fault. It is risky to seek to avoid liability by accusing others: the response from those accused is often counter-accusation. This aggressive mode of defence is sometimes referred to as 'cut-throat'.

Experience teaches that the cut-throat defence is a high-risk approach and best regarded as a last resort. The cut and thrust of accusation and counter-accusation between defendants can make the case for the claimant. Arguments between defendants over who is to blame tend to expose all potentially culpable actions to scrutiny. The more effectively each defendant argues that fault lies with others, the less the claimant has to do to prove their case and the more likely it is that all defendants will be found to share liability. Provided some or all of the defendants are found to be liable, the claimant does not have to show the extent of individual fault, as apportionment of blame is reserved to the court.

Assessment of damages

Damages – the money awarded by the courts to compensate an injured party for the losses caused by a culpable breach of contract – are assessed on the basis of the cost of putting the injured party into the position they would have been had the breach not occurred. There are, in practice, qualifications to this principle. These include the effects on the value of an award for a successful claim of:

- taxation of costs;
- mitigation;
- betterment;
- pre-estimated damages and agreed limits to liability; and
- equity or proportionality.

Taxation of costs

Where a claim is disputed and costs are incurred in prosecuting the claim, the money spent adds to the losses suffered by the injured party. The culpable party may be compelled to compensate the injured party for these costs but is rarely made to pay them in full. It is common practice for the costs to be awarded in ways which reflect the conduct and outcome of the dispute.

For example, if a defects claim is successfully pursued through the courts, the court would ordinarily require the defendant to compensate the claimant for their legal costs (subject to taxation). However, if claimants are awarded less than they claimed, their ability to recover their costs may be reduced proportionately and they may have to compensate the defendant for some or all of their legal costs.

Some protection can be sought in respect of costs:

Where a litigant fears that other parties may be unable to pay the costs if they lose, they can seek security of costs. This is sometimes appropriate where the other party has few visible assets, or is a company with nominal assets which may fold on losing a substantial claim.

A claim may contain several elements, some of which are stronger than others. A defendant can make a confidential offer based on an assessment of the strength and value of each part of the claim. By following the correct procedures, this offer will reduce the risk to the defendant of having to pay the legal costs incurred after the offer is made.

Take, for example, an employer's claim against a builder for the cost of correcting three defects, each of which will cost about £100,000 to rectify.

Let us suppose that:

- immediately proceedings were issued, the builder had offered £100,000 in settlement of the claim;
- this offer is rejected;
- the dispute goes to a full hearing;
- one of the defects is found to be due to fault in the builder's work;
- the other two defects are found to arise from design errors for which the builder is not responsible; and
- the builder's liability is found to be £100,000.

The legal costs incurred by both employer and builder after the offer was made are far more likely to be awarded to the builder than would be the case had the offer not been made. However, if the employer is awarded more than £100,000, the offer made by the builder is likely to have done little, if anything, to reduce their liability for costs.

Attributing blame

Complications arise where there is more than one culpable party to a defect. Anyone who has materially contributed to the damage is potentially liable. Whilst evidence may be adduced to show where blame is to be attributed, ultimately it is for the courts to decide on the apportionment of blame.

> Two recently constructed basements suffered from water-penetration problems. Both designs, prepared by engineers and architects, were found to be deficient to the extent that the construction was doomed to failure from the outset. However, it was also established that the contractors had deviated from the design in ways which led directly to water ingress.
>
> The problem in apportioning blame was that if the contractors had followed the specifications to the letter in each case the same part of the construction would have leaked, but failure might have been less rapid. The results of the contractors' breaches of contract were to accelerate fault but, it may be argued, their errant actions did not increase the cost of repairs that would, in due course, have been necessary. On this argument, no loss flowed from their actions and negligible damages were therefore recoverable from them.
>
> In one of the two cases, it was also argued that the design placed undue reliance on workmanship and that abnormally high standards were required for the waterproofing to function.
>
> The contracts were executed in the Standard JCT Form with Quantities and no special terms were incorporated regarding standards of workmanship. Insofar as the fault arose through deficiencies in workmanship and insofar as the work was of an ordinary good standard, a failure arising solely out of this workmanship may not give rise to a sustainable claim. If extraordinary standards are required it is advisable for the contract to state this. The JCT Form states:
>
>> *The Contractor shall upon and subject to the Conditions carry out and complete the Works in compliance with the Contract Documents, using materials and workmanship of the quality and standards therein specified, provided that where and to the extent that approval of the quality of materials or of the standards of workmanship is a matter for the opinion of the Architect such quality and standards shall be to the reasonable satisfaction of the Architect*[77]

Standards were specified by the incorporation in the contract bills of quantity of the expression:

> Where and to the extent that materials, products and workmanship are not fully detailed or specified they are to be in accordance with good building practice.

It is arguable that the expression 'good building practice' does not impart a requirement for extraordinary or exceptional standards. The counter-argument – that the contractor, in entering the contract for this work, implicitly warranted that his work would be of an appropriate standard – is also worthy of consideration. The inclusion of an express requirement that: 'where and to the extent that materials, products and workmanship are not fully detailed or specified they are to be of a standard appropriate to the Works and suitable for the functions stated in or reasonably to be inferred from the project documents' might have avoided such argument altogether.

Further complications arise in considering the deficiencies in the architect's and engineer's work. The waterproofing specification was thoroughly inadequate, evidencing negligence in design by the architect. However, the structure to which the waterproofing was to be applied was not appropriately designed – thus preventing, regardless of the method of applied waterproofing adopted, an adequate solution. Fundamentally, therefore, the fault lay in poor engineering design. However, the architect failed to identify the conflict between the engineer's proposals and the requirements for applied waterproofing, and incorporated the engineer's design unmodified into the contract.

Under the standard terms and conditions for the appointment of an architect, architects are not responsible for the competence of designs prepared by others. They may, in their defence say that they relied on the competence of the engineer in their own field of expertise. The engineers may argue that the waterproofing design is an architectural and not an engineering problem and that, as their design performs adequately from a structural viewpoint, they are not to blame.[78]

Clearly, as there is fault in the work performed by the architect, engineer and contractor and, as these faults relate directly to the failure of the built structure, there must be a sound basis for a claim. The deficiencies in design and construction can be identified and shown to be relevant to the failure of the construction. But the case against the designers is hypothetical insofar as detrimental effects of the design faults are masked by defective building work and the interrelationship of the designers' work is such that they both, in different ways, contributed to the same inevitability of failure. Neither designer is, therefore, uniquely responsible, nor has a direct causal link between the design errors and the immediate damage suffered been established. However, there is a need to remedy the faults in design to achieve satisfactory long-term performance and both designers have a potential liability for the resultant costs. There is, in addition, a need for temporary emergency measures, resultant upon the contractor's breach of contract, for which the contractor has a liability.

It can thus be shown that some part of the cost of rectification stands to be borne be each party. The apportionment of such cost must either be agreed between the parties or decided by a tribunal.

The lesson to be learnt from such experiences is that, at the outset, the role of each member of the project team should be precisely defined. Where overlaps occur between the activities of different team members, individual responsibilities should be clarified and preferably expressed in written contracts. This not only lends clarity to the attribution of blame, should matters go wrong, but it also reduces the risk of error or oversight while the work is being carried out.

Mitigation and betterment

Mitigation and betterment are related but distinct concepts. They are both, potentially, not recoverable at law.

Mitigation is the prevention of unnecessary and avoidable loss.

Betterment involves achieving more than the mere correction of a defect.

The existence of betterment or lack of mitigation does not negate a claim for damages, but the amount recoverable at law may be reduced by the cost of the betterment and by the increased loss arising out of the lack of mitigation. If betterment or lack of mitigation does not increase the sums claimed, they should have no effect on the claim. These are dealt with more fully under 'Legal terminology' below.

Legal terminology

In dealing with litigious matters it is sensible to be aware of certain terms which are customarily used. The definitions given below are based on the author's experience. A fuller definition of legal terms may be obtained from Phipson's *Manual of Evidence*.

Mitigation

Under English law there is a general duty on a claimant to mitigate loss. As a general principle, any loss suffered through lack of mitigation is not recoverable at law. For example, a defect left unattended can worsen and cause other (consequential) damage. Repairing the worsened defect and consequential damage is likely to be more expensive than prompt repair would have been. If this increased cost could have been mitigated by early action, the extra costs caused by the delay may not be a recoverable part of the loss suffered. If there is good reason for not carrying out early repair, the additional cost of delay may be recoverable.

A common reason to want to delay repair is the desire to win the money at law before spending it. This is rarely a good tactic. It does not convey the urgent necessity of repair, which is most often the basis on which a loss is argued. Additionally, pecuniary difficulties do not necessarily justify a lack of mitigation. English civil law rarely favours the impecunious litigant.

The need to mitigate loss can be an argument to spend money just as much as it is a reason to avoid overspending. Take, for example, the repair of a roof to an occupied building. The process of repair can temporarily expose the building to increased risk of water damage. This may, in a commercial tenanted building, cause large consequential losses. To obviate this risk, it may be prudent to provide temporary protection during the work. A temporary over-roof to protect a building while the permanent roof is rectified may be expensive but prudent. Working without temporary protection in the hope of saving this additional cost may be potentially less expensive but imprudent. It may result in very substantial consequential losses if a rainstorm occurs while the roof is open for repair. Depending on the circumstances, provided careful balanced judgement is used, the prudent route is more likely to be accepted as showing proper regard to mitigation of loss than is an imprudent alternative.

Betterment

Betterment, that is achieving – through the correction of certain defects – something better than would have existed had the building been built without these defects in the first place, may involve expenditure which is irrecoverable at law.

> For example, a flat roof was wrongly waterproofed and subsequently leaked, such that it would cost £100,000 to replace the waterproofing or £150,000 to over-roof with a pitched roof. If the defects could not be reliably eliminated by anything less than replacing the waterproofing, its replacement is probably justified and does not give rise to claims of lack of mitigation or betterment.
>
> If, nevertheless, the building owner, having lost faith in the building trades' capability to construct watertight flat roofs, wishes to construct a pitched roof in lieu of repairing the flat roof he may do so. He could still pursue a claim for the £100,000 loss he has suffered as the figure which is properly recoverable where due regard is given to mitigation of loss and to betterment. In this simplistic example, the additional £50,000 cost of using pitched rather than flat construction would have to be paid by the building owner.

Improvements to a building which are incidental to correcting defects may not be regarded as betterment for which damages are recoverable. Improvements which are not justifiable as part of the legitimate costs of correcting defects are likely to be excluded from any award of damages.

> An example of an improvement to a building not being considered betterment, for the purpose of assessing recoverable damages, occurred in connection with a claim for compensation for the cost of correcting the behaviour of building walls which were fracturing. The problem was stopped by encasing the walls in thermal insulation and over-cladding.
>
> The external insulation reduced thermal cycling in the masonry. The thermal cycling was causing fluctuating stresses in the masonry which was a contributory cause of the cracking. Thus the external insulation directly combated one of the causes of fracturing in the masonry.
>
> Naturally, the external insulation also improved the thermal resistance of the building envelope, thus improving comfort and reducing running costs. This could be argued to be betterment, as a non-defective aspect of the building's performance was improved by the repairs. It was eventually accepted that this 'incidental' betterment should not reduce the money recoverable as damages.

Proof

Proof is the process of testing an alleged fact to satisfy the courts or arbitral tribunal of the fact being tested.

In civil proceedings, establishing fact on the basis of a balance of probabilities is generally acceptable. In criminal proceedings, a higher standard is required – that is, the assertion must be demonstrated to be true beyond reasonable doubt. The burden of proof is generally upon the person making the assertion.

> Thus, if Archie, our architect, asserts that he instructed the removal from site of some defective work and Bert, our builder, disputes that Archie stated the work was defective, then, in accordance with the general principles of evidence, it would be for Archie to demonstrate that he had condemned the work rather than for Bert to disprove this. Conversely if Bert were to assert that Archie had approved the work, which approval Archie denied giving, then the burden of proof would be with Bert. In either case, if the tribunal is not satisfied, on the balance of probabilities, that the assertion is true, judgment should be given on the basis that the assertion has not been sustained as proven fact.

Evidence

Evidence includes statements made by witnesses, i.e. their testimonies and physical evidence, the latter including things such as contemporaneous documents, specimens and even the building itself – or at least the defective parts of it.

Such things as laboratory analyses of a defective building component, photographs, sketches, detailed drawings, survey notes, video recordings, etc. showing and recording a defect may be incorporated in evidence. It is better for these to be presented as part of the testimony of the witness who carried out the analysis, took the photographs, etc. rather than offered into evidence in isolation. A videotape recording of water entering a building and damaging the finishes, for example, is not itself proof that the building leaks. The person who made the recording and saw first-hand the water entering and the damage being caused is a 'witness of fact'. Although such witness evidence may be more credible and easier to understand when supported by a video recording, the videotape is best regarded as corroboration of the witness's statements regarding the defects and consequential damage.

A record of the investigation of a defect, however presented, unsupported by the testimony of the witness who made the record is arguably hearsay evidence, and potentially less satisfactory than the first-hand evidence of the person who made the records, supported by those records.

Recordings – whether electronic, photographic, taped, written or drawn – may be counterfeit. A genuine, undoctored record, such as a photograph, may be misinterpreted. Where it is not possible to have the photographer, etc. present to be examined before the tribunal documentary, photographic or other physical records may still be placed in evidence, subject to the discretion of the tribunal. For example, the clerk of works may at regular intervals have taken progress photographs, kept samples, etc. and the builder may have done likewise. These photographs may form part of the contemporaneous evidence. The clerk of works may have gone abroad, died or otherwise become unavailable to give evidence at the tribunal. Others involved in the project may, nevertheless, be able to state that the clerk of works did produce photographs at set intervals, that the photographs in evidence are – to the best of their knowledge – those that the clerk of works took and that they were accepted as being an accurate record of the condition of the site at the time they were taken. The clerk of works may, at the same time, have kept a site diary, and corroborative evidence in support of the authenticity of the photographs may be found in it.

The experts appointed to examine a building defect may jointly choose to rely on certain documents or records even if there are no witnesses of fact to attest to their authenticity. They may do so because their knowledge of the building process and familiarity with practices involved give them confidence in the validity of the records and allow them to interpret knowledgeably what these show. They will, in giving their evidence, be able to explain why they have relied on these records and how they have interpreted them. This may give greater credence to these records and assist the tribunal in understanding their significance. The weight given to this evidence will nonetheless remain at the discretion of the tribunal.

Expert witnesses often have to rely on old documents and records. Photographs, etc. taken during construction may show things that the expert has no other way of finding out. In fact, if expert witnesses have seen records which they believe have a bearing on the matters on which they are reporting, it is arguable that they are obliged to notify the tribunal. However, where experts rely on second-hand evidence they should make this clear.

Concrete cube tests, taken and logged during the progress of the works, may form part of the contemporaneous evidence on which experts rely. Laboratory analysis of the same concrete, carried out under the experts' direction as part of their investigations, is the evidence of the laboratory, or more precisely the laboratory technician, carrying out the analysis. Experts may append laboratory analyses to, and interpret the results in, their reports. These experts may be cross-examined on their interpretations of the test results and the testing itself, to the extent that this falls within their direct knowledge or fields of expertise.

The laboratory staff who analysed the concrete may reasonably be required to attend the tribunal to affirm, potentially under hostile cross-examination, the authenticity of the laboratory test results and the correctness of the procedures they carried out. It is for this reason, for example, that it is better for the testing laboratory themselves to take samples for testing, carry those samples to their lab and carry out the tests. They then know the provenance of the samples tested and the method of their removal, and can give informed comment as to whether the method of removal would have so affected the test results as to risk misleading rather than informing the tribunal.

Admissibility

If the law allows a fact to be proved by evidence, it is admissible – if not, then it is not admissible. The test for admissibility is whether or not the fact is 'in issue' (see below) or is relevant to matters in issue. Admissible evidence may be adduced before the tribunal, inadmissible evidence may not.

Relevance

Relevance is a matter of logic. If it can be shown that a fact which is not in issue bears upon matters which are in issue, it may be relevant. For example, if the building leaks in ordinary circumstances it is unlikely that meteorological evidence will be relevant. However, if it is argued that the building leaked because it was subject to a once-in-200-years meteorological event, and that designing for such conditions would be extraordinary, then meteorological evidence could well be relevant and may even become a matter at issue.

Best and inferior evidence

'Best' and 'inferior', or primary and secondary, evidence is a principle which gives preference to original over copied or reported evidence. For example, an original document is preferred to a copy of it or to a witness's description of it. Best and primary evidence is first-hand and original. Inferior and secondary evidence includes copied, second-hand and hearsay evidence.

Direct and circumstantial evidence

Direct evidence is either the evidence of a witness who perceived a fact, or the production of a document which proves the fact or the thing which is in question. For example, where the existence of a contract is in dispute the production of the signed contract and the testimony of a witness who is a signatory to it is direct evidence. Evidence that the parties to the alleged contract entered a room, reportedly for the purpose of signing the contract – and that thereafter they proceeded as if the contract were signed – is circumstantial. Although circumstantial evidence does not directly prove existence or non-existence of the disputed fact, it is admissible insofar it may assist the tribunal to decide whether that fact did or did not exist.

Original and hearsay evidence

Witnesses who testify to facts within their own knowledge give 'original' evidence. Witnesses who state facts which they have learnt from others, but of which they have no personal knowledge, give hearsay evidence. It is often necessary for expert witnesses to give hearsay evidence. For example, experts who have been brought in to investigate a building defect may well include, in their evidential reports, accounts of the description given to them of the incorrect performance of the building which gave rise to their being called in to investigate. Such descriptions are clearly hearsay evidence and equally clearly useful to the proper reporting of all of the facts which the experts have considered in reaching their conclusions. Hearsay evidence from witnesses of fact is less obviously useful to the tribunal, and its admissibility may be challenged.

Real evidence

The production of specimens taken from site or, better still, taking the tribunal to the site and opening up the defective construction in their presence so that they may directly observe the defects at issue.

Facts in issue

The facts 'in issue' are those facts which claimants must prove in order to sustain their claims, or those facts which defendants must prove in order to maintain their defence. Facts which are admitted are not in issue. Where formal pleadings or Statements of Case have been prepared, the facts – alleged and disputed – will have been set out.

Facts relevant to the issue

These are determined by logic. Any fact which has a bearing on the existence or non-existence of a fact in issue, so as to assist the tribunal to judge whether or not a fact in issue exists or does not exist, is 'relevant'.

Discovery of documents

The process whereby each side makes available or discloses to the other sides to the dispute the documents on which they intend to rely to prove their case. 'Discovery' of documents may be enforced by directions issued by an arbitral tribunal or court of law as part of the normal timetable of proceedings. Documents which are in the possession or power of the parties, unless privileged, are subject to discovery. Concealing documents which relate to the building project in dispute, whether or not they appear relevant to the dispute, can be reckless. It is, for this reason, prudent to keep the paperwork in good order throughout a building project.

Privilege

In civil litigation, whilst most documents relating to a dispute have to be made available (disclosed), if requested, to the other side, certain ('privileged') documents can be kept confidential. Privilege attaches to a solicitor's advice and is likely to extend to all correspondence between client and solicitor. In order that a client can take full rounded legal advice, the law permits that such advice may be kept confidential. For this reason disclosure of this advice would not normally be ordered by a court or arbitral tribunal.

There is some doubt as to whether privilege can attach to communications between clients and their technical advisors, such as an expert witness. It is prudent, therefore, to ensure that confidential communication between experts and their client is carried out via the solicitor. Thus pre-action advice given by the expert to the client is best sent to the client's solicitor, although it may be simultaneously copied to the client. Similarly, it is advisable that clients communicate with their expert via their solicitor and that the expert's instructions are issued by the solicitor. These instructions normally will be disclosed although, before they are finalised, they may be discussed between expert and solicitor to allow the experts to guide those instructing them on the best use of their expertise and to identify where other expertise is desirable. Because disagreements between experts can arise from differences in their instructions as much as from differences in their opinions, it is thought appropriate for the solicitors' instructions to the experts to be exhibited in the experts' reports.

Without prejudice

Privilege also attaches to 'without-prejudice' exchanges, which may be oral or written. 'Without prejudice' is a term used to protect negotiations from disclosure.

Merely stating that something is without prejudice does not necessarily cloak it in privilege. Equally, neglecting to write 'without prejudice' on part of a series of without-prejudice exchanges does not necessarily lift from it the cloak of privilege. For clarity it is better to write 'without prejudice' on all documents relating to without-prejudice negotiations and to agree in clear terms before starting each without-prejudice meeting or discussion that it is without prejudice.

Once proceedings are commenced, genuine attempts by the parties to negotiate out-of-court settlements can be carried out by them or their representatives on a without-prejudice basis. An agreement reached in without-prejudice exchanges may itself be disclosed and the courts may look behind the cloak of privilege to the extent necessary to resolve a dispute over whether or not an agreement has been reached during without-prejudice exchanges.

Where a dispute exists, the parties in dispute may negotiate openly or without prejudice in genuine attempts to resolve the dispute. This may give rise to correspondence which seeks to achieve an out-of-court settlement by compromising the claim. For example, a claimant may be willing, for speedy settlement, to accept less than their claim (without admitting that their claim is wrong). Alternatively, a defendant may offer to make a contribution to the cost of a repair for which they do not openly accept liability.[79] Such an offer, if presented to a court or arbitral tribunal, might be seen as tacitly conceding that a compromise settlement is just, and so prejudice the court against the claimant's or the defendant's stated case.

If such negotiation were, as a matter of course, disclosed it might discourage commercial negotiation and make out-of-court settlement more difficult to achieve. Negotiated out-of-court settlements are encouraged as they lessen the cost of disputes and reduce the workload on the civil courts. To encourage negotiated settlements there is a process of without-prejudice negotiation available to the parties. What is said as part of this negotiation is privileged and may not, except under special circumstances, be brought to the attention of the court or tribunal before they have heard the case and issued their findings.

A permutation on without-prejudice correspondence is to make an offer that is 'without prejudice save as to costs'. Such an approach is based on an intention to make the offer known to the tribunal after a decision is reached. If say, a claim for

£10,000 is brought, the defendant makes an offer to settle for £6,000 before legal cost are incurred and the tribunal in due course finds in favour of the claimant in any sum less than £6,000, it is likely that costs incurred after the offer was made will be awarded very much more in the favour of the defendant than would otherwise be the case.

Checklist for establishing a sustainable claim

1. Find the root causes of the defects.
2. Establish the acts or omissions which caused the defects.
3. Identify the person(s) responsible.
4. Compare what was done with what ought to have been done, to draw out the deficiencies or omissions in performance of duties which gave rise to the defects.
5. Assess the deficiencies or omission with what was required under the terms of contract where relevant or, otherwise, by the standard of ordinary competence.
6. Prove the loss arising from the defects.
7. Show a legally binding duty between those who caused the defect and the injured party.
8. Through all of the above trace a causal link between culpable actions and loss, and demonstrate a relevant legal obligation between the instigators of the damage and the party suffering loss.

[74] See Chapter 6 for an explanation of the differences between technical and forensic defect reports.
[75] See Chapter 12.
[76] Judge Newey in *Victoria University Manchester* v *Lewis Womersley* (1984) CILL 126.
[77] JCT Standard Form of Building Contract 1998 Edition, Private with Quantities, Incorporating Amendments 1 to 5 inclusive.
[78] Standard Form of Agreement for the Appointment of an Architect, published by the RIBA, Clause 4.1.7.
[79] Under the Civil Procedure Rules 1999 this may now be referred to as a 'Part 36' offer.

Litigation and the Alternatives

9

Failed building work often leads to conflict, caused by those involved being more anxious to protect themselves than to resolve the issues and correct the defects. The defensive stance, quick to allocate and slow to accept blame, is invariably unhelpful and often costly. An agreement to postpone arguing culpability – while co-operating in a methodical and scientific approach to establish the root causes of, and cures for, the problems – can be as preferable as it is less profitable for lawyers, claims consultants and the like. Once the mechanism of failure is known, remedies can be evaluated and priced. Culpability and the apportionment of cost may then be established on the basis of known fact, thus facilitating agreement. If agreement cannot be reached, the issues to be decided by judge, arbitrator or adjudicator have still been reduced, so limiting legal costs.

Claims and dispute-resolution procedures

Recourse to law can be a costly trap for the unwary. Disputes and the associated legal procedures can take more time and money than correcting the defects from which they arise. At the outset, the full costs of pursuing and defending claims cannot be forecast with any certainty. Litigation and arbitration rarely favour the impecuniary. There is no point in fighting a legal action unless to win, but expert advocacy is not cheap. If one side buys expert help, the other parties to the dispute will want equal representation and advice to avoid being disadvantaged. Keeping up in the face of escalating legal costs may become unmanageable, forcing the poorer parties to withdraw.

Confronting inexorably growing legal costs, litigants can find themselves in a dilemma – facing, on the one hand, having to risk still more money and, on the other, losing all by backing down first. Withdrawing a claim, like losing in court, carries with it not only the loss of money already spent on the dispute but also the risk of having to compensate the other side for their legal costs. These combined costs can rapidly grow to exceed the sums originally in dispute.

When facing legal action over building defects, always weigh the cost of proceedings against the value of the issues in dispute. It is rare to recover the full cost of a dispute.

> Say there is a dispute between a developer and a builder over defective work which would cost £100,000 to correct. Assume that it is a simple dispute, which goes to trial and that the developer spends £30,000 on legal costs while the builder spends £10,000.
>
> After 9 months of dispute, the judge finds entirely in the developer's favour and awards him costs. The builder will not agree the costs as he, having spent only £10,000 himself, thinks a claim for £30,000 by the developer is extravagant and unjustifiable.

In such circumstances, the court's taxing master assesses the awarded costs. The 'taxed' costs may, from experience, lie between 40 and 80 per cent of the actual costs. (In this context the word 'tax' has nothing to do with sources of government revenue. It is the process whereby the court reviews the parties' legal costs and decides which parts are recoverable from the losing parties and which parts are not.) In this example, 60 per cent of the developer's legal costs are awarded. That is, the builder is required to pay £18,000 toward the developer's legal costs.[80]

The builder therefore has to pay to the developer £100,000 for the rectification of the defects and £18,000 in recoverable legal costs. The net result is that the developer had to spend £130,000 but recovered only £118,000, a net loss of £12,000. The builder, on the other hand, is out of pocket by: £100,000 for the cost of rectifying the defects, £10,000 for his legal costs and £18,000 for the developer's taxed legal costs – making £128,000 in total. The lawyers are, of course, some £40,000 better off. That is the overall additional cost to the builder and developer of failing to reach an agreement without recourse to law.

The developer would have saved delay and effort if he could, at the outset, have negotiated a compromise settlement for about four fifths of his claim, and the builder stood to save something in the order of £40,000–£50,000 by accepting such a compromise.

The watchword is 'proportionality'. The more disproportionate the cost of a dispute to the value of the matter in dispute, the more desirable it is to avoid full-blown litigation or arbitration. Disputes rarely get to a final hearing; the parties usually settle out of court – often, regrettably, after the costs have grown alarmingly.

To minimise the waste of time and money when conflict is unavoidable – and to preserve working relationships – it is important to understand the different ways of resolving disputes.

At one end of the scale there are procedures that are imposed by law, externally regulated and binding. At the opposite end there are procedures which are intended to help disputants resolve their differences but which are voluntary, flexible, and which do not lead to legally enforceable findings. Although there are many shades in between these extremes it is conventional to subdivide procedures for resolving disputes into those which provide outcomes that are – largely – final and binding on the disputants and those that do not. Non-binding procedures are often referred to as 'alternative dispute resolution', or ADR.

In England and Wales, for disputes arising from building work, the available final and binding dispute resolution procedures include: litigation, arbitration and – within limits – adjudication. Non-binding dispute resolution can involve anything from direct negotiation between the disputing parties to more formal procedures. These are often conducted by disinterested third parties and include, for example, mediation, expert determination and mini-trial.[81]

Adjudication may now be imposed by statute and may be both mandatory and binding. For this reason, in this book, it is dealt with as part of the formal legal system alongside litigation and arbitration. Traditionally, it has been treated as an alternative dispute resolution procedure and is included in many books and articles on ADR.

Figure 9.1: **An illustration of the range of dispute resolution procedures.**

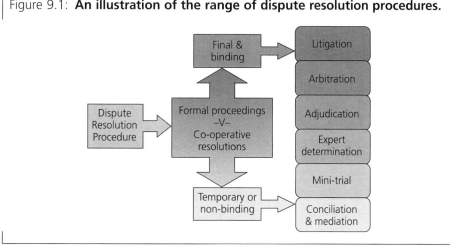

Alternative dispute resolution (ADR)

The term 'alternative dispute resolution' might originally have been applied to any method of resolving disputes other than litigation. Language changes, and ADR is now commonly used to describe alternatives to any imposed, externally-regulated and binding system of resolving disputes.

It may mimic processes such as courtroom trials or arbitration hearings, or adopt wholly dissimilar procedures. There are formal protocols or codes of conduct available which can be followed if wished. (Guidance on this may be obtained from various bodies, of which the Centre for Effective Dispute Resolution, CEDR[82] is one, and reference may usefully be made to the Commission of the European Communities' green paper which defines alternative dispute resolution as *'out-of-court dispute resolution processes conducted by a neutral third party, excluding arbitration proper'*.[83]).

Traditionally, alternative dispute resolution is entered into voluntarily and governed by agreement between the parties in dispute. More recently, ADRs which are conducted by the court or entrusted by the court to a third party (ADRs in the context of judicial proceedings) are taking on a greater significance in Europe. For example, pursuant to Rules 26.4 and 44.5 of the Civil Procedure Rules for England and Wales, which came into force on 26 April 1999, the court may suspend a case to allow the litigants to have recourse to mediation and can order the litigants to make financial penalty payments if they refuse mediation.

ADR can work well where all want a fair and equitable remedy – and badly where they do not. These voluntary and little-regulated processes can be disingenuously appropriated to obfuscate rather than resolve issues, so deferring the day of reckoning and delaying both technical and legal remedy. For this reason, non-binding dispute resolution procedures are useful only where those involved are capable of moderating self-interest with enlightened objectivity, in which the natural desire to avoid blame is balanced with the long-term benefit that comes from consensus rather than dispute.

Finding consensus between opposing interests, especially where the outcome is likely to be costly to one party, is difficult. It is useful for those involved to remember, when

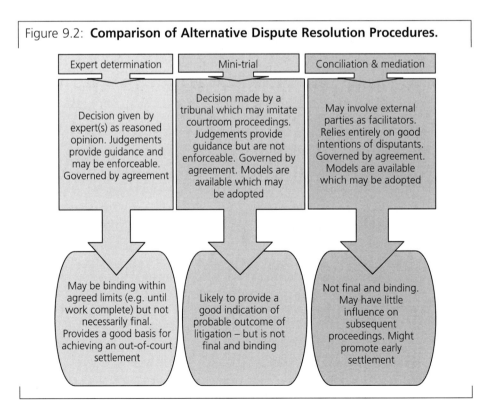

Figure 9.2: **Comparison of Alternative Dispute Resolution Procedures.**

Expert determination	Mini-trial	Conciliation & mediation
Decision given by expert(s) as reasoned opinion. Judgements provide guidance and may be enforceable. Governed by agreement	Decision made by a tribunal which may imitate courtroom proceedings. Judgements provide guidance but are not enforceable. Governed by agreement. Models are available which may be adopted	May involve external parties as facilitators. Relies entirely on good intentions of disputants. Governed by agreement. Models are available which may be adopted
May be binding within agreed limits (e.g. until work complete) but not necessarily final. Provides a good basis for achieving an out-of-court settlement	Likely to provide a good indication of probable outcome of litigation – but is not final and binding	Not final and binding. May have little influence on subsequent proceedings. Might promote early settlement

considering strict liability, that compromise over the cost of repair is often cheaper than litigation. If the parties can be persuaded that it is better to put their energies and money into resolution rather than dispute, alternative dispute resolution offers several tried and tested methods.

Expert determination

This is one of the best, yet least-used, methods of resolving building defects disputes. Expert determination involves the parties to the dispute referring the problem to a suitably independent expert individual or team – the 'experts' – who then investigate the drawings, specifications, building, etc. as appropriate. They generally take evidence from the parties as well as from their own investigations but there are no hard and fast rules and a good expert in this role will seek the most effective way of getting at the facts. In contrast to litigation, the experts' investigations will be carried out openly, allowing all parties to see the methodology and follow their progress. Customarily, the experts will, on concluding their investigations, report their findings and give their opinion on the appropriate remedies. Where their conclusions are not binding on the parties the success of the process depends, to some extent, on the experts' communication skills. A comprehensive treatment of the evidence and full exposition of their reasoning is a persuasive basis for forming opinions. If the conclusions are shown to flow inevitably from the established facts, they will be most compelling.

Experts cannot enforce agreement and, to be effective, must present the facts on which they have relied, and their interpretation of them, clearly.[84] Demonstrably correct facts and conclusions based on good research and well-reasoned arguments can be very convincing. The expert's findings should, therefore, be presented in sufficient detail to demonstrate that they are adequate in scope, thoroughly researched, logically interpreted and reliable.

If they have properly identified the causes of failure and provided reasoned descriptions of the causal links between faults, defects and damage, they have provided a good basis for resolving the dispute and for correcting the deficiencies in the building.

They may, if asked, go further and allocate blame. Usually, once the mechanisms of failure are clearly understood, matters of responsibility and liability will be self-evident to those concerned. The experts' decision on accountability may therefore not be required. It will, in any event, not assist if the experts are not legally competent. A good understanding of science and technology is not necessarily linked to a proper understanding of contract, and of the legal principles underlying the correct allocation and apportionment of blame. It is important, in selecting experts, to ensure they are not asked to go outside their areas of expertise, and it is often best to restrict experts to the authoritative explanation of the technical issues which are well within their area of competence.

An example of what may be regarded as an agreement for an expert's determination is to be found as an optional clause in a version of an Association of Consultant Architects (ACA) form of contract. In this clause it is agreed, at 25.1, that certain disputes are to be decided by the architect, whose decision is final and binding until the works have been handed over.

> If any dispute or difference of any kind whatsoever shall arise between the Employer or the Architect and the Contractor at any time prior to the Taking-Over of the Works arising out of or in connection with the Agreement or the carrying out of the Works (either during the progress or after completion or abandonment of the Works), as to:
>
> (a) the construction of this Agreement; or
> (b) any adjustment or alteration of the Contract Sum; or
> (c) the Contractor's entitlement to and length of any extension of time for the Taking-Over of the Works or any Section under Clause 11.5; or
> (d) whether the Works are being executed in accordance with this Agreement; or
> (e) the reasonableness of any objection by the Contractor under Recital E to this Agreement or under Clauses 9.5 or 10.2; or
> (f) any other matter or thing of whatsoever nature (including any matter or thing left by this Agreement to the discretion of the Architect the withholding by the Architect of any certificate to which the Contractor may claim to be entitled or any issue as to whether or not any certificate is in accordance with the provisions of this Agreement);
>
> then such dispute or difference shall in the first place be referred to and settled by the Architect who within a period of 5 working days after being requested by either party to do so shall give written notice of his decision to the Employer and the Contractor. Such reference shall not relieve either party from any liability for the due and punctual performance of his obligations under this Agreement.

Clause 25.2 makes it clear that the Architect's decision in resolving a dispute under clause 25.1 is an expert determination and that it is not final and binding after the works are practically complete in that it may be referred to arbitration.

> In giving a decision under Clause 25.1, the Architect shall be deemed to be acting as expert and not as arbitrator and his decision under Clause 25.1 shall be final and binding upon the parties until the Taking-Over of the Works and shall forthwith be given effect to by the contractor and by the Employer and the Contractor shall proceed with the Works with all due diligence whether or not either party requires arbitration as provided in Clause 25.4.

Not all expert appointments are so clear-cut. Typically, consideration is not given to this procedure until after a dispute has arisen. This occurred in the appointment of a joint expert to assist an employer, his architect and builder in a potential dispute over the repeated appearance of water in a new industrial building.

The building was typical of its kind, having a concrete floor, steel frame and insulated metal cladding. The water appeared as damp patches on the floor in the mornings.

The three parties wished to know the cause of the dampness so that cure and responsibility could be decided. The architect was appointed on standard RIBA terms. The building contract was based on a JCT form. Both of these agreements contained arbitration clauses; neither contained a clause requiring expert determination of disputes. No formal agreement for expert determination had been agreed between the parties when the expert was appointed. There was, however, an agreed intention that they would resolve the problem rather than enter into a dispute. From this intention the expert was able to adopt a role which combined, to some extent, that of mediator with that of expert.

He investigated the roof construction and found some hips and parapet junctions were poorly made. This brought into question some aspects of design but was mostly a simple matter of workmanship. He investigated some junctions in the roof cladding over the damp marking but could not find evidence of rain ingress.

Despite being instructed, at the outset, that the building had never been occupied and that there was therefore no activity inside it which could give rise to high internal humilities, the expert discovered that there was a caretaker in the building who used copious amounts of hot water both for cleaning and brewing tea. His habit in the early morning was to turn on an electric kettle and to leave it boiling until he had finished both cleaning and several brews.

A study of the conditions within the building in the early morning on a cold day, when the caretaker was carrying out his kettle-boiling ritual, showed it was probable that some part of the water damage was caused by condensation.

When he explained this, the employer had some difficulty in understanding that there might be a mechanism causing the water damage that was neither the fault of the architect nor of the builder. When he grasped this point, his interest in resolution by expert determination waned.

As resolution by expert determination is voluntary, the procedure foundered at that point. As is generally the case with alternative dispute resolution, it works when the parties wish it to but not where any key party decides to withdraw from the procedure. This is always tempting for a party who perceives the results to be contrary to their own interests.

It would be possible to make an expert determination final and binding, in which case it might be regarded as a form of arbitration.

Mediation and conciliation

Mediation has been defined as a voluntary, non-binding, without-prejudice, private dispute resolution process in which a neutral person helps the parties try to reach a negotiated settlement. Conciliation can sometimes be distinguished from mediation in that the third party takes a more active role in devising settlement terms or providing opinion. However, there is little consensus and meditation in one country may be conciliation in another.

Sometimes those involved in a building project need to step back when problems occur, to view them objectively. This can be difficult once a dispute has started. Often, all the technical knowledge required is present but effective progress is hampered by a lack of consensus, combined with concern over liability and cost. Bringing in a disinterested third party or mediator can assist.

Mediators need not be expert in the matters in dispute. They may draw on the expertise of others if required. They look for common ground and points of agreement, and facilitate discussion to help those involved in the dispute find ways in which they can settle their disagreements amicably.

Mediation may be done in informal discussion, follow protocols similar to those used in formal legal hearings or fall somewhere in between. The method used should be shaped to suit the participants and the complexity of the issues.

It is possible to adopt facilitative or evaluative processes. In the former, the mediator/conciliator aids or assists the parties' own efforts to formulate a settlement. In the latter, the mediator/conciliator gives an independent view of the issues.

Mini-trials

In a mini-trial, sometimes referred to as a 'mock' trial, the parties argue their case in front of a tribunal. Procedures are usually an abbreviated imitation of courtroom formality, but unlike litigation a mini-trial tribunal's findings are not binding.

The arguments for each side are rehearsed in front of the tribunal, weighed and judgment given. This process may be quicker and cheaper than the binding procedures it imitates and it forewarns the parties of the probable outcome should the trial be repeated in a court of law. This focuses the parties' minds on the difficulties they would face and the costs they would risk in litigation. It also makes them properly aware of the arguments for each side. This may assist them to reach agreement and avoid protracted dispute.

A variant is the 'executive tribunal'; a panel of senior executives from each party – usually with a mediator or expert as neutral chairperson. Following the presentations, the executives meet (with or without the mediator or expert) to negotiate a settlement on the basis of what they have heard.

Other forms of dispute resolution

The Centre for Effective Dispute Resolution (CEDR) promotes many other forms of alternative dispute resolution (ADR), or 'effective dispute resolution' (EDR) as a recent article they published proposed it be called. These are outlined below using CEDR's definitions and terms of reference.

Dispute review board

A 'standing' adjudication panel system used in major construction contracts. The board is normally appointed at the beginning of the project and stays in close touch with it, adjudicating disputes as they arise.

Early neutral evaluation (ENE)

A preliminary assessment of facts, evidence or legal merits. This process is designed to help parties avoid further unnecessary stages in litigation or – at the very least – to serve as a basis for further and fuller negotiations.

Independent interventions

The involvement of an impartial third party to facilitate negotiations, discussions, consensus-building, problem-solving and relationship-building or to manage existing or potential difficulties in a wide variety of situations.

Judicial appraisal

In this procedure, sometimes known as 'rent-a-judge', the parties appoint a judge to receive written presentations from each side and to make an appraisal of the likely result should the case go to court. The parties must agree the form and extent of submissions, and whether the appraisal is to be binding or not.

Med-arb

A process in which parties contract to give the mediator power to 'convert' to being an arbitrator and make a legally binding award, in the event that mediated negotiations do not lead to a settlement.

Neutral fact finding

Similar to expert determination, but restricted to the clarification of particular issues and non-binding in that the 'neutral' does not normally make an award.

Benefits of alternative dispute resolution

When used successfully, ADR may be quick, cost effective and preserve confidentiality. All disputes, whether in difficult negotiations or full-scale litigation, can become a drain on resources – sapping money, time and focus. Generally, with alternative dispute resolution, the parties remain in control. If no settlement is reached, they retain their legal rights. For these benefits to be achieved, at the commencement of alternative dispute resolution both sides must have a genuine interest in seeing an end to the dispute or in re-starting effective negotiations.

Judges, using their powers under the 1999 Civil Procedure Rules, may direct parties to attempt to resolve their dispute through non-litigious means. Anticipating this prior to such court intervention has the potential to save time and money. The earlier the dispute is resolved, the greater the potential benefits in terms of costs, timesaving and preservation of business relationships.

Some indication of the value of ADR in litigation is given by looking at the Commercial Court, which, since 1993, has been identifying appropriate cases for ADR. A study of 233 of these cases that were before the court between July 1996 and June 2000, where the court had directed the parties to attempt to settle through ADR, has revealed the following:[85]

- ADR was undertaken in a little over half of the cases in which an ADR Order had been issued;
- of the cases in which ADR was attempted,
  - 52 per cent settled through ADR,
  - 5 per cent proceeded to trial following unsuccessful ADR,
  - 20 per cent settled some time after the conclusion of the ADR procedure,
  - 23 per cent of cases were still 'live', or the outcome unknown, when the survey was carried out;
- there is some information on the results of cases in which ADR was not attempted following an ADR Order:
  - 63 per cent eventually settled (about one fifth of these said that the settlement had been as a result of the ADR Order being made),
  - 15 per cent proceeded to trial.

Figure 9.3: **The effectiveness of ADR.**

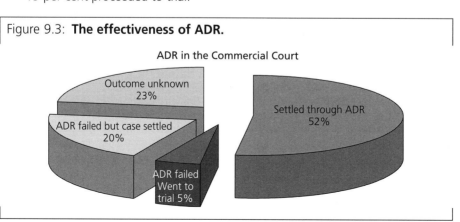

About 95 per cent of cases settle before a final court judgment. With hindsight, those to whom this happens often wish they had achieved this settlement before starting litigation.

In summary, alternative dispute resolution may be of particular benefit where:

* the cost of litigation is expected to be disproportionately large when compared to the value of the claim;
* negotiations are deadlocked;
* there are certain multi-actions involving common parties;
* the issues are of a complex technical nature, particularly if they involve multiple parties;
* the issues involved are sensitive or require the disclosure of sensitive information;
* the parties do not wish for any publicity.

Alternative dispute resolution is unlikely to be suitable when the dispute involves novel or unprecedented legal issues. It is better used for technical and commercial issues.

Similarly, it is not appropriate where summary judgment is available quickly and efficiently such as, for example, certain disputes arising out of party wall awards.

It cannot serve parties requiring emergency injunctive or other protective relief.

On the rare occasions where publicity is actively sought by one party but not the other, alternative dispute resolution may be the least suitable approach.

Most importantly, where there is no real interest in settlement by any of the parties to a dispute, commencing alternative dispute resolution can be a frustrating and expensive waste of time.

Binding and final dispute resolution procedures

Litigation and arbitration are similar in that both involve bringing disputes in front of a tribunal whose decision is binding (and final, unless successfully appealed to a higher court). Adjudication – under the Housing Grants, Construction and Regeneration Act – has similarities, but is subject typically to severe time constraints and the extent to which the findings of the adjudicator are binding are more limited.

Where the parties to a dispute cannot settle their differences, litigation is the only available option unless there is an agreed alternative or one is imposed by statute.

Adjudication will be implied into a contract dealing with construction work under certain circumstances. This is a consequence of the Housing Grants, Construction and Regeneration Act (commonly abbreviated to 'the Construction Act'). Ordinarily in England and Wales, adjudication will be implied into a contract under the Construction Act if:

Chapter 9

- it is a contract for construction work;
- the contract is evidenced in writing; and
- the project is not restricted to domestic building.

The Construction Act, and hence the implied terms relating to adjudication, are as likely to apply to professional contracts as they are to building work itself. Architects finding themselves in dispute with their employer regarding an architectural commission may be forced to resolve the dispute through adjudication if amicable settlement is unattainable.

Adjudication, at least as it is practised under the Construction Act, differs from arbitration as a consequence of the time restrictions imposed. The adjudicator is appointed in much the same way as an arbitrator would be and often by the same nominating bodies.

An adjudicator, as an arbitrator, is likely to be appointed on the basis of their knowledge of the type of work that is in dispute. Experience shows that both are likely to interpret the evidence placed before them in the light of their experience and knowledge of the matters that are in dispute.

In contrast, where litigation is adopted and the matter comes before the judiciary in courts of law, judges are selected not for their knowledge of building but for their knowledge of law. More firmly than for other tribunals, courts of law are required to judge the matter on the basis of the evidence presented to them, avoiding any reliance on the judges' personal knowledge or prior experience of the matter being tried.

Ordinarily a tribunal – whether judicial, arbitral or adjudicatory – may obtain technical advice at need through the appointment of experts. In this way, the tribunal need not contain members who are personally familiar with all aspects of the type of construction which is in dispute. Expert witnesses may assist the tribunal properly to understand the technical matters they are asked to decide. Expert witnesses are distinct from witnesses of fact in that they are allowed to provide evidence of opinion. This may involve interpretation and reliance on hearsay.[86]

Arbitrators and adjudicators have taken expert advice outside the formal boundaries of the tribunal over which they preside. This happened quite recently where an arbitrator, outside the hearing, telephoned an expert for technical advice. He described the complaints which were alleged against the builder and asked the expert to explain to him what these complaints meant in terms of the behaviour of a roof.

The arbitration concerned the noise caused in attic rooms by the movement (chatter) of the roof tiles in wind. The complaint, as expressed in the referral to the arbitrator, was simply that the chattering tiles caused annoyance to residents. No measurements of noise levels caused by chatter, or of ambient noise levels, were given. The use of the rooms within which noise nuisance was reportedly caused was not stated. The specification for the building work, which the arbitrator had read, was as silent on acoustic performance as the completed roof was allegedly noisy.

There appeared to the expert to be, in the submission made to the arbitrator, no statement of defective work. The complainant had identified something which might be symptomatic of a defect but had not followed this through to positively identify any fault in the work. He had described a nuisance without quantifying, by measurement, the annoyance caused – for example, by showing that the noise in the rooms, in relation to their intended use and the background noise levels, exceeded that which written authority gave as acceptable. There was probably a good case to be made but the evidence necessary to drive the claim home had not been collected and submitted to the arbitrator.

Roof tiles may move to dissipate wind load and, in so doing, may generate noise. If lightweight construction is used to form attic rooms, this noise may be audible in the rooms. The movement of the tiles and the audibility of the sound made was alleged, but this was not conclusive evidence of defective construction or of the need for remedy.

Had the expert been asked to provide this advice in an open hearing in front of the claimant and defendant, the claimant might have had an opportunity to amend his claim in the light of the technical advice obtained from the expert and the defendant and claimant might have been able to address properly the real technical issues in front of the arbitrator. As it was, the claimant's case was being explained to the arbitrator in a private conversation, depriving both the claimant and the defendant of the opportunity to challenge the expert advice at source.

In the above 'noisy-roof' arbitration there was a lack of objective evidence and, although there may have been defects requiring correction, these were probably to do with the design of the attic rooms, not the construction of the roof. Because this was not properly investigated or understood, it was not properly pleaded.

The arbitrator has to try the pleaded case, not the case that should have been pleaded. The behaviour of the roof was said to annoy occupants of attic rooms. These occupants could be exceptionally sensitive to noise or the noise could be loud enough to trouble the partially deaf. With no objective assessment of sound levels, it would not be safe to conclude that the roof was abnormally noisy – in which case the noise nuisance may not be symptomatic of a defect. As no evidence of fault in the construction was submitted other than that to be inferred from the annoyance its behaviour was causing, the claim was not sustainable.

A correctly functioning tiled roof may not be silent under wind load. A correctly designed attic room would take this into account and be built so as to adequately attenuate incoming noise. Traditional lath and plaster historically used in attic construction in the UK has a density 2 to 3 times that of most plasterboards. It is formed *in situ* in lime reinforced with combed hair to make a continuous, flexible, dense roof lining. Typically, this will better attenuate sound transmission than will lightweight, foamed-plastic, thermal insulants and modern plasterboards. This may well have been at the root of the problem.

> More recently, an adjudicator telephoned the same expert to ask about the correct method of constructing a sand-and-cement floor screed. The case the adjudicator was considering involved the incorrect placement of a reinforcing mesh in a screed.
>
> The expert described to him the alternatives which would have ensured correct construction. The expert gathered from his conversation with the adjudicator that the mesh was generally laid below the screed but was in some places poking out from it. No other fault was reported.
>
> Whilst the expert confirmed that the mesh, to perform its intended purpose, should be placed centrally in the screed, he also advised that the screed may work adequately without reinforcement – that, in fact, the incorrect incorporation of reinforcement may not cause widespread damage. The adjudicator had, however, already made up his mind that the claim was justified on the basis that the construction was faulty regardless of the consequences thereof.

In the above floor-screed adjudication, the defendant might have successfully argued that the fault in the placement of the screed had caused no more than minor damage which could be corrected at a much lower cost than the complete replacement of the screed. His argument that the work was not defective was weak but an argument that complete replacement of the screed was unnecessary would have had some force. Mitigation of loss should be taken into account.

Both of the above cases illustrate the importance of starting the proceedings with a well-drafted statement of case.

In an English court of law, judges would ordinarily be restricted to a consideration of the arguments and explanations given to them in the courtroom. It would be improper for them to consult privately and so take expert opinion, in a form which was not open to challenge in the courtroom, from an expert who was not available for examination by the parties to the dispute. Whether the arbitrators and adjudicators who have privately sought expert technical advice when making their decisions acted properly depends on the terms of the references to them. For justice to be seen to be done, it is arguable that the advice taken by arbitrators

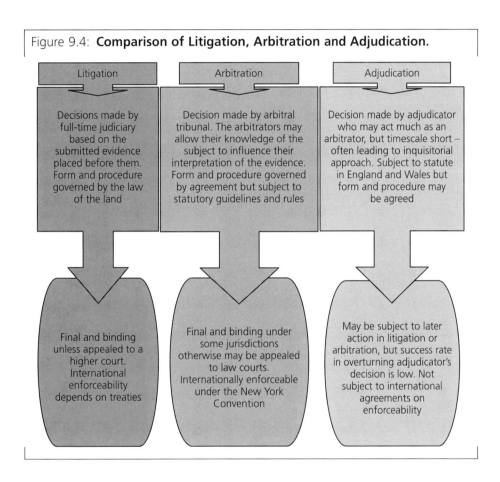

Figure 9.4: **Comparison of Litigation, Arbitration and Adjudication.**

Litigation	Arbitration	Adjudication
Decisions made by full-time judiciary based on the submitted evidence placed before them. Form and procedure governed by the law of the land	Decision made by arbitral tribunal. The arbitrators may allow their knowledge of the subject to influence their interpretation of the evidence. Form and procedure governed by agreement but subject to statutory guidelines and rules	Decision made by adjudicator who may act much as an arbitrator, but timescale short – often leading to inquisitorial approach. Subject to statute in England and Wales but form and procedure may be agreed
Final and binding unless appealed to a higher court. International enforceability depends on treaties	Final and binding under some jurisdictions otherwise may be appealed to law courts. Internationally enforceable under the New York Convention	May be subject to later action in litigation or arbitration, but success rate in overturning adjudicator's decision is low. Not subject to international agreements on enforceability

and adjudicators should be made known to the parties before the hearings are closed.

Applicable law

The law of the contract

The parties' choice will usually be upheld unless it is contrary to public policy of the place where the proceedings are to be held or the choice is not exercised for bona fide reasons and for a legal purpose.

In 1948 Lord Denning stated what is probably still the approach of the English courts, as follows:

I do not believe the parties are free to stipulate by what law the validity of their contract is to be determined. Their intention is only one of the factors to be taken into account.[87]

Substantive law

This is the law governing the interpretation of the contract. For example, the parties may agree that the law of the contract is English law, even if the contract is for work done in Austria. Very often, countries having their embassies built in foreign countries will prefer the law of the contract to be their own domestic law.

Procedural law

Whatever the substantive law, the procedural law (the law which governs the proceedings) will be that of the country in which the proceedings take place.

Where the procedural law is that of England and Wales and the claim is in the County Court or in the Technology and Construction Court, the process of bringing a claim to court is as follows:

- first, the claimant issues proceedings;
- court rules state that they must serve the opposing side within 4 months of the proceedings;
- if they do not serve within this 4-month period, they must start again by drafting proceedings, issuing, etc.;
- under the court rules, once served the defendant(s) will have to file an acknowledgement of service (a form that says whether they intend to defend or accept the claim) within 21 days of service;
- 14 days after that, the defendants will need to file their defence;
- thereafter, proceedings may be stayed for an agreed period.

Generally, it is appropriate for the proceedings for building disputes to be in the Construction and Technology Court unless the sums involved are very small, in which case they may be suitable for the small-claims procedure.

Once the initial procedures of service and response are dealt with, the courts will commonly issue directions which set out such matters as the timetable, disclosure, permission for expert evidence, etc. Because of the restrictions applying to English courts these matters are normally dealt with by solicitors and barristers, although litigants in person may act for themselves. In arbitration, very similar procedures are often followed but the timescales may differ and the participants may be represented by people who are neither solicitors nor barristers.

In litigation in England and Wales where the litigants hire others to run the case for them, it is customary for solicitors to have 'care and conduct' of the case and for barristers to advocate their clients' claim. Put very simply, the solicitors do the paperwork and the barristers argue the case both orally in the court and in preparing written arguments before the case is heard.

Advocacy may effectively start in interlocutory (or interim) hearings before the case is heard. There is often, in major cases, some cut and thrust over what is permitted or required by way of evidence, amendment to claims or defences, etc. – all of which may be subject to hearings attended by the lawyers in front of the trial judge long before the case proper is heard. These may be crucial.

A wrongly pleaded case may fail because of weaknesses in the way it is stated, despite there being an underlying good case with overwhelming merit. The defence, knowing their weaknesses, may know how a pleaded case against them could be re-stated so as to be irresistible. The claimant may suspect this but lack key facts from which it could see how to make its claim more compelling. It may go on 'fishing expeditions', hoping broad requests for disclosure will uncover useful ammunition for its claim. The defence may resist this with legal argument and may seek awards relating to costs in respect of interlocutory hearings to deal with applications for disclosure, etc. and any late changes in the pleaded case.

The sparring over these issues may be as significant to the commercial outcome of the litigation as the hearing of the substantive case.

The current governing guidance to running civil litigation over building defects comes from the Wolf reforms and is set out in the Court Procedure Rules (CPR). The objective of these rules is introduced at Section 1.1 as follows:

(1) *These Rules are a new procedural code with the overriding objective of enabling the court to deal with cases justly.*
(2) *Dealing with a case justly includes, so far as is practicable –*
  (a) *ensuring that the parties are on an equal footing;*
  (b) *saving expense;*
  (c) *dealing with the case in ways which are proportionate –*
    (i) *to the amount of money involved;*
    (ii) *to the importance of the case;*
    (iii) *to the complexity of the issues; and*
    (iv) *to the financial position of each party;*
  (d) *ensuring that it is dealt with expeditiously and fairly; and*
  (e) *allotting to it an appropriate share of the court's resources, while taking into account the need to allot resources to other cases.*

In line with these objectives, Part 5 of the CPR gives a protocol for a pre-action meeting in a defended claim, which encourages the litigants to talk and agree – where they can – so as to try and avoid litigation and minimise cost. For this purpose they are to meet as soon as possible after receipt by the claimant of the defendant's letter of response, or (if the claimant intends to respond to a counterclaim) after receipt by the defendant of the claimant's letter of response to the counterclaim.

At the meeting (or meetings) the parties should try to agree clearly what they are in dispute over and the root causes of the disagreements which have caused them to commence litigation.

They are to review ways of resolving their disagreements without litigation or, failing this, to consider what steps should be taken to ensure that it is conducted in accordance with the overriding objective as defined in Part 1.1 of the Court Procedure Rules.

The format for these meetings is not prescribed. Attendance will normally include: each party (or authorised representative, if the party is a corporate body); their legal representatives (if appointed); and, where applicable, their insurers. If there is a multi-party action, the meetings should extend to include all parties.

For each element of the dispute they should look at using ADR instead of litigation. If they cannot agree on ADR they should try to agree on the most cost-effective way to litigate in respect of appointing experts, disclosure and conduct. In particular, the appointment of joint experts in preference to each party having their own experts should be considered.

Who attended or refused to attend such meetings, including the stated reasons for non-attendance, can be disclosed to the court as well as any agreements concluded between the parties. The meetings are otherwise 'without prejudice'.

Consolidation and joinder

In litigation, subject to certain possible impediments such as arbitration agreements, it is possible to bring together related disputes into a single action. In this way, several disputes between the same parties or linked disputes between separate parties can be brought together before one tribunal. This amalgamating of related legal disputes into a single action is referred to as 'consolidation' or 'joinder'.

Stay of proceedings

If a party takes a dispute or difference, which is eligible for arbitration, to the courts, the other party (or parties) may apply to the court to stay the proceedings and the court may order this.

If no application to stay to arbitration is made, the matter will proceed in the courts despite the existence of an arbitration agreement.

The application to stay can be made at any time after appearance and before delivering any pleadings or taking any other steps in the proceedings. Appearance is the formal step by a defendant, after they have been served with a writ, by which they advise the claimant that they intend to contest the claim. That, however, would appear to be the final step that the defendant may take before applying for a stay. The following constitute steps which have in the past been held to bar application:

- application for security costs – *Adams* v *Cattley* (1892) 66 LT 687;
- issue of a summons for discovery – *Chappell* v *North* (1891) 2 QB 252;
- attending a summons for directions – *County Theatres* v *Knowles* (1902) 1 KB 480.

Opposition to an application for summary judgment under O14 (RSC) may constitute a 'step'.

The test to be applied is whether the act of the defendant implicitly affirms the institution of proceedings in court and shows a willingness to go to law.

A dispute over the existence of a written contract can be material, as an insurance claim showed. The respondent denied that a policy had been issued but nevertheless subsequently (but unsuccessfully) sought to rely on the arbitration clause which would have been incorporated if the policy had been issued.[88]

Similarly, when Tarmac Construction denied the existence of a subcontract which provided for arbitration and were then served a writ by the subcontractor, the Court of Appeal rejected Tarmac's application to stay proceedings to arbitration as they had not been *'ready and willing etc.'*[89]

Refusal of a stay

The current Arbitration Act provides for the enforceability of arbitration agreements. Examples of situations in which, from precedent, an English court *may* refuse a stay are those where:

- the agreement provides for no immediate arbitration;
- there is a delay in applying for a stay – e.g. 18 months after issue of writ in *The Elizabeth H* (1962) *1 Lloyd's Rep 172*;
- hardship would be caused to a claimant who would be legally aided as a plaintiff in the courts (legal aid is not available in arbitration);
- a stay would result in two sets of proceedings arising out of the same facts, one set of which is in court;
- a claim alleges fraud and the person charged with fraud wishes the matter to be held in court, in which case a stay will be refused – *Russell* v *Russell* (1880). Where it is the party alleging fraud that opposes a stay then the court will use its discretion, in all the circumstances, as to whether to refuse a stay;
- If the only question is one of law, which, if made to the arbitrator, ought to be referred to the court as a preliminary point, a stay will not be granted.[90] A stay

was thus refused where the question was whether, as a matter of law, the contracts were live or dead.[91] On the other hand a stay was granted where the route of the dispute was the true construction of part of an agreement.[92]

A dispute as to whether a contract has come to an end (e.g. by frustration) falls within the usual arbitration clause, for it is a dispute as to the construction or application of the express or implied terms of the contract.[93]

The mere fact that a claim involves points of law is not sufficient reason to refuse a stay[94] but, if difficult questions of law are likely a court may do so.[95]

Where there is no arbitration clause in the contract, or where, in spite of an arbitration clause, the parties have commenced litigation which has not been challenged, the matters in dispute will be settled in the courts.

Offers to settle

A method of compromising an action is to make an 'offer to settle'. This can be made at any stage prior to the tribunal making its decision. There are established procedures for settlement offers in both litigation and arbitration.

It is in the parties' interests to settle the dispute before the tribunal comes to a decision, thus saving costs. The earlier proceedings settle, the lower the incurred costs. A party rarely obtains all their costs even if they succeed in an action, because of the effect of the scales of costs normally awarded. The more unscrupulous may well bring actions of doubtful validity knowing the other party may prefer compromise to risk and may concede some part of the claim to achieve early settlement.

Offers to settle may be made 'openly' or 'without prejudice', which latter may be 'sealed' or 'paid into court' and referred to as 'Calderbank' or 'Part 36' offers.

The methods of making offers in arbitrations to cushion the losing party from having to pay the abortive costs have been said in the English courts to be one of three kinds: 'without prejudice', 'sealed' and 'open'.[96]

The distinction between these types of offer is important but can be confusing. They are reviewed briefly below.

Without-prejudice offers

A 'without-prejudice' offer can never be referred to by either party at any stage of the proceedings. This is because it is in the public interest that there should be a procedure whereby the parties can discuss their differences freely and frankly and make offers of settlement without fear of being embarrassed by these exchanges if, unhappily, they do not lead to a settlement.

Open offers

An 'open offer', properly so called, is one to which either party can refer at any stage of the proceedings. In an appropriate case, it may influence the tribunal both in its decision on the matters in dispute and on the order as to costs.

Payments into court and sealed offers

The normal method of making an offer during litigation in the UK is to pay the money into court in settlement of the litigation, or of particular causes of action in that litigation. This is placed formally on record by means of a 'notice of payment into court'. The fact that this has been done is not made known to the trial judge until judgment has been given and submissions on costs are to be heard. This is to prevent such payments influencing decisions on liability but to allow them to be taken into account in orders for costs.

A 'sealed offer' is the arbitral equivalent of making a payment into court. For similar reasons, it is convenient for arbitrators to make their awards exclusive of costs and then to make a separate costs orders having enquired about offers.

An example copy of a notice used in a civil action in connection with a payment into court is given below:

Take notice that the defendant has paid the sum of £.... into Court.

The said £.... is in satisfaction of all causes of action in respect of which the plaintiff claims and after taking into account and satisfying the above-named defendant's cause of action for damages in respect of which he counterclaims.

Calderbank and Part 36 Offers

An alternative system devised in the courts, which has spread to arbitration, is called a Calderbank Offer.[97] It is an offer to settle which is made 'without prejudice save as to costs'. The tribunal is invited to make an award dealing with the substantive issues, reserving for a further interim or final award the decision or liability for costs. When submissions are made on costs, the 'Calderbank' letter may then be produced. Costs will then be decided in the same way as they would be in a 'sealed offer'.

Offers to Settle and Payments into Court are addressed in Section 36 of the Civil Procedure Rules, which now replace the use of Calderbank offers in litigation. There are in effect three alternatives:

- an offer to settle before proceedings are begun (Section 36.10);
- an offer to settle after proceedings are begun; or
- a payment into court after proceedings are begun.

They are all without prejudice save as to costs. That is, they are concealed from the judges so as not to influence the trial of the substantive case and then opened for consideration when the award of costs is to be decided.

The CPR give precise instructions for the expression of Part 36 offers. They have to clearly state what they are and what their potential effect is on costs. They must be open for acceptance for 21 days and include an offer to pay the offeree's cost up to the end of the 21-day acceptance period. The offers come into effect when they are received.

If an offer is made under Section 36.10 before proceedings are commenced it should be followed by an equivalent payment into court within 14 days of the service of the claim form.

Even where a full and final settlement has been agreed between litigants, the settlement may prove less than final for one or other of the parties. If, for example, a builder settles a claim with a building owner, the builder may subsequently be brought by the architect into an action between, say, the building owner and architect. For this reason, it is sometimes prudent to seek an indemnity when agreeing to make an out-of-court settlement.

An example of such an offer, drafted with reference to CPR Part 36 and made in anticipation of a multi-party litigation, is set out below:

> *Defendant's Solicitors*
> *Chambers of Law*
>
> *17th July 2003*
>
> *WITHOUT PREJUDICE SAVE AS TO COSTS*
>
> *Claimant's Solicitors*
> *Law Chambers*
>
> *BY RECORDED DELIVERY*
>
> *Dear Sirs,*
>
> **The Owners of the Disputed Building v The Developers Limited**
>
> *We are writing on behalf of the Developers Limited in respect of the above matter.*
>
> *The Civil Procedure Rules 1999 (the 'CPR') incorporate, under Part 36 thereof, a mechanism for either party to make an offer in settlement of all or part of a claim and/or counterclaim (a 'Part 36 Offer').*

Acceptance, or in some cases rejection, of a Part 36 Offer may have financial consequences as set out in that Part.

Our Client seeks to tender an offer in respect of full and final settlement of its liability to your client and any Part 20 claims by the Architect and the Sub-contractors.

In accordance with the provisions of Part 36 of the CPR, our Client hereby offers to make payment to your Client the sum of £50,000.00, a figure which is exclusive of VAT and interest up to 21 days after receipt by you of this letter, in settlement of these proceedings (the 'Settlement Sum').

This offer is made on the following conditions:

The Settlement Sum is to be paid in full and final settlement of all claims and counterclaims including, but not limited to, claims for interest of either party against the other whensoever, howsoever and wheresoever arising out of or in connection with the alleged liability of our Client.

Your Client shall be responsible for, indemnify, defend and hold harmless our Client against any and all claims or proceedings, any loss or expense, injury or damage to any property real or personal, whether arising whensoever, howsoever and wheresoever out of or in connection with the alleged liability of our Client. This indemnity shall extend to, but not be limited to, any Part 20 claims that may be instigated by third parties against our Client.

For clarity, the Settlement Sum shall be deemed and held by your Client to represent the net contribution of our Client in respect of any liability that arises between your Client and our Client. No further contribution shall be offered by our Client and any further contribution requested or ordered shall be indemnified by your Client as per the provisions of this Condition 2.

It is open for acceptance for 21 days from the date of this letter. Thereafter, this offer shall only be able to be accepted if the parties agree the liability for legal costs and interest incurred after the said 21 days or, in the absence of such agreement, by leave of the court, arbitrator or adjudicator.

This letter is written on a 'without prejudice save as to costs' basis, in contemplation of legal proceedings, it may therefore not be revealed to any Tribunal before a court, arbitrator or adjudicator has determined all matters of liability.

If you require any clarification of the above offer the provisions of Part 36 stipulate that you request it within 7 days.

As a matter of courtesy, we would be grateful if you would let us know in writing at the expiry of the said 21 days whether or not this offer is accepted.

Yours faithfully

For an explanation of the reference to *any Part 20 claims that may be instigated by third parties* in the above letter; see Third party/section 20 actions in Chapter 8.

Checklist for evaluating a potential claim

1. Consider who caused defect to arise by identifying cause of defect and the roles of the parties involved:
    1.1. Do defects arise from faults in design, workmanship or materials?
    1.2. Consider contracts used for consultants, contractors, subcontractors, suppliers, etc.
    1.3. Look for extension of liability under collateral warranties, product warranties, guarantees, any other express undertakings, statutes and implied terms.

2. Obtain information on contractual relationships:
    2.1. Typical relationships in building contracts:
        • Employer–contractor;
        • Employer–consultant;
        • Employer–inspector;
        • Contractor–subcontractor;
        • Contractor–supplier;
        • Subcontractor–supplier.
    2.2 Typical extended relationships under warranty:
        • employer–nominated/named subcontractor;
        • employer–nominated/named supplier;
        • consultant–building owner;
        • contractor–building owner.
    2.3. Typical relationships in design-and-build contract:
        • contractor–consultant;
        • contractor–employer;
        • employer–inspector.
    2.4. Take care not to imply relationships based on knowledge of what actually happened if this contradicts express terms of the contract.

3. Check dates having regard to the Statute of Limitations:
    3.1. For simple contract, action must be brought within 6 years of accrual of cause of action.
    3.2. For speciality/contract under seal, action must be brought within 12 years of accrual of cause of action.
    3.3. In the case of fraud, limitation shall not begin to run until discovery of fraud.

4. Where no breach of contract can be established, action may be possible under tort.

5. Defects are not of themselves necessarily evidence of a culpable act or that compensation can be obtained through litigation.

5.1. For design-and-build contracts, unless expressly excluded, product is judged on 'reasonable fitness for its intended purpose'.

5.2. Under normal terms of engagement for consultants, performance is judged by comparison with 'what an ordinarily competent equally skilled or qualified practitioner would have done'. Therefore, to assess the performance of an architect, an architect's view is of value, and so forth.

5.3. Consultants' responsibility may be extended by express terms in their conditions of employment or by collateral warranty.

6. Remedies normally lie in damages, not in specific performance.

7. There is no obligation to allow culpable parties to put right their mistakes themselves or to accept their nominees.

8. There is an obligation to minimise loss. Therefore, it is generally advisable to show that the costs of rectifying defects are reasonable and that they have not been increased by unnecessary delay.

9. Check, if possible, that the defendant(s) has adequate funds or relevant insurance before commencing action.

Litigation is a last resort where outcome and cost are unpredictable. Even where fully successful in pursuing or defending a claim, a litigant is unlikely to recover the full cost of the action. A negotiated settlement, even where this involves conceding strongly held contentions, is preferable. If relationships between potential litigants have broken down to the point that they can no longer discuss the matter, consider alternative dispute resolution (ADR).

[80] Costs are discussed further in the section on Damages in Chapter 8.
[81] Variants of alternative dispute resolution procedures are incorporated in some contracts in terms which bind the contracting parties to them, to allow disputes to be determined with similar finality to arbitration. Used in this way they may be considered to be a kind of arbitration.
[82] *www.cedr.co.uk*
[83] 'Commission of the European Communities, Brussels, 19.04.2002, COM(2002) 196 Final Green Paper on Alternative Dispute Resolution in Civil and Commercial Law'.
[84] Some agreements incorporate expert determination clauses which are binding, e.g. some rent review clauses in leases.
[85] 'Court-Based A. D. R. Initiatives For Non-Family Civil Disputes: The Commercial Court And The Court Of Appeal' by Professor Hazel Genn.
[86] The role of the expert witness is dealt with more fully in Chapter 11.
[87] *Bouissevain* v *Weil* (1948) IKB 482.
[88] *Toller* v *Law Accident Insurance Society Ltd* (1936) 2 All ER 952 Court of Appeal.
[89] *G Dew & Co* v *Tarmac Construction* AC: 996730 (1978) CA (1981) 15 BLR 22–26.
[90] *Carlisle Place* v *Wimpey Construction* (1980) 15 BLR 109.

[91] *Grey & Co v Tolme* (1915) 31 TLR 137.

[92] *Metropolitan Tunnel and Public Works Co v London Electric Railway Co* (1926) Ch 371.

[93] *Heyman v Darwins* (1942) AC 356.

[94] Re Phoenix Timber Co's Application (1958) 1 All ER 815, (1958) 2 WLR 574, 1 Lloyd's Rep 305, CA.

[95] *Clough v County Livestock Association Ltd* (1916) 85 LJKB 1185, 32 TLR 526.

[96] Mr Justice Donaldson (as he then was) in *Tramountana Armadora SA v Atlantic Shipping Co. SA* (1978) 2 All ER 870.

[97] Named after a procedure in a divorce settlement between a Mr and Mrs Calderbank (1975).

Arbitration and Adjudication

10

Arbitration

Overview

Arbitration antedates legal systems and courts. Litigation in ancient Rome was a form of arbitration facilitated by the state. The role of arbitration in international disputes grew towards the end of the 20th century, but has diminished in UK building disputes since the imposition of adjudication. This is binding, formal and closer to a quasi-judicial procedure than to alternative dispute resolution, as arbitrators' awards replace judicial decisions.

Arbitration can be entered into by agreement, is decided by an independent tribunal and has the force of law. Many standard forms of building contract and forms of appointment for building professionals contain arbitration clauses, i.e. agreements to refer disputes to arbitration.

Persons commencing arbitrations are called 'claimants'. Those against whom the actions are brought are called 'respondents'. Those who sit in judgement may be referred to as the 'arbitral tribunal'. In England the members of the tribunal are called 'arbitrators', and in Scotland 'arbiters'. A decision issued by the arbitral tribunal is called an 'award'.

If arbitrators lack either legal or technical knowledge they may appoint legal and/or technical assessors to assist them. This may vary from arbitration to arbitration and be facilitated or constrained by each arbitration agreement.

The arbitrating parties may be represented or may represent themselves. What usually happens is that if one side appoints a barrister the other side does likewise, and matters can escalate into something akin to a full-blown court hearing with witnesses being examined under oath.

International rules

Arbitration is the subject of a certain number of legislative instruments in member states of the European Union. At wider international level there are rules and agreements such as the 1958 New York Convention on the recognition and enforcement of foreign arbitration decisions, or, within the framework of the Council of Europe, the 1966 European Convention providing a Uniform Law on Arbitration.[98] Adopting the 1958 New York Convention allows arbitration to be internationally enforceable.

In 1985 the United Nations Commission on International Trade Law published a Model Arbitration Law (UNCITRAL Model Law).[99] This has been adopted for international arbitration in Scotland, but not in the rest of the UK.

The Paris-based International Chamber of Commerce's (ICC) Rules are perhaps the most commonly used procedure in international construction contracts.[100] According to these, the court fixes the place of arbitration unless agreed by the parties (Article

241

12). However, it is usual (unless the contract provides otherwise) for the arbitration to be held where the chairperson of the tribunal resides (or where the single arbitrator resides, if only one arbitrator is required). The ICC usually appoints a chairperson from a country other than those from which the parties are nationals (unless otherwise agreed by the parties).

The relationship of arbitration procedures to national laws varies.

Arbitration in the UK

In England, arbitration was given a statutory footing in1698 by *'An Act for determining differences by Arbitration, ... It shall and may be lawful for all merchants and traders and others desiring to end any controversy, suit or quarrel ... by a personal action or suit in equity, by arbitration whereby they oblige themselves to submit to the award or umpirage of any person or persons ... so agreed.'* Over time the Act has been updated and new Acts introduced. Of particular significance was the adoption of the 1958 New York Convention on the Recognition and Enforcement of Foreign Arbitral Awards in the Arbitration Act 1975.

The extent to which arbitrators' awards made under English law can be challenged in the courts was restricted by the Arbitration Act 1979, which made it possible to contract to exclude appeal of an arbitrator's award to the court on a point of law. Otherwise, the courts may, as a result of the 1979 Act, become involved in a dispute during, or after, the arbitration in two ways:

- to decide a point of law (Section 2). One of the parties, with the consent of the other party or with the consent of the arbitrator, may refer the matter to the High Court, and – providing the point in question is likely to produce substantial savings in costs (should it be determined in the reference to the High Court) and/or is one which would qualify as grounds for leave to appeal – then the courts will deal with it.
- to deal with an appeal on any question of law (Section 1). One of the parties, with the consent of the other party or by leave to appeal granted by the High Court, may appeal on a question of law.

The Arbitration Act 1996 updated arbitration law in England, Wales and Northern Ireland to be broadly consistent with the UNCITRAL Model Law, although it has substantial differences to arbitration in Scotland. Many parts of the world which were once under British rule have legal systems, including arbitration, modelled on English practice.

National variations in arbitration

Arbitration procedures can vary from one country to another and may take a variety of forms within each country. The following table illustrates characteristic differences between arbitrations carried out under English and under some other jurisdictions.

English	Civil Law Countries
1. Tribunals consisting of one arbitrator are common.	1. Tribunals usually consist of three persons.
2. Arbitrators are often not lawyers.	2. Arbitrators are usually lawyers.
3. Primary procedure is by short pleadings, followed by oral evidence and argument.	3. Primary procedure is by written submissions incorporating pleadings, evidence, law and argument.
4. Parties normally determine speed and method of proceedings.	4. Arbitrators often control speed and method of proceedings.
5. Each party calls one or more expert witnesses as it thinks fit.	5. Arbitrator decides whether to receive expert evidence and, if so, which expert should be selected. Experts normally report in writing.
6. Each party calls its witness.	6. Arbitrator invites witnesses to the hearing, and questions the witnesses before they are questioned by the parties.
7. A party may, by using powers of the court, compel a witness to attend and give evidence.	7. No one can be compelled to attend or to give evidence.
8. Arbitrators may take evidence on oath or affirmation.	8. Arbitrators have no power to require evidence to be given on oath or affirmation.
9. Each party has a duty, if so ordered, to produce for inspection all relevant documents in its custody, possession or power, whether they support or are adverse to its case.	9. No general duty to produce documents; but if an arbitrator orders production and a party fails to comply, the arbitrator may take that fact into consideration.
10. Arbitrators' general function is to decide the issues put to them on the evidence that the parties choose to put before them.	10. Arbitrators' general function is to discover the truth (but in general they do not call a witness who has not been nominated by either party).
11. The parties fully prepares their cases, and all the issues are normally decided at one hearing.	11. Arbitrations proceed by stages.

Chapter 10

Arbitration clauses

The extent to which matters fall to be dealt with by arbitration rather than litigation depends on the wording of the arbitration agreement. Ordinarily this is a clause in the contract.

Probably the first standard 'building' arbitration clause was contained in the RIBA form of contract published at the beginning of the last century. The early RIBA arbitration clause was limited and set out in complex terminology. Modern standard forms of building contract typically contain clear all-embracing arbitration clauses. For example, a 1980 edition of the JCT Standard Form of Building Contract contains the following provisions:

> *Article 5*
> *If any dispute as to the construction of this contract or any matter or thing of whatsoever nature arising thereunder or in connection therewith shall arise between the Employer or the Architect on his behalf and the Contractor either during the progress or after the completion or abandonment of the Works, it shall be and is hereby referred to arbitration in accordance with clause 41.*

> *41·1*
> *If a dispute or difference as referred to in Article 5 has arisen including: any matter or thing left by this Contract to the discretion of the Architect, or the withholding by the Architect of any certificate to which the Contractor may claim to be entitled, or the adjustment of the Contract Sum under clause 30·6·2, or the rights and liabilities of the parties under clauses 27, 28, 32 or 33 or unreasonable withholding of consent or agreement by the Employer or the Architect on his behalf or by the Contractor then such dispute or difference shall be referred to arbitration and final decision of a person to be agreed between the parties to act as Arbitrator, or failing agreement within 14 days after either party has given to the other a written request to concur in the appointment of an Arbitrator, a person to be appointed on the request of either party by the person named in the Appendix.*

Some contracts provide alternative dispute resolution procedures which may be selected at the time the contract documents are prepared, arbitration being one of the options available. An example of an arbitration clause in such a building contract (based on an ACA form) is given below:

> *Upon receipt of the Architect's notice of his decision under Clause 25.1, if either party is dissatisfied with the same or if the Architect shall fail to give notice of his decision within the time or in the manner required by Clause 25.1, then either party may within 20 working days after receiving the Architect's notice of his decision or of the expiry of the time within which it should have been given, give notice to the other requiring that the matter should be referred to the arbitration of a person to be appointed under Clause 25.4. If no claim to arbitration has*

> *been notified by either party to the other within 20 working days as aforesaid, the Architect's decision shall remain final and binding upon the parties.*
>
> *Appointment of Arbitrator*
> *All disputes or differences in respect of which a decision (if any) of the Architect has not become final and binding under Clause 25.3 shall be referred to the arbitration and final decision of a person to be agreed between the parties, or failing agreement within 10 working days after either party has given to the other a written request to concur in the appointment of an arbitrator, a person to be appointed on the request of either party by the President or a Vice-President for the time being of the Chartered Institute of Arbitrators. The Arbitrator so appointed shall have full power to open up review and revise any decision, opinion, direction, certificate or valuation of the Architect.*[101]

Building disputes are often multi-party. For example, the architect may condemn some work, causing the contractor in turn to require the subcontractor responsible to correct the condemned work. The subcontractor may deny fault and challenge the architect's opinion. To safeguard their own position, the contractor may adopt the subcontractor's view in discussion with the architect and the architect's view in discussion with the subcontractor. Potentially, this could put the contractor in two separate arbitrations over a single piece of allegedly defective work – one with the employer and another with the subcontractor. A disadvantage of arbitration is the difficulty of bringing multi-party disputes to a single tribunal unless the potentially multi-party nature of the dispute is foreseen before the contracts and their related arbitration clauses are written. A clause in an ACA form of building agreement dealing with referrals to arbitration illustrates an approach to dealing with this, as set out below:

> *Reference to Arbitration*
> *. . . Provided always that if, in the Employer's opinion, any dispute or difference to be referred to arbitration under this Agreement raises matters which are connected with matters raised in another dispute between the Contractor and any of his subcontractors or suppliers and provided that such other dispute has not already been referred to an arbitrator, the Employer and the Contractor agree that such other dispute shall be referred to the arbitrator appointed under this Agreement and such arbitrator shall have power to deal with both such disputes as he thinks most just and convenient.*[102]

Provided the subcontracts contain suitable arbitration clauses, the above clause would allow related disputes to be dealt with by a single arbitrator.

Arbitration clauses incorporated by reference

An arbitration clause may be incorporated in a contract by reference to some other document. The courts had to decide whether or not the arbitration clause in a standard form had been incorporated in a letter which said:

> To supply adequate labour, plant and machinery to carry out and complete ventilated and non-ventilated ceilings at the above contract, within the period stipulated in the programme of work and in full accordance with the appropriate form for nominated subcontractors (RIBA 1965 Edition). All work to be carried out to the complete satisfaction of the Architect and in full accordance with our detailed programme which can be inspected on site or at this office. All as your quotation.[103]

The parties agreed that there was a contract between them, but an RIBA (or JCT) form of contract had not been executed, nor was there in existence a 1965 edition of an RIBA or JCT form. The Court of Appeal took the view that 'the appropriate form for nominated subcontractors' was to be taken as meaning the National Federation of Building Trades Employers/Federation of Associations of Specialists and Sub-contractors (NFBTE/FASS) 'Green Form', commonly used with JCT 63.

It is argued that an advantage of arbitration is that it is capable of being operated as an international system outwith local legal peculiarities. To limit the risk of dispute over the arbitration itself, it is always advisable to state the legal jurisdiction under which an arbitration agreement falls. For example:

> Law of this Agreement
> The Law of England shall be the proper law of this Agreement and any arbitration under this contract which, unless the parties shall so agree, shall take place in England.

Principles of arbitration

There are certain principles that govern arbitration under UK law – these are summed up in Section 1 of the Arbitration Act 1996 as follows:

(a) *the object of arbitration is to obtain the fair resolution of disputes by an impartial tribunal without unnecessary delay or expense;*

(b) *the parties should be free to agree how their disputes are resolved, subject only to such safeguards as are necessary in the public interest;*

(c) *in matters governed by this part the Court should not intervene except as provided by this part.*

The Arbitration Act gives guidance on the role of the arbitrator as follows:

(i) *The tribunal shall –*
  (a) *act fairly and impartially between the parties giving each party a reasonable opportunity of putting his case and dealing with that of his opponent, and*
  (b) *adopt procedures suitable to the circumstances of a particular case, avoiding unnecessary delay or expense, so as to provide a fair means for the resolution of the matters falling to be determined.*

(ii) *The tribunal shall comply with that general duty in conducting the arbitral proceedings, in its decisions on matters of procedure and evidence and in the exercise of all other powers conferred on it.*

The Arbitration Act also gives guidance on the behaviour expected of the parties to the arbitration:

(i) *The party shall do all things necessary for the proper and expeditious conduct of the arbitral proceedings.*
(ii) *This includes –*
    (a) *complying without delay with any determination of the tribunal as procedural or evidential matters, or with any other directions of the tribunal, and*
    (b) *where appropriate, taking without delay any necessary steps to obtain a decision of the Court on a preliminary question of jurisdiction or law.*

Cost of arbitration

In the UK, parties to arbitration are jointly and severally liable for the arbitrator's reasonable fees and expenses. This is a mandatory requirement set out in Section 28 (1) of the Arbitration Act and means that, if one of the parties fails to contribute to the arbitrator's fees, the remaining party may have to make up the shortfall.

The referring party usually pays for the arbitration venue, and the costs thus incurred are dealt with as part of the overall costs of bringing the action.

Mandatory provisions under UK law

In Schedule 1 to the Arbitration Act there is a definition of those matters which are mandatory under UK law in arbitration. Provided these mandatory provisions are not traversed, the parties are free to decide by agreement all matters relating to the arbitral procedure adopted.

For example, many contracts provide for arbitration in accordance with a certain set of established rules and procedures, either in bespoke terms or based on models published by such bodies as the International Chamber of Commerce (ICC); the Society of Construction Arbitrators, who publish the Construction Industry Model Arbitration Rules (CIMAR) 1998; and the Institution of Civil Engineers, who publish arbitration rules for civil engineering contracts.

Where the contract giving rise to arbitration does not define the arbitration rules, the arbitration should be conducted in accordance with the applicable legislation, in the UK the Arbitration Act, subject to the terms of the contract between the parties. This may be referred to as *ad hoc* arbitration.

Starting arbitration

Unless the parties have agreed otherwise, arbitration commences when one party writes to the other requiring it to agree to the appointment of an arbitrator in respect of the matter in dispute.

Appointing the tribunal

In standard building contracts it is commonly left to the parties to agree arbitrators between themselves after a dispute has arisen. If they are unable to agree within a stipulated period, many contracts nominate an independent body to appoint an arbitrator. Relevant bodies include the RIBA, the ICC, the Royal Institute of Chartered Surveyors (RICS) and the Chartered Institute of Arbitrators (CI Arb). If all else fails, the court has power to appoint an arbitrator.

Arbitral tribunal – composition and behaviour

In his book *Introduction to Arbitration*, Harold Crowter offers that an arbitrator is bound to apply the rules of natural justice, which he summarises thus: *'The arbitrator must be, and be seen to be, impartial and disinterested; and each party must be given a full and fair opportunity of putting its case and rebutting the case made against it.'*

It is normal for an arbitral tribunal to contain either a single arbitrator or a panel comprising an odd number of arbitrators including one who chairs the tribunal.

Where three arbitrators are appointed, this may be in the form of two arbitrators and an umpire. The two arbitrators, representing the appointment of each party to the arbitration, appoint the third arbitrator (umpire). All three attend the whole of the proceedings, but the umpire's function is limited to that of deciding between the two arbitrators on any issue where they are incapable of reaching agreement.

Powers and jurisdiction

Arbitrators' powers and jurisdiction depend on the arbitration agreement under which they are acting, the relevant national legislation and the notice of arbitration – that is, the matters covered by the document(s) referring the matter to the arbitrator.

An arbitrator may lack jurisdiction for any of the following reasons:

- no valid arbitration agreement;
- invalid appointment as arbitrator;
- the arbitration agreement is not sufficiently widely worded to allow the matter in dispute to be referred to an arbitrator;

- the matters on which the arbitrator has been asked to decide have not been validly referred to arbitration; or
- the arbitrator has been asked to decide a matter that should be decided not in arbitration but in the courts (e.g. a criminal matter).

In deciding whether or not an arbitrator has jurisdiction in respect of any matter in dispute, reference should be made to the precise wording of the arbitration notice.

Arbitrators have power only where they have jurisdiction. Their powers derive from the arbitration agreement, relevant national legislation (e.g. the UK Arbitration Act 1996) and, in the UK, common law or precedent.

The powers conferred on them by the arbitration agreement may be amended by agreement of the parties. The arbitration agreement may refer to established arbitration rules, which may confer power upon the arbitrator.

A distinction between an arbitrator and a judge is that the arbitrator may use their own expert knowledge and experience in relation to the matters under dispute, but the way in which they may use this is limited.

In construction disputes, arbitrators may rely on their expertise as a basis for coming to grips with the technical arguments involved in the arbitration. If the arbitrator believes they have expertise, which is pertinent and on which they wish to rely, they should put that to the witnesses so that the parties and the experts they have employed may deal with it openly in the hearing. The courts may remove arbitrators if they make an award based on their own experience and expertise without allowing this to be considered in the hearing by the witnesses. As with a judge, an arbitrator should make a decision based on the evidence put before them and not on the basis of their own private knowledge.

An arbitrator may act inquisitorially. The extent and nature of this may be settled at the preliminary meeting. They may, for example, make their own investigations and enquiries and seek independent advice.

Directions

At the outset of arbitration it is customary to hold a preliminary meeting to set out and agree procedural matters. As well as addressing fundamental issues – such as the arbitrator's jurisdiction, the seat of the arbitration, applicable law and so forth – this may also cover matters such as the form of evidence, including that of experts and witnesses of fact. In court proceedings strict rules of evidence apply, dealing with matters such as hearsay. Such strict rules do not have to apply in arbitration and arbitrators can be allowed to use their judgment in assessing evidence.

Statement of case

In arbitration there is some flexibility in the way a claim may be put. Lawyers tend to write a formal statement of case (pleadings). For arbitration a statement of case could be a plain English narrative, stating what has happened, why this has lead to a claim, what the claim is and what evidence there is to support it.

Whichever method is adopted, the other side then customarily is allowed to write a defence and, if they have one, their own claim. It may be that the first side is then permitted to write a reply to the defence and, if appropriate, counterclaim. Done well under good direction, these exchanges serve to make the issues clear and to set out fully the arguments which are to be relied upon, although not necessarily setting out in full the detail of each and every argument.

Witnesses

As with litigation, two types of witness may be called: witnesses of fact and experts.

The witnesses of fact are people who were involved in the matter or the dispute and have direct knowledge of it. It is preferable for witnesses of fact to be restricted to stating that which they know first hand, rather than what has been reported to them. Thus, evidence such as: 'I, as architect, approved the work and informed the site agent of this on Tuesday' is better than: 'the architect said to me on Tuesday that the work I had completed was satisfactory', which itself is preferable to a statement that 'the site agent told me that the architect said to him that our work was satisfactory'.

Where strict rules of evidence are applied, a statement of hearsay evidence by a witness of fact may not be permissible. Such restrictions do not necessarily apply to experts.

Joint arbitrations

An issue that often arises in dealing with arbitration in construction is the question of distinguishing between matters of workmanship and matters of design, in work carried out under a conventional building contract. For example, the employer and the building contractor may seek to resolve a dispute under arbitration proceedings in respect of incorrect workmanship. The contractor, in their defence, may seek to demonstrate that the part of the works which they have allegedly built incorrectly was, in fact, incorrectly designed and that this design was a matter for the architect not for the contractor.

It may be perfectly true that the problem arose out of incorrect design by the architect, either in part or in whole. However, the dispute referred to the arbitrator is that between the employer and the building contractor, not the potential dispute between the employer and the architect. It may be within the arbitrator's jurisdiction to decide that the building contractor is not at fault, or is only partly at fault, by way of considering the issue of defective design. It is not, however, in the arbitrator's power to decide that the architect is at fault, or to seek to apportion the blame between the architect and the contractor.

This is one of the commonly encountered difficulties with building arbitration. There may, in any dispute arising under a building contract, be the possibility that the contractor, subcontractors (including nominated and specialist subcontractors) and the design consultants are each to some extent to blame.

Most arbitration proceedings are written on the assumption that the dispute to be resolved by arbitration is a matter between two disputing parties only. An employer might wish to consider bringing claims against the architect, a nominated sub-contractor and the general building contractor – all of whom they believe to some extent have contributed to a defect in the building. They will not be able to do this through a single arbitration unless the arbitration clauses in their contracts with the architect, the building contract, and the agreement relating to the nomination of the specialist subcontractor(s) have each been written with an arbitration clause which allows this.

It is possible to overcome this by agreement – i.e. in the above example, if the nominated subcontractor, the architect, and the building contractor all voluntarily agree with the employer that they should proceed by way of a single combined arbitration, ordinarily they may do so. They may all jointly appoint an arbitral tribunal which has the power to decide whether or not each of them has any liability for the defect and, if so, to apportion blame.

There have been cases where such joint proceedings would have been in the employer's interests but the offending parties, after the dispute had arisen, would not agree to multi-party arbitration. Seeing no benefit in helping the employer prosecute a claim against them they may use judicial and disingenuous negotiations over every detail of the proposed joint arbitration to frustrate or delay the day of reckoning.

A single joint arbitration with several respondents may lead to vigorous open debate. Each of the respondents may, in mitigation of their own fault, forcefully argue the flaws in the work of others. For example, the general contractor, in seeking to divert attention from faulty workmanship, may reveal a better facility for describing deficiencies in the design than ever they had for constructing buildings on site. In anticipation of this, the architect may portray the progress of the building work by such a tale of builder's blunders as would convict a master craftsman of incompetence with, for good measure, a detailed recital of contract and warranty, aptly demonstrating that all defective things were designed exclusively by specialists, subcontractors, other consultants, etc. And so on. Thus, the respondents may make the case for the employer and it becomes not so much a question of who will win but how the cost of meeting the claims will be apportioned between the defendants.

In such a situation, the employer does not risk losing the arbitration if the cause of fault has been wrongly ascribed to design when it is a matter of workmanship, or vice versa. It simply changes the parties against which the claim is most successful. The employer is also not faced with the cost of pursuing several separate arbitrations, either simultaneously or sequentially.

In litigation, the employer does not ordinarily require prior agreement of the other parties in order to join them into a single legal action. The other parties may themselves choose to join other people into the action, and there are mechanisms under UK law that allow for this.

It is not possible in the building contract for the arbitration agreement to be so written that the employer or building contractor automatically has the right to bring in others to an arbitration. The building contract is between the employer and the building contractor and of itself can deal, therefore, only with arbitration proceedings between them. Similarly, the contract between the architect and employer cannot create arbitration agreements involving other consultants, the builder or subcontractors. In order for there to be a contractual basis with a clear procedure for binding all of the project team to one arbitral proceeding, it is necessary for this to be dealt with in all of the contracts. The arbitration agreement in each of the contracts would have to be written in a 'back-to-back' form. Thus, for example, the contract of employment of the architect would need to contain an arbitration clause which allowed – where there was a dispute between the employer and the architect and the employer and building contractor over a common matter – that this dispute could be settled by a single arbitration between all three parties. The building contract would have to contain a like arbitration clause.

There is a move in this direction in some building contracts. These contain arbitration agreements which allow the appointment of the same arbitrator for a dispute between the employer and building contractor and for the same, or a related, dispute between the building contractor and their subcontractor.[104]

Even where there is no provision in the contract for combining the disputes it may be possible for them to be consolidated, particularly where it can be shown that they are sufficiently related and that the resolution thereof will turn on the same facts and matters.[105]

In the UK, the High Court has the power to join parties in legal proceedings. Where the parties do not consent to consolidation of disputes in arbitration, the courts can, in some circumstances, exercise the power to appoint the same arbitrator in more than one arbitration.[106]

There are many practical issues involved in multi-party arbitrations. It is not unusual for more than a score of subcontractors to be in dispute with the main contractor (particularly where delays have occurred) and for the main contractor to be in dispute with the employer. The facts are very often entangled and are all (partially) relevant to each individual dispute. This situation may lead to proceedings that are unmanageable and/or extremely costly. Sometimes only a few subcontractors will proceed whilst the others wait on the sidelines to see how things develop. However, once more than one subcontractor is roped into the same proceedings time and costs may become prohibitive.

The award

To end the arbitration, the decision given by the arbitral tribunal is called an award. This award must:

- be final;
- comply with the submission;
- show what the arbitrator has determined;
- be made within the prescribed time (if any);
- comply with any other special directions in the arbitration agreement (for instance as regards its form, method of publication, or delivery to one or other of the parties);
- be in writing, unless a contrary intention is expressed in the arbitration agreement;
- be certain in meaning;
- be consistent in all its parts and not contradictory or ambiguous;
- be directed to all matters referred to therein;
- not decide issues not referred to the arbitrator by the parties;
- be clear and precise;
- be capable of being executed (an award for specific performance, for example, that involves entry on to a person's property should not be made unless the permission has been given for such entry); and
- be legal.

A 'reasoned' award, that is an award which contains the tribunal's explanation of the reasons for the decisions contained in the award, may be required by the parties to the arbitration.

Interim and specific performance awards

Awards on parts of the dispute referred to arbitration may be given at an interim stage in an arbitration. These awards, although interim, are final as to the matters they cover. For example, there may be a point of law which has to be decided and which will determine the context in which certain technical or cost issues stand to be judged. The legal issues may be determined as a preliminary issue, and an interim award issued. This can avoid having to deal with arguments over the technical and cost issues that are founded on an interpretation of the law which, in the tribunal's view, is invalid. This can reduce the cost and duration of an arbitration.

An interim award on a fundamental issue can bring the arbitration to an early conclusion and make a full hearing unnecessary.

An arbitration over a new-build industrial development included a disputed assertion that the work was practically complete as defined by the JCT 'With Contractor's Design' form of contract. A site visit was arranged for the arbitrator to view the work and decide whether or not, in his view, the work was practically complete. If it was not practically complete at the date alleged by the builder, the damages due for late completion would undermine the builder's case and, regardless of the decisions on the other issues, the builder would be liable for a substantial payment to the employer.

Each side was represented during the visit by their building expert. The parties to the arbitration were also present. The lawyers were not. Those accompanying the arbitrator were allowed to point to the defective items which had been cited but not to rehearse their arguments in front of the arbitrator.

The arbitrator stated unequivocally during his visit that certain of the patent defects shown to him precluded his agreeing that the work was practically complete.

Before the arbitrator could issue an interim award, the builder reopened negotiations on terms which were very much more favourable to the employer. On the Sunday following the arbitrator's visit an early morning settlement was reached on site, the settlement agreement signed and a cheque handed by the builder to the employer.

Awards for specific performance[107] can be made in addition to, or as an alternative to, the award of damages. Such awards are difficult only because of the problem of enforcement. If, for example, the specific performance requires workmanship of a specific standard for work with materials of a specific quality at a stated time, who is to judge compliance and how is the award to be enforced? Ordinarily, the tribunal is not empowered to supervise and compel performance.

An interim award for specific performance keeps the arbitration alive and offers a method for the effective use of specific performance. Such an award has to be carefully drafted if the arbitrator is not to become *functus officio*[108] before the work required by the specific performance award is performed.

Comparison between litigation and arbitration

Arbitration	Litigation
Private hearing	Public hearing in court
Private award	Public judgment
Choose your own arbitrator	Judge allocated
Choose your own venue	High Court or County Court according to size and nature of dispute
Hours, dates, flexible with agreement	Court decides, normally inflexible
Can be less formal, greater party autonomy	Rules of court apply
Right of appeal restricted	Normal rights of appeal
Less suitable, and often impossible, for multi-party disputes	Suitable and adaptable for all disputes
Costs of arbitrator and venue payable by parties	Judge and court provided 'free'
Lawyers optional	Solicitors, and in the High Court and above normally barristers, are obligatory save if litigant in person
Unfettered right of representation	Normally lawyer advocate, unless litigant in person
Powers and jurisdiction of arbitrators variable by consent	Courts' jurisdiction and power laid down in rules of court/statutes
Less easy to deal with reluctant party	Court more robust, sanctions available
Can be quicker and easier	Set pattern, with less opportunity for fast-track procedures
Documents only, and other short forms of procedures, if agreed by parties	Hearing according to rules of court
Can award compound or simple interest	Can only award simple interest under statute
View of site, etc. can be insisted upon	At judge's discretion
Standard form of construction contracts normally contain arbitration clause	Litigation can be stayed if valid arbitration agreement
Legal Aid scheme not applicable	Legal Aid available subject to means

Adjudication

Since the introduction of the Housing Grants, Construction and Regeneration Act 1996 adjudication is now the first (and often the last) formal step in resolving construction disputes in the UK. In common usage, this Act is often referred to as the 'Construction Act' – which abbreviation is adopted hereafter.

Under this Act adjudication is regulated by the Scheme for Construction Contracts[109] but agreements under statute, Private Finance Initiative (PFI) contracts, finance agreements and development agreements are excluded from the scope of the Act by the Construction Contracts (England and Wales) Exclusion Order 1998.

Under these statutory provisions, adjudication may be likened to fast arbitration. Allowing for differences in terminology such the substitution of 'adjudicator' and 'adjudication' for 'tribunal' and 'arbitral proceedings', it is similar to arbitration and much of Section 42 of the 1996 Arbitration Act applies.

Strict time constraints are imposed, in view of which it is sometimes said to offer quick but rough justice – letting the 'heat' out of the dispute while the contract is completed. The adjudicator's decision is binding and the parties must comply with it until, if either of them wishes, the dispute is finally resolved by arbitration or litigation.

Confidential documents remain confidential, other than to the extent that the adjudication proceedings require disclosure of them.

Unlike arbitrators and judges, adjudicators generally cannot award costs unless the adjudication agreement provides for this. In broad terms, all parties to the dispute are jointly and severally liable for the adjudicator's reasonable fees and expenses.

Adjudicators have no liability for their actions as adjudicators, unless they act in bad faith.

Duties of an adjudicator

In compliance with the Construction Act and the Scheme for Construction Contracts, an adjudicator may:

- require peremptory compliance with their decision or any part thereof;
- in deciding the matters in dispute, take into account anything which the parties to the dispute agree should be within the scope of the adjudication – and may take into account anything under the contract which the adjudicator considers necessarily connected with the dispute;
- open, revise and review any decision under the contract, except where that decision is stated by the contract to be final and conclusive. This includes all certificates, etc. Unless the adjudicator directs otherwise, the parties in dispute are to comply with their decision immediately it is issued;
- ascertain the facts and the law necessary to determining the dispute;

- request any party to supply them with documents, written statements, etc.;
- decide the language or languages to be used for the adjudication, and on the provision of translated documents;
- meet and question any of the parties or their representatives;
- visit the site and inspect, subject to obtaining necessary consents;
- carry out any tests or experiments, subject to obtaining necessary consents;
- obtain and consider such representations and submissions as they require;
- appoint experts, assessors or legal advisors, provided the adjudicator has notified the parties;
- issue directions for the adjudication timetable, deadlines and limits to the submission of oral evidence etc.;
- if their directions are not followed, proceed to adjudicate and give such weight as they think appropriate to late evidence; etc.

Adjudicators must:

- provide reasons for their decisions, if any of the parties to the dispute request this;
- consider any relevant information submitted to them;
- make available to all other parties in the dispute any information they use in reaching their decision;
- act impartially and in accordance with the relevant terms of the contract;
- reach a decision in accordance with the law applicable to the contract; and
- avoid unnecessary expense.

Enforcement of an adjudicator's award

Adjudicators decisions have, if not complied with voluntarily, to be enforced at law. Developing case law gives guidance on the effective finality of adjudicators' awards.

In *Macob Civil Engineering Ltd* v *Morrison Construction Ltd*, Mr Justice Dyson found that an adjudicator's decision could not be stayed for arbitration:

> *29. But what the defendant could not do was to assert that the decision was a decision for the purposes of being the subject of a reference to arbitration, but was not a decision for the purpose of being binding and enforceable pending any revision by the arbitrator.*[110]

In the case of *Outwing Construction Limited* v *H Randell & Son Limited*, His Honour, Judge Humphrey Lloyd QC discussed in detail the correct method of enforcing an adjudicator's decision:

> *Action to enforce an adjudicator's decision is not comparable to the ordinary process of recovering an apparently undisputed debt. The Rules of the Supreme Court provide a reasonable time for the defendant in an ordinary case to take stock of its position in case there is a defence to the claim. The Housing Grants, Construction and Regeneration Act 1996 (and the statutory instruments made*

under it) constitute a remarkable (and possibly unique) intervention in very carefully selected parts of the construction industry whereby the ordinary freedom of contract between commercial parties (without regard to bargaining power) to regulate their relationships has been overridden in a number of areas, one of which is dispute resolution. The overall intention of Parliament is clear: disputes are to go to adjudication and the decision of the adjudicator has to be complied with, pending final determination. There is no provision for a "stay of execution" (unless it is part of the decision itself), presumably since that would undermine the purpose which is final, at least temporarily. In addition the provisions in the Scheme for the enforcement of peremptory orders via what is thought to be a quick and effective procedure reinforce the conclusion that Parliament intended that adjudicator's decisions and orders, if not complied with, were to be enforced without delay. It is clear that the purpose of the Act is that disputes are resolved quickly and effectively and then put to one side and revived, if at all, in litigation or arbitration, the hope being that the decision of the adjudicator might be accepted or form the basis of a compromise.[111]

In the decision in *A & D Maintenance and Construction Ltd* v *Pagehurst Construction Services Ltd*, two important issues were decided. Firstly, did the right to refer a dispute to adjudication survive a determination of the contract? His Honour Judge David Wilcox made this clear as follows:

Even if the contract had been terminated, the matters referred to the Adjudicator remain disputes under the contract. Where there is a contract to which the Act applies, as in this case, and there are disputes arising out of the contract to be adjudicated, the adjudication provisions clearly remain operative just as much as an arbitration clause would remain operative.[112]

Secondly, the judge confirmed the provisions of the Construction Act, which define a contract in writing, widely:

Also material to this submission is Section 107(5) which provides:

" . . . an exchange of written submissions in adjudication proceedings, or in arbitral or legal proceedings in which the existence of legal proceedings otherwise than in writing is alleged by one party against another party and not denied by the other party in his response, constitutes as between those parties an agreement in writing to the effect alleged . . . "

There was clearly a contract within the Act. The contract did not expressly make provision for adjudication compliant with Section 108 of the Act. Accordingly Part 1 of the Scheme applies pursuant to Section 108(5) of the Act. Pursuant to Section 114(4) the provisions of the Scheme take effect as implied terms of the contract.[113]

The decision in *John Cothliff Ltd* v *Allen Build (North West) Ltd* upholds the principle that, under the Scheme, an adjudicator can award costs. His Honour

Judge Marshall Evans stated:

> But, primarily, I decide that the adjudicator has got power to award costs, at least where, as in this case, costs have been expressly sought in the application placed before the adjudicator, and where he has allowed representation, at least on behalf of the defendant by lawyers, and apparently on behalf of the claimant by a firm of dispute pursuing quantity surveyors, whom I am told are the leads in that specialised field of extracting money from contractors up the line, or it may be denying it to contractors down the line.[114]

The finality of an award comes from the parties being at best content or at worst resigned to accept the adjudicator's decision. By 2003, about one in sixty adjudication awards had been referred to the courts. Of these about one fifth were not enforced. That is approximately 299 out of 300 awards proved, in effect, to be final and binding. His Honour Justice Humphrey Lloyd noted in the recent case of *Balfour Beatty Construction Ltd* v *Lambeth London Borough Council* that:

> It is now clear that the construction industry regards adjudication not simply as a staging post towards the final resolution of the dispute in arbitration or litigation but as having in itself considerable weight and impact that in practice goes beyond the legal requirement that the decision for the time being has to be resolved … Lack of impartiality or of fairness in adjudication must be considered in that light. It has become all the more necessary that, within the rough nature of the process, decisions are still made in a basically fair manner so that the system itself continues to enjoy the confidence it now has apparently earned …[115]

The Housing Grants, Construction and Regeneration Act 1996

In July 1993 the Government announced the Joint Review of Procurement and Contractual Arrangements in the United Kingdom Construction Industry. This led to the publication, in July 1994, of a report called 'Constructing the Team'.

Some of the recommendations set out in 'Constructing the Team' are given legal force by Part II of the Housing Grants, Construction and Regeneration Act 1996, which deals with, amongst other things, adjudication in construction contracts.

The Construction Act defines a construction contract as *'an agreement to carry out construction operations, or the arranging for others to carry out construction operations under a subcontract and the provision of one's own labour or the labour of others for the carrying out of construction operations'*.

Under the Act, construction contracts include the provision of professional services for building work, such as architecture, surveying, engineering, decorating and landscaping. A contract of employment, as identified in the Employment Rights Act 1996, is excluded.

Construction operations covered by the Construction Act are all normal building and civil engineering activities, including site preparation, new work, alterations, services, external or internal cleaning, and decoration of any buildings or structures.

The Act expressly excludes certain activities from its definition of 'construction operations', viz:

- the extraction of oil or natural gas;
- mineral extraction;
- contracts where the primary activity is plant or machinery for chemicals, pharmaceuticals, gas, oil, food and drink, nuclear processing, power generation or water-effluent treatment;
- the manufacture or delivery of components, equipment and materials, plant or machinery – except where the contract also provides for the installation of that component, equipment and/or materials;
- the making, installation and repair of artistic works.

There is no minimum contract value in the Construction Act, and therefore it will apply to all construction contracts regardless of size.

The Construction Act does not apply to 'operations on a dwelling' – i.e. a construction contract with a residential occupier in which one of the parties to the contract resides or intends to reside in the dwelling.

Work to domestic properties carried out for developers, local authorities, housing associations, commercial landlords and managing agents fall within the Act.

The provisions of the Construction Act apply only where the construction contract is evidenced 'in writing' – defined as 'recorded by any means'.

Even if a contract were not evidenced in writing, it may fall within the scope of the Construction Act if a dispute is submitted to adjudication, in which submission the existence of the contract is affirmed by one party and not denied by the other.

This arises from Clause 107(5) of the Construction Act, which states: '*exchange of written submissions in adjudication proceedings, or in arbitral or legal proceedings in which the existence of an agreement otherwise than in writing is alleged by one party against the other party and not denied by the other party in his response constitutes as between those parties an agreement in writing to the effect alleged*'.

This means that if the parties involved in arbitration agree that they have an oral rather than a written contract, under the statute it has exactly the opposite effect, i.e. it is treated as a written contract.

The Act introduces a right for either party to a construction contract to refer any dispute to adjudication '*under a procedure complying with Section 108*'.

The contract shall therefore:

- enable a party to give notice at any time, referring a dispute to adjudication;
- provide a timetable with the object of securing the appointment of the adjudicator and referral of the dispute within seven days of notice;
- require the adjudicator to reach a decision within 28 days of referral or such longer period as is agreed by the parties after the dispute has been referred;
- allow the adjudicator to extend the period of 28 days by up to 14 days with the consent of the party who referred the dispute;
- impose a duty on the adjudicator to act impartially; and
- enable the adjudicator to take the initiative in ascertaining the facts and the law.

The adjudicator's decision shall be binding until finally determined by legal proceedings, arbitration or by agreement, and the parties may agree to accept it as finally determining the dispute.

If the contract does not comply with these requirements, the adjudication provisions of the Scheme for Construction Contracts will apply.

As adjudication is an additional provision for resolving disputes, it is necessary to consider in what ways it differs from arbitration:

- adjudicators will be experts who will make their decisions based upon their own knowledge and experience;
- to achieve a speedy decision – a 'quick fix' – there will be constraints upon the time available for the parties to present their case, submit documents and cross-examine;
- where a speedy decision is made, not all of the facts may have been considered and, therefore, the decision must only be binding on the parties in the short term – with each having the right to refer the decision, at a later date, to arbitration or litigation.

The rules of natural justice are unlikely to be upheld where parties have not been given full opportunity to present their case or defend themselves.

The Construction Act provides that all contracts which are within its scope are subject to adjudication. The parties to the contract are free to agree how to deal with these matters, but if the contract does not include provisions for adjudications or if its provisions do not comply with the requirements of section 108 (1)–(4) of the Act, then a clause as set out in the Scheme for Construction Contracts will automatically be implied into the contract and either party will be entitled to rely on it.

Commencing adjudication

Any party to a construction contract can start adjudication. The party that does so is the 'referring party'.

To start adjudication, the referring party serves written Notice of Adjudication on all parties to the contract. The Notice of Adjudication must state:

- who are in dispute (including their addresses);
- what is in dispute;
- where and when the dispute started; and
- what redress is sought.

Subject to any express provisions of the contract, the referring party requests the person named in the contract to act as adjudicator or, if none, requests the appropriate nominating body to provide an adjudicator.

Timetable for adjudication

- Any nominating body for adjudicators must inform the referring party of the selected adjudicator within five days. If the nominating body fails so to do, the referring party may request any other adjudicator-nominating body to make a nomination or, alternatively, may agree the selection of an adjudicator with the other parties to the dispute.
- Any person requested to act as an adjudicator must accept or decline within two days.
- Once an adjudicator is in place, the referring party provides a Referral Notice to the adjudicator. The Referral Notice must be issued within seven days of the Notice of Adjudication.
- The parties to the disputes may agree to extend the period within which the adjudicator may reach a decision.
- The adjudicator is to decide the dispute within 28 days of the Referral Notice, or 42 days of the Referral Notice if the referring party so consents, or any period exceeding 28 days from the Referral Notice if all the parties to the dispute agree.

The Referral Notice should be accompanied by copies of, or extracts from, such documents as the referring party relies upon. The Referral Notice and accompanying documents must at the same time as being sent to the adjudicator be sent to all other parties to the dispute.

A nominating body may be any public body which will nominate adjudicators.

Any adjudicator to be appointed under the Act is a person, not a company or organisation. The persons that are appointed must not be any employee of the contracting parties who are in dispute, and must declare any interest that they have in any matter relating to the subject of their appointment.

If a person has been named as an adjudicator within the contract but is, for some reason, unavailable or unwilling to act when a dispute arises, the referring party may adopt similar procedures to those which would have been available to them had the person not been named in the contract.

The adjudicator may, with the consent of all the parties to those disputes, adjudicate simultaneously on related disputes under different contracts whether or not one or more of those parties is party to those disputes.

Procedures for operation of adjudication

The Construction Act states that a party to a construction contract has the right to refer a dispute arising under that contract for adjudication and it defines a dispute as including *'any difference'*.

It may prove impracticable to investigate a building defect or to assess build quality properly during the restricted time limits for adjudication, particularly where built work has been concealed and the performance required of the work is disputed.

The Act requires the adjudication provisions in a contract to set out a timetable for the appointment of the adjudicator and for the party requiring the adjudication to refer the dispute to them within seven days of the notice of the dispute – ideally providing a detailed but concise submission both to the adjudicator and to the other party.

Adjudicators need not model themselves on judges, and sit back listening or reading the points raised and reaching their decision only on those points. They can investigate and interview, acting as an expert enquiring into the dispute. The rules of natural justice apply and adjudicators must be open in what they do.

The amount of investigation or interviewing the adjudicator will be able to carry out is likely to be limited, as they have to reach a decision within 28 days unless a longer period is agreed by both parties. There is also provision allowing the adjudicator to extend the 28-day period by 14 days if this extension is agreed by the party who referred the dispute – it does not require the agreement of the other party – however, adjudicators cannot extend the 28-day period on their own.

The intention with adjudication is that there should be a concise submission by one party with a similarly concise defence from the other party without any hearings, calls for further and better particulars or legal representation. Although the submission to the adjudicator should be concise, it will have to be supported by relevant documentation such as contract documents. It is possible to have a meeting of the parties, perhaps in the form of a hearing with the adjudicator presiding.

Rarely do disputes arise on one clear-cut issue – there are usually many issues involved and probably several subcontractors, manufacturers and suppliers. Consideration needs to be given to whether all the related matters are dealt with as a single adjudication, joining all parties, or whether it will be limited to the dispute between the two directly contracting parties. Unless all the contracts name the same adjudicator it may not be possible to have a joinder provision (see Chapter 9, Consolidation and joinder). Even if the contracts make suitable provisions it may be difficult to instigate joinder proceedings.

Removing an adjudicator

- The adjudicator may resign at any time, whereupon the referring party has to seek the appointment of another adjudicator, repeating the exercise it initially undertook.
- If the adjudicator finds that the dispute is substantially the same as one which has been previously been referred to adjudication, in which a decision has been given, the adjudicator must resign.
- Parties in dispute may at any time jointly revoke the appointment of an adjudicator. The objection of any party to the appointment of an adjudicator does not invalidate that adjudicator's appointment or decisions.
- If adjudicators fail to give decisions within the stipulated time, any of the parties may replace them with new adjudicators and transfer all papers, etc. to their replacements.

Presenting a case before an adjudicator

There is no formal procedure or format for making a referral or for the response from the other party, and each of the standard forms of contract outlines slightly different requirements. The following particulars should, however, be considered in a referral under any form of contract.

A Notice of Adjudication and Referral Notice must be given. The following details must be included:

- the contract particulars;
- the parties to the contract;
- the parties involved in the dispute;
- the nature and a brief description of the dispute,
  - where and when it arose,
  - the nature of redress being sought.

The details should be supported by a copy of the contract, or extracts from it, and by any other relevant documents in support.

Adjudication is intended to be a quick fix. Long, detailed, complicated or rambling submissions are inappropriate.

The referral should be:

- as simple as possible;
- easily understandable;
- clear, precise and brief;
- a document (including photographs and diagrams as appropriate) explaining the whole of the overall case and individual items separately.

In addition to the general information required in any referral of a dispute or difference, specific details will be needed dependent upon the matter being referred to adjudication.

Referral requirements under various forms of contract

The Scheme for Construction Contracts states that the Notice of Adjudication should set out the nature and brief description of the dispute, the parties involved, where and when the dispute arose, the nature of redress that is sought, and the names and addresses of the parties.

The Scheme states that copies of, or relevant extracts from, the contract and other documents the referring party intends to rely upon shall accompany the Referral Notice.

- JCT forms of contract state that the Notice of Adjudication should set out briefly the dispute or difference identified. The Referral Notice should include particulars of the dispute of difference, summary of contentions, a statement of relief or remedy sought and the material the referrer wishes the adjudicator to consider.
- The Institution of Civil Engineers (ICE) Contract, 6th Edition Amendment, states that, in the first instance, a matter will be an item of 'dissatisfaction' and it will only become a dispute or a difference after the engineer has given a 'Clause 66 decision' or the period of time for that decision has expired.
- An adjudication under the ICE contract (see above) is required to be conducted under the ICE Adjudication Procedures (1997). This procedure requires the Notice of Adjudication to include the date of the contract, issues the adjudicator is to decide and the nature and extent of redress sought. The Referral Notice should include a full statement of case, a copy of the Notice of Adjudication, a copy of adjudication provisions in the contract, and the information upon which the referrer relies (including supporting documents).
- Government Contract GC/Works/1–1998 states that the Referral Notice should set out the principal facts, arguments and relevant documents.
- DOM 1, the domestic form of subcontract for use with JCT 80, states that the Notice of Adjudication should include details of the dispute or difference briefly identified and the Referral Notice should include particulars of the dispute or difference, summary of contentions, a statement of relief or remedy sought, and material the referrer wishes the adjudicator to consider.
- The Civil Engineering Contractors' Association (CECA) Blue Form of subcontract for use with ICE 6th Edition refers to matters of 'dissatisfaction' as in the main form, and this does not become a dispute or difference until the engineer has given a decision under the main form – or the period of time for that decision has expired. When adjudication is to take place it should be in accordance with the ICE Adjudication Procedures (1997).

Response to a referral

Both the Construction Act and The Scheme for Construction Contracts are totally silent as to what, if anything, is to be submitted.

There is no consensus in the various forms of contract on how to address the party and the document that may be used in responding to a referral to adjudication. Some of the titles used include 'defence', 'respondent', 'party not making referral', and 'other party'.

The various provisions include the following:

- The Joint Contracts Tribunal (JCT) forms of contract state that the party not making the referral may, within seven days of the date of the referral, send a written statement of contentions and matters they wish the adjudicator to consider.
- GC/Works/1–1998 states that the project manager, the quantity surveyor, and 'the other party' may submit representations to the adjudicator not later than seven days from the receipt of the Notice of Referral.
- The ICE Adjudication Procedures (1997) for use with ICE 6th Edition, and the CECA Blue Form of subcontract state that the other party may submit their response to the statement under the referral within 14 days of the referral, and that this period may be extended by agreement between the parties and the adjudicator.
- DOM 1 (a JCT subcontract form) states that the party not making the referral may send to the adjudicator, within seven days of the date of the referral, a written statement of the contentions on which they rely and any material they wish the adjudicator to consider.

[98] *European Treaty Series – No. 56: European Convention Providing A Uniform Law On Arbitration, Strasbourg, 20.I.1966* (see *http://conventions.coe.int/treaty/en/reports/html/056.htm*).

[99] See *www.uncitral.org*

[100] See *www.pbh.org.uk/PDF/rules_arb_english.pdf*

[101] The Association of Consultant Architects; see *www.acarchitects.co.uk*

[102] The Association of Consultant Architects; see *www.acarchitects.co.uk*

[103] *Modern Buildings Wales Ltd v Limmer & Trinidad Ltd.* (1975) 2 All ER 549.

[104] E.g. JCT '80, Clause 41·2 and International Federation of Consulting Engineers (FIDIC) Subcontract 1994, Clause 19.2.

[105] *Schindler Lifts v Shui On* [1986] HKLR 1177.

[106] *Abu Dhabi Gas Liquefaction Co v Eastern Bechtel Corporation* (1982) 21 BLR 117.

[107] Specific performance is a remedy of a breach, for example by the correction of defective work.

[108] Free from further obligations, having discharged their duty.

[109] The Scheme for Construction Contracts (England and Wales) Regulations were introduced by Statutory Instrument made by Parliament early in 1998. Part I of the Scheme provides rules for the conduct of adjudication. Similar regulations have been introduced for Scotland. The England and Wales Regulations were introduced for Northern Ireland by an Order in Council to the Northern Ireland Act 1974, as the Scheme for Construction Contracts in Northern

Ireland Regulations (Northern Ireland) 1999, which came into operation on 1 June 1999.

[110] *Macob Civil Engineering Ltd* v *Morrison Construction Ltd* (1999) BLR 93.

[111] *Outwing Construction Limited* v *H Randell & Son Limited* (1999) BLR 156.

[112] *A & D Maintenance and Construction Ltd* v *Pagehurst Construction Services Ltd* (1999) 29 BLISS 1.

[113] *A & D Maintenance and Construction Ltd* v *Pagehurst Construction Services Ltd* (1999) 29 BLISS 1.

[114] *John Cothliff Ltd* v *Allen Build (North West) Ltd* (1999) BLISS 14.

[115] *Balfour Beatty Construction Ltd* v *Lambeth London Borough Council* (2002) BLR 288.

The Expert

Expert witnesses

As a general rule, under UK law witnesses may not express opinions when giving evidence; they are limited to giving their personal perceptions of the facts without drawing inferences from them. The courts sometimes find that they require more assistance than is available to them under such restrictive rules of evidence. Where the issues being tried require an understanding of specialist matters of which the judges do not have knowledge, they may permit the introduction of evidence of opinion by someone who is expert in the specialisms concerned:

> . . . if matters arise in our law which concern other sciences or facilities, we may commonly apply for the aid of that science or faculty which it concerns. Which is an honourable and commendable thing in our law. For thereby it appears that we don't dispute other sciences but our own, but we approve of them and encourage them as things worthy of commendation.[116]

The role of the expert witness developed to serve the needs of the courts and is defined accordingly. In the 18th century, the eminent engineer, Mr Smeaton, was called to give his opinion to the court as he: 'understands the construction of harbours, the causes of their destruction and how remedied'.[117]

More recently the courts set out the duties of an expert witness as follows:

> Their duty is to furnish the judge or jury with the necessary scientific criteria for testing the accuracy of their conclusions, so as to enable the judge or jury to form their own independent judgement of the application of these criteria to the facts provided in evidence.[118]

The role of the expert in UK law is now addressed in the court procedure rules.

In civil proceedings an expert may give evidence on any issue in a proceeding.[119] The experts first give their evidence-in-chief under questioning from their client's advocate.[120] They may then be cross-examined by the opposing side's advocate and thereafter re-examined by their own client's advocate. In practice, in building disputes experts' reports are normally accepted as their evidence-in-chief. This places constraints on the form and content of such reports. In particular, an expert's report must be a personal statement written in the first person singular. Where reference is made to information which experts have by report, unverified by their own observations, they should make this clear. To the extent that such references are to hearsay evidence, they may be inadmissible.

Experts' duties

An expert may be called upon to do any or all of the following:

- investigate the facts;
- form opinions;

- advise their client and their client's lawyers;
- prepare evidence;
- propose remedial works.

In all of this, within their own role and competence, they owe a duty of care, both in contract and tort, to their client. Unless they are legally qualified their responsibility is restricted to technical matters, excluding advice on legal procedures or on the likelihood of success should litigation or arbitration be pursued. The extent of their responsibilities is defined by the skills they hold themselves out as having, and the agreement they enter into with their client. As with any appointment for professional services, it is important that they agree, at the outset, the extent of their responsibilities.

They have a duty to the court to be truthful, which overrides their duty to their client and makes it most unwise for them to deliberately omit or falsify facts to disguise the truth. Accordingly, to ensure that they feel able to speak freely in court, experts' liability to their clients is limited.[121] They should not address matters which are outside their brief, and on which they are not questioned.

Court may appoint experts,[122] in which case their role may have some similarity to that of an arbitrator in respect of the issues within their expertise. Their role is, nonetheless, advisory.

Expert witnesses' duty to the court overrides any obligation they have to the person who instructs or pays them. To discharge this duty, experts must be completely open in revealing to the court all relevant matters whether or not they go against their client. Accordingly, to ensure that they feel able to speak freely in court, experts' liability to their client is limited.[123]

It has long been held that expert witnesses are immune from civil action for any error they make in court provided they do not commit perjury. Lord Salmon spelt this out in 1974 in the following form: 'it is well settled that judges, barristers, solicitors, jurors and witnesses enjoy an absolute immunity from any form of civil action being brought against them in respect of anything they say or do in court during the course of the trial'.[124]

Following the House of Lords' decision in 2000, immunity from suit for actions in negligence for professionals engaged in court proceedings is now limited to judges and those giving expert-witness testimony.[125]

The immunity enjoyed by expert witnesses extends to evidence given by them in court and to work which is preliminary to giving such evidence.[126]

Work done by experts prior to legal proceedings being started or for the principal purpose of advising the client on the merits of their case or on the suitability of the expert, are not covered by this immunity.[127]

There are two forms of liability to consider: negligence and defamation. Lately, immunity from suit for negligence has been put into question. Current thinking is illustrated by the following recent example:

A consultant was appointed as expert for a defendant. He declared in his expert report that he understood his duty to the court and had complied with that duty, pursuant to the court procedure rules (CPR) section 35 and CPR PD 35. (These are the court rules which confirm the experts' duties to the court.). In its ruling the court effectively rejected this expert's evidence.

An application was made for this consultant to be joined as a respondent to the issue under CPR 48.2 for the purpose of costs only. It was argued that the court should order an expert witness to pay compensation to parties who have suffered loss due to the expert's gross dereliction of duty. It was proposed that the liability of experts should be regarded as being strongly analogous to that of (for example) advocates, who have long been subject to sanctions as regards wasted costs. Part of the problem with this submission was that experts enjoy immunity from suit in respect of evidence given.

The court considered the scope and nature of an expert's duty in a way which indicates that experts may enjoy less protection in UK courts than was traditionally the view. The following summary points illustrate some of the current thinking:

- The question should be looked at in the light of modern developments of the law in relation to litigation.
- Wasted-costs applications against advocates have been decoupled from immunity.
- The court should not remove from itself the power to make a costs order against experts who, by their evidence, cause significant expense to be incurred, and do so in flagrant reckless disregard of their duties to the court.
- In these circumstances the proper sanction is the ability to compensate a person who has suffered loss by reason of that evidence.
- Experts will not, by reason of this potential exposure, be inhibited from fulfilling their duties.
- The high level of proof required to establish the breach would deter a flood of claims.
- If the experts are in difficulty, under CPR 35.14 they can approach the court – allowing the court to ensure that they are given a full opportunity to present their case. (These are court rules which provide a right to expert witnesses to approach the court directly.)

Most commonly, in proceedings under English Law, the parties in dispute each appoint their own experts. Experts hold themselves out to have special skills or expertise in certain areas, and have a duty of care to their clients for the advice they give in those areas.

In a building dispute, the expert will usually give advice before proceedings commence – advice which may be relied upon in deciding whether or not to proceed with legal action. If the advice is negligent, it may result in a hopeless case being taken to trial or a good case being needlessly abandoned. The former will waste the court's time and both defendant's and claimant's money. The latter may delay or stop potential claimants from recovering the damages to which, at law, they are entitled.

False encouragement, which leads to a hopeless claim being pursued, is more likely to come to light than is overly discouraging opinion. Pessimism, however, is unlikely to secure a commission and it is the expert with a positive view of the strength of a prospective client's case who is likely to be appointed.

In substantial cases barristers often like to test the experts before the hearing. Indeed, counsels' 'friendly' cross-examinations of their own experts in chambers can be the most penetrating. By contrast, the 'hostile' cross-examination in court is often less incisive as the advocate, lacking the expert's detailed knowledge of the matters the expert has addressed, is often at a disadvantage.

If litigants discover their experts to have been negligent, they may seek compensation from the experts. The traditional immunity from civil proceedings for a witness's actions in court does not impart immunity to the witnesses for their actions prior to the trial.

Experts usually obtain employment by claiming extensive knowledge and/or experience in a particular field. In taking on a commission, an expert owes the client a duty of care. This is similar to the duty of care an architect, engineer or other building professional, carrying out their normal work, owes to their clients – and is discussed under 'Roles' in Chapter 1.

With due regard for professional liability, it is wise – whether formally engaged as an expert, or casually consulted by a potential client – to ensure that any advice given is limited to the area of true expertise and that, where appropriate, the limits of the reliance which may be placed on it are clearly stated.

Without-prejudice meetings of experts

Where the experts appointed by the parties are directed by the tribunal to meet so as to see if they can reach any agreement, it is advantageous if they can talk freely and openly about all aspects of the matter they have to consider. In such conversations they may explore the basis on which their clients may be at fault. In order that they can do this openly, without any risk of inadvertently compromising their client's position, their discussions are normally 'without prejudice'. They may, however, reach agreements which they may jointly and openly report. These joint reports are not themselves without prejudice, no matter that the conversations from which they arose were.

Reliability of evidence

Factual evidence and witnesses of fact are not necessarily reliable. This was tested experimentally by an American Professor of Psychology who arranged for four people to enter one of his classes unannounced, each of whom was to carry out a singular individual act. The class were not forewarned and immediately after the event were asked to write a description of what they had seen. None of them properly and accurately recorded the event. Errors were made as to the appearance and number of the people who came in and the actions that they undertook. This despite the fact that they were in a controlled environment, without other distraction and were required to describe the event immediately after its occurrence. The witnesses were all disinterested and had no reason to lie. They were not put under pressure or tutored in any way as to the evidence they should give.

Expert witnesses may learn two lessons from this experiment. The first is that experts, in giving evidence, should be very clear to state as fact only that of which they are certain. The other is that where experts need to rely on second-hand or hearsay evidence that they obtain as many pieces of confirmatory evidence as is reasonably practicable, so as to be as sure as possible of the truth of the reported facts on which they rely.

Even where experts are relying on first-hand observation, the accuracy of their observations can vary. This can be an issue where, as is often the case, several experts look together at the same evidence but record disparate facts. Sometimes this may be due to an expert's view being blinkered by a wish to see that which supports their (or their client's) preconception of the facts. Sometimes it is natural human error.

An outbreak of blinkered sight occurred during joint expert investigations of cracking in brick walls. There were five experts, each of whom was acting for a different party. The investigations were arranged by the claimant's (who was the building owner) expert and were attended by an expert for each defendant including the contractor, architect, engineer and clerk of works. The employer's expert had arranged for some brickwork to be cut open so that all could look at parts of the concealed structure contained within the wall.

The first opening was made. Each expert in turn ascended the ladder to examine the exposed steelwork.

The group moved on to the second opening position and, whilst waiting for the bricks to be cut out, discussed what they had seen. This quickly revealed that they had not all seen the same thing. In particular, the experts for the engineer and builder could not recollect the loose bolts which the rest of the experts saw.

Thereafter, for each opening up, the employer's expert announced each thing he found as he found it and then moved aside to allow each expert to confirm the findings by their own observation. Proceeding in that fashion, all ended up with similar records of what was found during the opening-up.

Even where there is a common understanding of what has been seen, the way in which the observations are described can lead to apparent disagreement over the observed facts.

A dispute arose over cracking in the roof sheets on an agricultural building. Including third parties, there were 13 defendants. Each party to the litigation appointed an expert. The experts visited site together to examine the cracks. Although they each saw the same thing, they each described what was there in different terms. Writing a joint statement became more of a semantic than a technical issue. It was difficult to agree neutral terms to describe what they had seen, so that all were satisfied that the way in which the faults were described was both impartial and comprehensive.

Achieving the degree of neutrality necessary to allow a joint statement of the facts to be written down necessitated agreeing the words that would be used and the meaning that would be ascribed to them in the context of a joint report.

Thus, one expert would describe the crack as a surface crack, another as a superficial crack, the third as a shallow crack, etc. Whilst, strictly speaking, 'superficial' and 'surface' crack have the same meaning, 'superficial' in common usage may suggest that the crack is not regarded as significant. A 'shallow' crack may be the same as, or deeper than, the crack which is contained in the surface of the material.

All were from the UK, and all qualified building professionals, yet the way in which they used language was not consistent enough to allow them to describe simple observations without first carefully agreeing the terminology.

Expert's evidence-in-chief

The expert's evidence-in-chief in building litigation is now customarily given as a written report, relieving experts of the need to introduce their evidence orally in court.[128] As experts' reports may be used extensively in the drafting of a statement of claim, experts should work closely with their clients' legal advisers and stay available to advise on the other parties' experts' reports/statements of claim and to amend or supplement their own report as necessary.

It is not necessary for experts to attempt to use legal terminology, but they should understand the rules of evidence sufficiently to:

- understand what evidence is relevant and therefore admissible;
- understand, and be capable of stating properly, the relevance of the facts to which they allude in their evidence;
- be aware which types of evidence are likely to be regarded as more compelling when conflicting evidence is placed before a court or arbitral tribunal.

Guidance on the content of an expert report can be drawn from decided cases. (The one most commonly cited is referred to in short as '*Ikarian Reefer*' from the name of the ship involved in the dispute.[129]) From these cases the following conclusions can be drawn:

- Expert witnesses in civil cases have several duties and responsibilities, including the duty to give independent and unbiased evidence. If an expert witness did not have expertise in a certain area, or had insufficient information to reach a properly researched conclusion, then they should say so.
- Expert evidence presented to the court should be, and should be seen to be, the independent product of the expert, uninfluenced as to form or content by the exigencies of litigation.[130]
- Independent assistance should be provided to the court by way of objective unbiased opinion regarding matters within the expertise of the expert witness.[131] An expert witness in the High Court should never assume the role of advocate.
- Facts or assumptions upon which the opinion was based should be stated, together with material facts which could detract from the concluded opinion.
- Expert witnesses should make it clear when a question or issue falls outside their expertise.
- If the opinion was not properly researched because it was considered that insufficient data was available, then that has to be stated with an indication that the opinion was provisional. If the witness cannot assert that the report contains the truth, the whole truth and nothing but the truth, then that qualification should be stated on the report.[132]
- If, after exchange of reports, expert witness change their minds on material matters, then the change of view should be communicated without delay to the other side through legal representatives and, when appropriate, to the court.
- Photographs, plans, survey reports and other documents referred to in the expert evidence have to be provided to the other side at the same time as the exchange of reports.

Expert's reports

As with all reports, clarity, brevity, relevance and completeness are important watchwords. True experts are writing from a position of familiarity with their subject. Those who read their reports may not be acquainted with the terminology and customs associated with the area of expertise. Acronyms, common colloquial and slang terms and the like can frustrate the lay reader if not explained, and are generally best avoided. For example, architects may be familiar with the concept of damp-proof courses and be familiar with the site contraction to 'damp' and the written abbreviation, d.p.c. In writing an expert report to be read by lay clients and lawyers, it is not safe to assume that the readers will know what a damp-proof course is, let alone understand tracts of writing which refer to it by initials or other contractions. The need to explain the terminology used should be balanced with the avoidance of condescension to the reader.

Expert's reports should be drafted as stand-alone documents in the first person singular and express the expert's honest opinion uninfluenced by the contingencies of litigation no matter how hard the clients and their advocates may press for the adoption of a more favourable outlook.

Reports should be the experts' own work and express their own opinion. They may contain matters researched and drafted by others. To the extent that this is done it is better for it to be under the experts' control, so that the experts can confidently speak to the reliability of the work of others that they incorporate in their report. The opinions expressed must be those of the expert, or adopted by the expert, who should make clear which is their own work and where they rely on others.

The systematic ordering of the report, in headed sections with numbered paragraphs, helps to make it digestible and assists in clarity when reference has to be made to its contents.

Opinion and fact should be clearly identified as such and kept separate from each other. Conclusions should be either at the end of the section to which they relate or be in the final section of the report, before any appendices, and refer to the text that supports them. Appendices should be used where and to the extent that putting the information into an appendix rather than into the body of a report helps make the report readable and easy to follow.

It is often useful for each part of the report to be cross-referenced to each related part. This is particularly necessary where appendices are used. Each appendix should be clearly titled.

The first step in preparing the report is to marshal the facts. Once this is done, the issues should be reviewed to see if proceeding to a formal report is worthwhile. There is no point in writing a report for a claimant if, on a plain study of the facts, an expert's report would not help to substantiate the claim. It would be better to advise the claimant of this as early as it becomes apparent – so avoiding, as far as reasonably practicable, abortive costs in writing unhelpful reports.

The facts on which the writer relies should be clearly set out and distinguished as follows:

- first-hand knowledge – that is, information that the author of the report has by their own observations, i.e. site inspection, laboratory test, etc.;
- hearsay or second-hand knowledge – that is, matters of which the report's author has been informed but which they have not verified by their own direct observations;
- the results of investigations, experiments, tests, etc. carried out for the report's author at their request or under their direction;
- assumed facts on which the report's author has relied;
- established authorities, including the opinions of others, which the expert has adopted or which have influenced the expert's opinion.

Not all who, because of their expertise, are appointed as witnesses are skilled writers. Expert's reports often confuse direct observation, hearsay and opinion, use obscure language and run to unnecessary length.

For civil litigation a judicial committee[133] has produced a model for experts' reports.[134] While this is offered as a framework, it is not a standard to which experts are required to comply; it is intended as a guideline for expert's reports in all areas, not especially building. Its format is informed by the experience of lawyers who have had to read and use expert's reports, and, as such, offers a useful insight to those drafting such reports. It can be adapted for each individual task, and additional sections can be introduced at need.

Format

The report may have to be copied several times. To facilitate this, single-side printing on A4 sheets, punched and bound in ring binders or the like, is often preferred. If fully bound copies are required, the front cover should be transparent or should be the first page of the report. It is not helpful to obscure the report with an opaque cover.

The source of the facts on which experts rely in preparing their evidence should be given each time a fact is introduced. For example, if experts have been asked to assume something as fact, they might say *'I am instructed that...'*. Whereas, if the experts have relied on something they read in the contemporaneous documents they might say *'I understand from A's letter to B of such a date that...'*.

Experts' first-hand observations – e.g. the results of experiments, investigations etc. carried out by the experts themselves – should be distinguished from facts which others, acting on behalf of the experts, observed. In this latter case those assisting the expert should be identified.

If experts draw on the opinions of others in forming their own opinions they should refer to the sources on which they rely. Any written authority consulted by the expert should be stated, and the text cross-referenced to any rules, regulations or other published material which supports their conclusions. Matters of fact should be referred to so far as may be necessary to the understanding of the opinion.

Photographs

Depending on the type of dispute the following may be advisable:

- Photograph all work as it stands, showing the overall context of the building or engineering work as well as the detail of the areas in dispute.
- Keep a full set of record photographs of any investigation or exposure work. If remedial work commences before the dispute is settled, keep photographic records of the progress of the works including any defects exposed.
- Immediately photographs are printed (if film cameras are used) note, on the reverse of the print, the name of the photographer, the date the photograph was taken and the subject of the photograph.
- Give each photograph incorporated into the report a unique number.
- Provide a plan showing the position from which each photograph was taken and the direction in which the photographer was facing. This can often usefully be combined with a plan on which the locations of the defects are shown.

Drawings, etc.

Depending on the issues being dealt with, drawings can help explain the matters the expert addresses. Drawings showing the nature of each defect, alongside or overlaid with drawings showing the correct construction which would have prevented each defect occurring in the first place, are particularly effective.

If full drawn details of the proposed remedial works are not required, diagrammatic illustrations can assist in explaining the expert's proposals.

Schedules

It often necessary to itemise the costs of remedial works. A schedule of priced works is a useful format for this. It may also be useful to summarise defects in schedule form. If cost and defects schedules are developed into Scott schedules (see Chapter 6), this is usually kept separate from the expert's report.

Experts' report contents

First page

The first visible sheet should contain key information as follows:

Status: e.g. *'preliminary draft'*, *'final report'*, etc. as appropriate. It is advisable to label each copy issued before the report is finalised, 1st draft, 2nd draft, etc., so that the final copy can be simply be *'final'* or just *'report'*. If the report is *'private'*, *'confidential'* or written *'in contemplation of litigation'* it is useful to say so. If it is written after litigation is commenced, the case reference may be quoted.

Report of: name of author(s).

On: describe or name the building or project being considered, e.g. new office and warehouse at 11 Road Street, New City.

Dated: give the date of issue, revised each time the report is amended, updated, etc.

Specialist field: state the areas of expertise of the author(s), e.g. architecture, civil engineering, etc.

On behalf of: give the name of the client commissioning the report.

On the instructions of: give the name and office of the person from whom the expert received formal instructions to write the report. This is usually the instructing solicitor but need not be, particularly if the dispute is not in litigation.

Report subject: give a concise statement of the issues in dispute, e.g. the alleged defective workmanship in the construction of a new tiled roof.

Inspection dates: state the dates on which the building was inspected.

Address: give the expert's business address and contact details.

Second page

For long and complex reports, give a brief synopsis stating what is covered by the report and the conclusions drawn.

Third page

List the contents of the body of the report and of appendices. Where appropriate, list illustrations, tables, photographs, diagrams, etc. (for brief reports – say about half-a-dozen pages – this may be omitted) .

The body of the report

This can usefully be divided into sections, which may typically include some or all of the following: introduction, surveys/inspections, discussion, opinion and appendices.

Section 1: Introduction

This part of the report is factual only; no opinion should be expressed in it. It explains to the reader the value, purpose and scope of the report.

Foreword: Give the experts' qualifications and experience. This should draw out the relevance of their expertise to the special technical aspects of the matters in dispute as well as reviewing in general terms their practical and academic background. It is important to establish that the expert is an authority on matters contained in the report, so that appropriate weight will be given to their views. Where applicable, describe those who have assisted in the preparation of the report. Full details of the personnel are better set out in an appendix, not in the body of the report.

Instructions: The expert should state briefly what they have been asked to do, e.g. to identify the issues within their area of expertise that arise in this case, to make a technical investigation and to express their opinion with full reasons on each issue. It is desirable for the instructions to be in writing and for a copy of the instructions to be appended to the report.

Scope of the report: State the information on which the report is based, i.e. the instructions received, the documents reviewed, site inspections, laboratory tests, etc. The general nature of the investigations carried out should be set out concisely, stating what has been done and, where relevant, the limits to the investigations on which the expert relies, e.g.:

> *This report is based on a reading of the documents made available to me on a single site visit. I have made no destructive or invasive investigations. This report is limited to a consideration of the defects set out in the statement of claim. Defects other than those covered in this report may exist and this report should not be taken to be an exhaustive account of the defects in the building.*

(Note: the documents made available to the expert should be identified – either in this paragraph or listed in the appendix)

Background: This may sometimes be part of the introduction, a separate section or contained in an appendix. Give the history of the defect or dispute. The relevant parties should be set out briefly in short itemised paragraphs, giving their role in the relevant events.

Assumed facts: The facts (if any) the expert has been asked to assume, or which they have for other reasons assumed, should be set out in short itemised paragraphs.

Matters to be addressed: Set out the issues that are to be dealt with. Identify, in short itemised paragraphs, each of the allegations and issues that the expert is asked to address. Where appropriate cross-reference each item to the case papers.

Disclosure of interests: State any association or acquaintance between the expert and the parties to the dispute or others involved in the building project, whether or not these might cause a conflict of interest. For example:

> *I have previously invited the Claimant to quote for carrying out building work on projects that are wholly unrelated to the subject matter of this report. In doing this I have made general enquiries into the quality of the Claimant's work. I have*

not otherwise, prior to being appointed to write this report, any knowledge of the parties involved in this dispute or of the building project to which it relates. The opinions expressed in this report are not influenced by my prior knowledge of the claimant company.

Section 2 – Surveys, investigations, tests and research

This section of the report is factual only, containing statements of the investigations carried out and the results obtained. No opinion should be expressed. Bear in mind that interpretation of test results, site observations etc. involves opinion, and thus goes beyond factual reporting.

Depending on the length of the report it may be better to describe the investigations in separate technical reports. These can then be referred to as appropriate in the body of the expert's report and appended to it. Alternatively, if the reporting of investigations is minor or incidental it may be a sub-section within the introduction. Supportive documents, such as survey sheets, may in any event be better appended than inserted into the body of the report. There is no hard-and-fast rule; it is a question of what makes the report easiest to follow.

The full range of enquiries or inspections should be stated in simple, factual, succinct paragraphs giving:

- the date, time, place and method of investigation;
- details of who carried out the investigations and who witnessed them; and
- simple factual statements of what was found, without interpretation or embellishment.

It is desirable to avoid mixing second- or third-hand hearsay with evidence gained by direct observation. This is not an inflexible rule. An independent investigation of defects almost always benefits from the judicious use of contemporaneous reported observations of those who first noted the defects, and the memories of those involved in the building project. The reliability of hearsay should be tested where reasonably practicable, and its sources stated in the report. Contemporaneous written records may be preferred over uncorroborated memory. An expert familiar with the way building projects are customarily carried out will recognise the abnormal and extraordinary in hearsay evidence, and know where to focus doubt and enquire further.

Section 3 – Discussion

This is the link between the facts on which experts rely and the conclusions they draw. It allows the expert to set out their reasoning and to explain, where relevant, the matters on which they are expert. This should assist the lay reader to assess the level of confidence to be placed on the expert's assessment of matters, and assist other experts to identify any flaws in the report. The need for, and extent of, this section depends on the complexity of the matters addressed. A separate discussion section is not included in many expert reports, and on some views it is unnecessary.

If the report deals with a technically complex aspect of a building, set out the basic principles on which it is supposed to work. The discussion may typically cover the following:

- The alternative possible causes of the defects, etc. A process of elimination is often helpful. Each cause can be examined in turn, in relation to the available evidence. This can provide grounds for eliminating some causes and evaluating the probable effect of each of the remaining causes.
- The responsibilities of the parties may be similarly reviewed, where this is within the expert's brief. Where remedial measures are to be considered the options should be reviewed and explained.
- At all stages the reasoning behind any opinion which experts give as a result of their examination of the facts should be clearly expressed.

Section 4 – Opinion

Conclusions: To the extent that the instructions require, conclusions should be drawn – based on the matters set out in the forgoing discussions – as to:

- the causes of the defects, etc.;
- remedies for the defects; and
- liabilities and responsibilities for the defects.

This should relate to the issues to be addressed, as set out in the introductory section of the report. The arguments for and against the conclusions drawn should be explored at appropriate length in the discussion section, and the reasoning adopted made clear before coming to a conclusion. On some views, the discussion section can be left out and the reasoning and conclusions combined. For short reports and simple matters this can make following an expert's reasoning simpler.

Recommendations: Where it forms part of their instructions, experts should set out their recommendations for remedying the defects. Where remedial works are to be fully detailed by the expert, it may be better for the remedial works documents to be prepared separately and appended – and the remedial works referred to, in summary form, in the body of the report. Where the investigations are to some extent inconclusive, the recommendations should include such further investigations as the expert considers advisable.

Expert's declaration:

Following the Wolf reforms, experts are expected to include a signed declaration in their reports. The declaration should form part of the body of the report and is most commonly placed between the end of the report and the expert's signature. At its minimum it needs to say: *'This report includes everything which I regard as being relevant to the opinions which I have expressed in it and I have drawn to the attention of the court any matter which would affect the validity of my opinions.'*

By reference to CPR the following statements can be seen to be desirable in a report prepared for litigation in England and Wales:

> *I understand my duty to the Court and have complied, and will continue to comply, with that duty.* [CPR Rule 35.10(2) and Paragraph 2.2(9) of the Practice Direction 35 CPR];

> *I confirm that insofar as the facts stated in my report are within my own knowledge I have made clear which they are and I believe them to be true, and that the opinions I have expressed represent my true and complete professional opinion.* [Paragraphs 2.3 and 2.4 of Practice Direction 35 CPR.]

The Academy of Experts provides a model which can be followed if desired.

Appendices

The form and content of the appendices can be adjusted as necessary to suit each report. Where it is necessary to be able to look at pages of the appendix whilst reading the main body of the report, they should be bound separately from the report.

Typically, copies of the documents to which reference has been made should be exhibited in the appendix. These may include extracts from contemporaneous documents and written authorities. The documents exhibited should not be altered or marked in any way. Due regard should be given to copyright when copying other people's work.

It is usual to exhibit a copy of the letter(s) of instruction and of the expert's curriculum vitae.

For short or simple reports, illustrations and photographs can be incorporated in the body of the report. Otherwise these should be set out in appendices and clearly cross-referenced to the text.

Copies should be appended of such technical reports, surveys, drawings, site notes, photographs, etc. as have been referred to in the body of the expert's report.

Experts' reports checklist

Experts' reports must be seen to be objective. Expert witnesses are not advocates for their instructing parties and, even where technical advocacy is involved, disinterested objectivity is more persuasive than perceptibly biased argument.

Experts should aim above all for clarity, and start from readily comprehended principles:

- Write for an ordinary, reasonably intelligent layperson, not for close study by a fellow expert.
- Develop the report in a format required for a trial.
- A single report for each party, amalgamating the work of all their experts, is preferred.
- Supplemental reports should, if possible, be incorporated as amendments to the main report.
- Reports should be dated and clearly headed, and the date and nature of each amendment and addition indicated at the front.
- An index/contents page should be provided for long reports.
- The report should be divided into headed sections and numbered paragraphs, with sub-headings for long reports.
- For very long reports, a short summary of the purpose, content and conclusions of the report should be provided.
- Where reference is made to a Scott schedule (see Chapter 6), the items in the schedule need not be repeated in full but the schedule should be appended.
- The report should be written in the first person singular, stating where evidence is obtained from others.

---

[116] J. Saunders, 1553, in *Buckley* v *Rice-Thomas* [1554] Plowden 118, Court of Common Bench, 6 ConLR 117.

[117] *Folks* v *Chadd* [1782] 3 Doug KB 157.

[118] *James Pennycook Davie* v *The Lord Provost, Magistrates and Councillors of the City of Edinburgh*, AC: 999052, First Division [1953] SC 34.

[119] Refer to Section 3 of the Civil Evidence Act.

[120] The 'evidence-in-chief' is the term used to describe the evidence witnesses went to court to state, in line with their written witness statements.

[121] Court Procedure Rules, R 35.3(2).

[122] Order 40, rule 1.

[123] Court Procedure Rules, R 35.3(2).

[124] *Sutcliffe* v *Thackrah and others* [1974] AC727, 1 All ER 319.

[125] *Hall* v *Simons* [2000] 3 WLR 543.

[126] *Stanton* v *Callaghan* [1999] 2 WLR 745.

[127] *Palmer and Another* v *Durnford (A firm) and David J. Neve* [1992] 2 WLR 407.

[128] See Chapter 6 on 'Reports' in general, and below for expert's reports.

[129] *National Justice Compania Naviera SA* v *Prudential Assurance Company Ltd* ('Ikarian Reefer') [1993] Times Law Report, 5 March 1993, 2 Lloyds' Reports 68.

[130] *Whitehouse* v *Jordan* [1981] 1 WLR 246, 256, per Lord Wilberforce.

[131] *Polivitte Ltd* v *Commercial Union Assurance Co plc* [1987] 1 Lloyd's Rep 379, 386, per Mr Justice Garland, and *Re J* [1990] FCR 193, per Mr Justice Cazalet.

132 *Derby & Co Ltd and Others* v *Weldon and Others*; AC: 999997 [1990], Times Law Reports 9 November 1990 p. 34, per Lord Justice Staughton.

133 In 1989 the Lord Chancellor approved the formation of the Judicial Committee consisting of seven senior judges representing the English, Scottish and Northern Irish Benches. The Committee members were: The Rt Hon The Lord Slynn of Hadley (Chairman); The Rt Hon Lord Justice Neill, Court of Appeal; The Rt Hon Lord Justice Saville, Court of Appeal; The Rt Hon Lord Justice MacDermott, Supreme Court of Judicature, Northern Ireland; The Hon Lord Prosser, Court of Session, Scotland; The Hon Mr Justice Garland, Queens Bench Division; His Honour Judge Bowsher, QC Official Referees Court; Julian Cohen, Secretary to the Committee.

134 The Model Form of Expert's Report has been prepared by the Judicial Committee to further assist experts and their clients by indicating a format that the judiciary would find of assistance (a 'judge-friendly' format). A model form of expert report is published by the Academy of Experts in their members' handbook.

Liability – Insurance and Limitation

Insurance

It is useful to have an understanding of any insurances which may be in place. Where the cost of correcting defects is underwritten by insurers, both insured and claimant need to be aware of what is covered, which policies apply and how to proceed.

> A housing estate was developed by a well-known UK house builder. They contracted a general builder who in turn subcontracted each part of the work. A fault occurred in the groundworks. A process of investigation was started, partly to establish the remedy but also to discover how the work went wrong.
>
> The house builders were insured for certain risks.
>
> The geotechnical surveys had been commissioned from specialist surveyors who were insured for such work.
>
> The consultant designers had professional indemnity cover.
>
> The general builders had separate professional indemnity and all-risks cover.
>
> The subcontractor held a combined insurance policy.
>
> All agreed that whoever was at fault, repair was covered by insurance. The problem was knowing which insurances to call upon. To identify the appropriate insurance policy, the delinquent actions which led to the damage had to be established in as much detail as would have been required had the matter been settled by High Court litigation between uninsured parties.

Insurance can attract claims. There is no point entertaining the cost of litigation or arbitration unless funds are available. The well-insured are, from that point of view, worth pursuing. Learned counsel, for example, when hired to pursue a claim, may well focus on the deficiencies in an insured architect's performance rather than on the culpability of the poorly funded and uninsured builder.

There are various types of insurance which may come into play:

Single-project insurance

One approach to the inevitable risk of something going wrong on a building project is to insure against the risk. The parties to a project can collectively enter a contract of insurance. Such 'single-project insurance' could obviate the need to allocate blame and prove culpability – whoever is to blame, the insurer picks up the bill. However, where an insurer has to pay for a building failure the insurance company may investigate the cause of loss and seek to recover from those responsible. The insurer then takes the place of the injured party and must establish cause and effect, as would the injured party had the insurance not been in place.

An alternative is for the employer to seek single-project insurance in their own name. If defects arise, they may call on their insurer to foot the bill for remedy. The insurer may then seek redress from the delinquent members of the project team.

Individual elements may be subject to insurance-backed warranties which are written specifically for the project. These insurances are more limited in scope than, but otherwise similar in intent to, full single-project insurance. Such policies are typically limited to covering specific matters only and are likely to stipulate what must be done if a fault is found. Failure to follow the rules set out in the policy may invalidate the warranty.

The following example is taken from a warranty written for a project where the law of the contract was that of England and Wales, the warranted product was manufactured by a firm in the USA and the work was carried out in Europe but outside the EU. It had therefore to be written with an eye to the legislation in three different jurisdictions. The incorporated terms illustrate what is typically covered in such documents.

The first section names the parties to this agreement and states the scope of the works it covers:

---

12 Year Weatherproofing Warranty

THIS WARRANTY is made this day of . . . . between . . . . of . . . . ("the Contractor") and . . . . of . . . . ("the Employer").

WHEREAS
  1 *The Employer has entered into a construction contract dated . . . . with the Contractor whereby certain repair works are to be undertaken to . . . . ("the Construction Contract").*
  2 *The Contractor is to undertake certain works including the weatherproofing works – namely the repair or replacement of the roof, the supply and installation of over-cladding and the replacement of certain windows, which works and the works ancillary thereto are defined in the Construction Contract ("the Envelope Works").*
  3 *It is a condition of the Construction Contract that the Contractor enter into this warranty.*

The next section sets out the detail of the warranty given:

> *Now it is hereby agreed as follows:*
>
> *1 The Contractor will install the over-cladding as described in the Specification and defined in the Construction Contract ("the Cladding System"), in accordance with the manufacturer's current published application instructions, specifications and details for the Cladding System. All designs, materials, methods and uses of the Cladding System will have the approval of the manufacturers.*
> *2 The Contractor warrants that for a period of 12 years, from the date of substantial completion of the Envelope Works (hereinafter referred to as the "Warranty Period") that the Envelope Works*
>   *(i)   will meet the requirements of the Specification in all respects and will be installed using good and proper workmanship and using materials that are fit for their purpose;*
>   *and in the case of the Cladding System*
>   *(ii) will function as an air barrier and*
>   *(iii) will perform suitably as a weather barrier.*

What is excluded from the warranty is then stated:

> *3 No warranty is made whatsoever for any damage caused in whole or part by any of the following:*
>   *(a) Acts of God, or natural phenomena, such as but not limited to falling objects, fire, earthquakes, etc.*
>   *(b) Architectural, engineering, or other deficiencies in the design of elements, other than the Envelope Works, where such deficiencies are outside of the Contractor's control.*
>   *(c) Failures of the substrate, where such design or failure is outside of the Contractor's control other than those movements and cracks referred to in the Specification.*
>   *(d) Damage or injury not solely and directly caused by a failure of the Envelope Works as installed by the Contractor to perform as warranted.*
>   *(e) Defects in the Envelope Works which are a consequence of matters clearly outside of the Contractor's control; inter alia vandalism, physical damage by residents, change of use of the structure, water penetration from any other source than through the Envelope Works are not covered by this warranty.*

The warrantor's obligations and rights in respect of repair or replacement and the limits of their liability under this warranty are then stated:

> 4 The Contractor warrants that defects in the Envelope Works shall be repaired or replaced (at its option and cost).
> 6 The Contractor undertakes promptly to make such repairs or replacements as are necessary in order to return the Envelope Works to their originally specified standard. All costs of inspection, testing, investigation, repair or replacement and associated access by the Contractor or others on their behalf will be paid for by the Contractor. No other expenses or charges will be permitted.
> 7 The Contractor shall be allowed a reasonable period of time and authorisation to take samples in order to perform any testing which the Contractor deems necessary to investigate and determine the cause of the alleged defects.

There is usually a provision requiring timeous notice to be given to the warrantor by the warrantee and stipulations with regard to such matters as routine maintenance and emergency repair:

> 8 The Contractor shall not have any obligation under this Warranty, unless the Employer notifies the Contractor in writing at the above address within thirty days of discovery by the Employer of the alleged defects.
> 9 Where practical, the owner shall effect temporary repairs to mitigate any consequential or further damage, which may arise out of the defects, until the cause of the problem is determined and permanent repair recommendation made.

It is sometimes necessary to include as a beneficiary of the warranty the end user or subsequent owners, etc. and therefore to deal with the transferability of the benefits:

> 10 This Warranty is issued to .... and .... only. It may not be transferred or assigned, except to a subsequent owner or management company, without the written approval of the Contractor.

Whilst a general disclaimer is common, any attempt to restrict liability has to contend with local law and with the terms of the contract to which the warranty relates. The disclaimer below may prove less robust than it appears on a bare reading of the words:

> 11 This constitutes the entire Warranty agreement, for the installation of the Envelope Works. Except for the warranties expressly stated above, the Contractor does not make any other warranties express or implied, and disclaims any implied warranties of merchantability, or fitness for purpose.

The above warranty dealt with the contractor's liability. There was a comparable supplier's warranty in the following terms. The two warrantees were written together to ensure that the contractor's obligations stood back-to-back with the manufacturer's obligations. Again, the first part of the warranty sets out the parties to the agreement and the scope of the cover:

12 Year Limited Materials Warranty

. . . . . of . . . .
(hereinafter referred to as "the Cladding System Supplier") hereby warrants that

. . . . .
. . . . .
. . . . .

(hereinafter referred to as the "Cladding Products"), manufactured and/or sold by the Cladding System Supplier or its authorised distributor shall be free from manufacturing defects at the time of sale. The Cladding System Supplier further warrants that for a period of twelve (12) years from the date of substantial completion of the application of the Cladding Products (hereinafter referred to as the "Warranty Period"), that the Cladding Products, when installed by the Cladding System Supplier's authorised Contractor in accordance with the Cladding System Supplier's current published application instructions, specifications and details for the Cladding System:

(i)   will not lose their bond, peel, flake or chip and will meet the requirements of the Specification as defined in the Contract between . . . . and . . . . dated . . . . , in all respects;
(ii) will prevent water penetration into the cavity of the wall, so long as the surface integrity of the Cladding Products are maintained;
(iii) will function as an air barrier; and
(iv) will perform suitably as a weather barrier.

The warranty then sets out what is excluded;

It is specifically agreed and understood that no warranty whatsoever is made with respect to any materials other than the Cladding Products specifically identified above, even if such other materials are used in the installation of the Cladding Products unless and to the extent that the other products have been used with the knowledge and approval of the Cladding System Supplier.

Further, no warranty is made whatsoever for any damages caused in whole or in part by any of the following:

> (a) Acts of God or natural phenomena, such as but not limited to falling objects, fire, earthquakes, floods, tornadoes, hurricanes or pests; unusual air pollution or chemical fumes in the atmosphere;
> (b) Architectural, engineering, or other design deficiencies by any party other than the Cladding System Supplier unless such design has been approved by the Cladding System Supplier;
> (c) Failure of the substrates other than those movements and cracks referred to in paragraph . . . of the Specification;
> (d) Defective or improper workmanship by the Contractor in installing the Cladding Products or failure on the part of the Contractor to follow the Cladding System Supplier's current published application instructions, specifications or details;
> (e) Nor for other damage or injury not solely and directly caused by a failure of the Cladding Products to perform as warranted hereunder.
>
> This warranty shall be void, and the Cladding System Supplier will make no warranties whatsoever with respect to the Cladding Products if they are intermixed with other chemicals or materials not specifically required by the Cladding System Supplier, or if there is a substitution of any of the components included in the Cladding Products.

It is usual for a supplier to seek to restrict their warranties to the replacement of their defective products and to exclude any incidental or consequential damage. The duty and rights of the warrantee and warrantor in the event of a claim are usually set out. The extent and detail varies greatly between warranties, and that set out here is of average length and detail:

> The Cladding System Supplier shall not be responsible for incidental or consequential damages of any kind. The sole responsibility and liability of the Cladding System Supplier under this warranty shall be to repair or replace, at its option and by a Contractor selected by it, the Cladding Products shown to be defective during the Warranty Period. The Cladding System Supplier shall undertake to make such repairs or replacement as are necessary in order to return the Cladding Products to the originally specified standard. All costs of inspection, testing, investigation, repair or replacement and associated access by the Cladding System Supplier or others on their behalf will be paid for by the Cladding System Supplier. No other expenses or charges will be permitted.
>
> The Cladding System Supplier shall not have any obligation under this warranty unless the owner notifies the Cladding System Supplier in writing at the above address within thirty (30) days of discovery by . . . . or . . . . of the

> *alleged defect(s). The Cladding System Supplier shall be allowed a reasonable period of time and authorisation to remove samples in order to perform any testing the Cladding System Supplier deems necessary to investigate and determine the cause of the defect. The owner shall cause temporary repairs to be made if necessary to avoid further damage until the cause of the problem is determined and permanent repair recommendations can be made.*

The full extent of those benefiting from the warranty and the transferability of these benefits is usually set out at the end, along with any general disclaimers. Again, the disclaimers are subject to the applicable laws, which may limit their effect, and have to be considered alongside the warrantor's obligations under their contract of supply (and, in this case, of design):

> *This warranty is issued to . . . . and to . . . . and may not be transferred or assigned except to a subsequent owner of the structure upon written notice to the Cladding System Supplier.*
>
> *This constitutes the entire warranty agreement for the Cladding Products and its components. Except for the warranties expressly stated above, the Cladding System Supplier does not make any other warranties expressed or implied and the Cladding System Supplier expressly disclaims any implied warranties of merchantability or fitness for a particular purpose.*
>
> *This warranty shall be governed by and interpreted under the laws of . . . .*

An insurance policy was taken out to back these warranties. As the warranties ran alongside the building contract and contract of supply, the insurers had not only to satisfy themselves that the warranties were in acceptable terms but also that the terms contained in the related contracts were acceptable. In doing this they had to take into account the relevant national laws. The work was then subject to regular periodic inspection by the insurer. The contractor undertook during the construction period to correct any defects discovered by the insurer in the insured work as and when they were brought to the contractor's attention.

It is common practice for insurers underwriting these types of cover to pay independent inspectors to check both design and site work. These inspections may, at the outset, evaluate risk and assist the insurer in setting a suitable premium. Thereafter they may check for compliance with certain standards, and the cover may lapse if deficiencies in the standards required by the policy are found.

Where the finished work is flawed and a claim made on the insurance, the insurers may then look to the competence of the inspectors they employed and contemplate recovering their losses by way of claims for negligence.

Professional indemnity insurance

Where there is more than one culpable party, each of whom has materially contributed to the causes of the damage, blame is customarily apportioned between them pro rata to their contribution to the damage. This may be in the form of joint and several liabilities. Thus, for example, where an employer claims the designers and builder are jointly responsible for defective work the court may decide that the project engineer is 20 per cent to blame, the project architect 20 per cent to blame, and the builder is 60 per cent to blame. With individual liabilities, the employer would have to obtain compensation proportionately from each culpable party. In the case of joint and several liability, the employer could pursue any of them for any sum up to the full amount of awarded damages, subject only to the total obtained not exceeding the damages awarded. This is useful if one of the culpable parties is under-funded and thus unable to pay their contribution in full.

In a similar way, the contribution to the damage caused by the claimant can be taken into account. This may arise with, for example, a claim for poor workmanship which could, and ought to have, been picked up on inspection by the employer's in-house inspectors. Some of the blame may be apportioned, through the inspectors, to the employer thus effectively reducing their claim on the builder.

This is normally taken into account in contracts and warranties for those carrying professional indemnity insurance. It is customary for professionals to limit their liability to that which they would have if all others involved were given similar indemnities. Thus, for example, architects would seek to avoid liability for the work of engineers, even though they will adopt and incorporate into the building the engineers' designs. The following example clause follows fairly typical lines:

> *Further, the Warrantor's liability to the Employer under this agreement shall be limited to the proportion of the Employer's losses which it would be just and equitable to require of the Specialist having regard to the extent of the Specialist's responsibility for the same on the basis that all other contractors, suppliers and consultants shall, where appointed, be deemed to have provided to the Employer contractual undertakings in respect of their services and be deemed to have paid to the Employer such contribution as may be appropriate having regard to the extent of their responsibility for such loss or damage.*

Where claimants have contributed to the loss they have incurred, this will ordinarily be taken into account when damages are awarded. Each defendant's liability can be reduced proportionately to the claimant's contribution to the damage.

The way in which blame is apportioned is for the courts to decide – and this has, from time to time, caused professional indemnity insurers concern. A case which tested this principle, to the concern of architects' professional indemnity insurers, arose in January 1998 when a factory was destroyed by fire:[135]

The building owners were the claimants and the architects the defendants. The claimants contended that the fire damage had been caused, at least in part, by the defendants' negligence. The defendants denied liability and alleged contributory negligence on the claimants' part, because the fire had been caused by inappropriate use of the room in which it had started.

The owners conceded at the trial that they were 50 per cent responsible because they had caused the fire. The judge ruled that the contributory negligence was not relevant and found that the architects had been in breach of contract and breach of duty by failing to exercise reasonable skill in their designs and specifications in order to prevent the spread of fire.

The building complied with the fire regulations under the Building Act and the premises had a fire certificate.

The fire started in one room due to the owner's negligence but spread, because the room was not built in fire-resisting construction, to the rest of the building.

The fire had been started when oil was left in a bratt pan with a faulty thermostat, and the gas was left on. The experts agreed that the fire would not have occurred had the bratt pan been switched off and the thermostat been functioning correctly. Additionally, had the room been constructed as a fire compartment capable of containing a fire for one hour, the fire would not have spread outside that room. However, the room had not been built to such a specification and had not been protected by non-combustible panels.

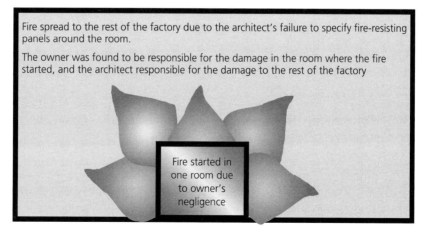

Fire spread to the rest of the factory due to the architect's failure to specify fire-resisting panels around the room.

The owner was found to be responsible for the damage in the room where the fire started, and the architect responsible for the damage to the rest of the factory

Fire started in one room due to owner's negligence

Figure 12.1: **Diagrammatic plan of fire damage to factory.**

The architects appealed, denying that they had been in breach of contract or had been negligent. Alternatively, they argued that if they were liable to building owners in principle, the judge had been wrong not to take into account this building owner's contributory negligence.

The judge had held that the architects had been in breach of their duty in failing to advise the owners to fit fire-resistant panels. The issue in the appeal was whether the architects should have given that advice.

The question of the architects' negligence revolved around whether they should have carried out a proper risk assessment and, from this, recommended the use of fire-resistant panels. It was found that they had not, despite prudent advice from the specialist subcontractor and that, if they had, they should have recommended fire-resisting construction – and that the owners would have accepted this recommendation if made.

The decision on contributory negligence was changed at appeal. It was argued that the owners contributed to the design in that they participated in the risk assessment leading to the decision not to use fire-resisting construction. It was accepted on appeal that the owners' production director had wrongly advised the architects that the room was used for steam cooking and that he did this in breach of a duty of care. It was held that the owners were guilty of contributory negligence and the award against the architects reduced accordingly.

It is necessary to take into account the potentially imprudent behaviour of building users. This was brought home by the findings in a claim for a domestic injury:

Ten pints of beer were drunk by a Denbigh man before he tried to change a light bulb, fell down the stairs and injured his spine. The bulb was positioned over the top of the stairs, rather than the landing.

Judge Derek Halbert ruled at Chester Crown Court that, although the injured man had to take 50 per cent responsibility, Denbighshire County Council, which owned the house, and the electrical contractor, which installed the fitting in 1988 each had to take 25 per cent responsibility. The main contractor did not have to pay.

Product insurance

Technological developments make reliance on design advice from manufacturers, suppliers and specialist contractors increasingly necessary. Employers all too readily look to the insurance policies of the traditional design consultants. It would be advisable for these consultants, where they rely on specialist advice obtained from others, to advise on the need for each party to hold suitable insurance cover.

Figure 12.2: **Designers may have to allow for drunken or foolhardy behaviour when making provision for routine maintenance of the buildings they design.**

Suppliers are more likely to have insurance against the risk of their products being found not to be fit for purpose than for design. Thus, where a supplier is brought into the design process, it would be advisable to check that suitable insurance is in place.

A difficulty with a supplier and their insurers has recently arisen because of the supplier's contribution to the design of a building.

The product they supplied was not fit for its purpose because it was wrongly selected, not because it was badly made or due to faults in the materials used. The supplier had been involved in the design development and, through the advice they gave, had directly caused the error in selection of the component they supplied. Their insurance did not provide indemnity for errors in the design of the buildings which used their products but would indemnify them for errors in the design of the products themselves. The sum in dispute is large and the supplier is resisting the claim because his insurance is inappropriate. Had the nature of their insurance been looked into earlier, appropriate insurance cover could have been obtained.

Insurances within building contracts

Insurances required under building contracts may cover many forms of risk. The most basic is cover for the works, as they progress, from ordinary perils.

To the extent that the contracting parties are compensated through insurance for problems arising from defects, defects are less likely to provoke disputes leading to litigation, etc.

The JCT standard forms of contract illustrate the typical situation where all-risks cover is specified.[136] They give the meaning of insurance on an all-risks basis as follows:

Insurance which provides cover against any physical loss or damage to work executed and site materials and against the reasonable cost of the removal and disposal of debris and of any shoring and propping of the Works which results from such physical loss or damage but excluding the cost necessary to repair, replace or rectify:

Wear and tear
Obsolescence
War risks
Nuclear risks
Deterioration, rust or mildew
Sonic bang
Inventory losses
Northern Ireland terrorist exclusion
Defective design.

The exclusion of defective design limits the form of design cover required.

Policies offered by insurers vary, making it necessary to accept variations to the insurance cover set out in the contract terms, depending on what is commercially available at the time the insurance is required.[137]

For new-build work, the contractor is usually required to take out a policy in joint names for all-risks insurance on both the works and site materials. As an option, the employer may take out this insurance. In either case, the employer pays; the only question is whether they pay directly or through the building contract. Employers are more certain that cover is maintained if they buy the policy.

For alteration of or extension to existing buildings, the employer/principal can take out joint-names building and contents insurance (under the JCT standard forms, this is limited to certain 'specified perils')[138] and a joint-names all-risks cover for the contract works and site materials.[139] The JCT approach is for this insurance to cover the employer and main contractor, and to include (nominated) subcontractors – either as joint policyholders or, by waiver of subrogation rights,[140] in respect of the range of specified perils.[141] Insurance against delay to completion can also be included under some forms of contract.[142]

Legal-costs cover

A robust way of deterring claims is to take out insurance for the cost of litigating over defective works, rather that for the cost of correcting them. Such insurance has the advantage of allowing the insured to deal vigorously with vexatious claims. Many claims achieve some success just because it is potentially more expensive to defend that to settle. Letting a claimant know that they are facing someone with legal-costs insurance is likely to discourage the claimant from pursuing a weak or dubious claim in the hope of an early out-of-court settlement.

Building insurance

Sometimes the cost of remedying building defects can be obtained from building insurers. It depends entirely on the terms of the policy, which will generally cover actual rather than potential damage.

A roof, which had a deteriorating covering due to a defect in manufacture, was especially susceptible to high winds. After three separate windy occasions, each followed by an insurance claim for the reinstatement of the parts which had blown off, the underlying fault was established.

The building insurers had, under the policy, to accept liability for the wind damage but not for the manufacturing flaws which made wind damage more probable. Having learnt through experience of the propensity of this roof to suffer storm damage, they increased the insurance premium when the policy came up for renewal and contemplated refusing to renew it. Once the building owner had discovered the flaw in manufacture, he was in possession of a material fact which, under the terms of the insurance policy, he was obliged to disclose to the insurers.

There is clearly a distinction between a building component wearing out naturally and failure due to a defect. When seeking insurance cover it is necessary to be clear which eventualities are to be covered.

> Several school roofs in the USA failed in sub-zero temperatures within two or three years of the expiration of their ten-year warranty period. The contractor had assured his client that the roofs had service lives of 15–20 years.
>
> The roofing was in pvc sheets, which shattered in sub-zero temperatures. Pvc roofing contains plasticizer, as otherwise it would be rigid and lack the elasticity and plasticity required to accommodate movement without fracture.
>
> Plasticized pvc, to retain its flexibility, needs stabilisers and inhibitors – otherwise the volatile plasticizers will gradually be lost. These roofs failed after the expiration of the warranty period but sooner than expected, due to gradual plasticizer loss.
>
> The school board sought to recover from their insurers. The insurers accepted liability for consequential damage but not for the cost of replacing the defective roofs themselves, arguing that the loss did not arise from a fortuitous incident.[143] The insurers contended that the failure was inevitable at the time of construction, and therefore not covered by the policy.
>
> It was found, as a matter of fact, that failure was not inevitable – two such roofs having survived. Further, the terms of the policy did not expressly exclude liability in these circumstances.

Notification and compliance

Any insurance cover can be invalidated if its terms are not followed and the insurers notified as required.

It is common to many insurance policies that where the insurers become exposed to potential liability they reserve to themselves the right to take control of the conduct of any dispute and/or settlement procedures. Detail of how this is done varies from policy to policy, but it generally starts with a requirement that they be notified as soon as a potential claim becomes known to the insured. It is prudent for the insured to notify their insurers as soon as they become aware of a matter which could give rise to a claim against them, and to seek their insurer's approval before attempting to resolve the matter. For this reason, a cautious claimant may advise those against whom they intend to claim to notify their insurers.

For the same reason it may be prudent, when contemplating entering a contract for services or goods, to obtain evidence from the providers of the services, goods, etc. that they are insured. There is little, if any, purpose in a claim where successful prosecution does no more than bankrupt the defendant.

It is sometimes not enough merely to see that insurance is in place, it is important also to know what is covered by that insurance.

> An example of inappropriate insurance came to light when a major building-products manufacturer undertook the role of main contractor in remedial works to a refurbishment project. Their building system and materials had been used for the refurbishment work, but performance when finished was flawed. Believing the faults lay in the site work, not in their products, they undertook to confirm this to the building owner by implementing repairs.
>
> They ably set about correcting the installation. This done, the work failed. They had created an excellent test bed for a relatively new product. By minimising workmanship error and having full control over design and materials, they had ensured there was a full-sized example of their building system, which was correctly set up and exposed as intended to the elements. This was a much more robust way of evaluating the system than the laboratory tests and computer modelling upon which all had hitherto relied. The failures were limited and allowed specific flaws in the computer modelling to be identified, with benefits for the future development and use of the system.
>
> Although the failures following the remedial works were much less severe than had originally occurred, they were unacceptable to the building owner who brought a claim against the manufacturers. They turned to their insurers. Their insurance covered product quality and the design of the system – normally supplied under a contract of sale, not a contract for the supply of services. The insurer stated that, by taking on the role of main contractor, the manufacturer had extended their liability beyond the cover the insurers provided.
>
> To carry out the remedial work, they had engaged a quantity-surveying firm to act both as quantity surveyor and project manager. It turned out that although this firm held professional indemnity insurance this covered them for quantity surveying but not for project management. It was through their project-management services that the quantity surveyors had contracted to control the quality of the works. In dereliction of this duty they had failed to recognise bad workmanship, which negligence they compounded with commendable regularity by certifying monthly payments for faulty work. The quantity surveyor's professional indemnity insurers firmly stood aside when faced with a claim for negligence in project management.
>
> Following out-of-court settlements and substantial rejection of the claims against their product insurer and against the project manager's professional indemnity insurer, the manufacturers turned to their parent company, on whose research and development work they relied, and were finally successful in recovering a substantial part of their losses. This was largely due to being able to claim that the

> root of the failures which occurred arose from demonstrable negligence in research and development, for which risk the parent company was insured.

Under English law, the principle that a contract must not contain agreements which are contrary to law applies equally to a contract of insurance. This can cause insurers to have to pay out very much larger sums than they anticipated:

> A factory building was substantially damaged by fire, causing extensive collapse. The local authority required the reconstruction of the fire-damaged factory to comply fully with current Building Regulations. The factory had been partially demolished by the fire to ground level but parts of the structure were still largely intact. The building could – but for the Building Regulations – have been rebuilt, retaining the parts of the factory which were still intact, to the original standard of construction. This would have complied with the regulations current at the time the building was built but not those current at the time of the fire damage.
>
> The local authority pointed out that where a building was to be reconstructed from within eight metres of the ground the Building Regulations would apply to the whole of the fabric including the retained part, and that the retained part would have to be brought up to current Building Regulations standards. The result was, to all intents and purposes, that the factory had to be rebuilt as a brand new building.
>
> This increased the claim on the insurance by about £1m. The insurers, an American company, were not familiar with this peculiarity of English Building Regulations and had not foreseen, in setting the premium for the insurance, their exposure to this risk. They nevertheless could not insist that they had a right to limit cover to the cost of reconstruction to a standard below that required by statute and so accepted that they would have to pay for a new building which complied fully with the Building Regulations but which was otherwise the same as that which had been fire damaged.

Such requirements, if not properly considered, can lead to a building being under-insured, as the need to comply with current Building Regulations in reconstruction can increase the cost of reconstruction each time the regulations are upgraded. Thus, the cost of reinstating a damaged building can increase much more rapidly than would be calculated by reference to building-cost inflation only.

Personal and company liability

Individuals who are members of companies may, through their actions, create liabilities – both on the companies and on themselves. This is true also of individuals who work for partnerships.[144]

Insurance policies will generally be taken out by companies or partnerships rather than by individuals. These policies, which protect the companies or partnerships, will not necessarily automatically provide the same protection to the members of the companies and partnerships – whether they be principals, employees or owners.

For this reason, some professional organisations advise and/or require their members to be expressly covered by the insurances taken out by the organisations for whom they work. Even where this is in place, the insurance cover is unlikely to extend to protect individuals when acting in their own capacity rather than on behalf of their company, etc.

Therefore, professionals who give advice not in pursuit of a commission given to the organisation with which they work may expose themselves to liabilities for which the insurance taken out by the company or partnership offers no protection.

Limited liability

A registered company could be 'limited by guarantee' (a now-defunct designation) or 'limited by shares'. In either case, it will be what is commonly called a 'limited liability company'.

The members of a limited liability company have only limited liability for debts incurred by that company. They are not similarly protected in respect of criminal actions, where liability may attach both to the company and to its officers. For example, a breach of health and safety regulations may result in the company being fined or the employees responsible for the breach being punished, or both. Insurance to indemnify employees against fines imposed by the courts as punishments for criminal offences is not available.

The executive directors of a limited company gain some protection from liability whilst acting as employees of the company. The protection given to a design professional, such as an architect-director of a limited liability company, is unlikely to be all-embracing. Individuals may rely on the advice of an architect because they have confidence in that architect. They may engage the architect's services by contracting with that architect's limited company. Under such circumstances, the architect has a duty to both company and client.

There is a contractual relationship between the client and the company. If the architect, through negligence, caused a breach of that contract, the company, not the architect, would be liable to the client for that breach. However, the architect may have liabilities to the company under a contract of employment and to the client in tort.

Pre-estimated damages or agreed limits to liability

Where a genuine pre-estimate of the loss arising from a foreseeable breach of contract has been made and has been set out in the contract, this may determine the damages which are recoverable for a breach of the contract. This is common in building contracts in respect of the pre-estimates of the losses that will be caused by late completion. In the main forms of contract published by the JCT, this is customarily referred to as 'liquidated and ascertained damages' or LADs. LADs could be applied to other terms of a contract where a genuine pre-estimate of loss can be made for a foreseeable breach of the contract. The agreement to be bound by this pre-estimate of damages could then limit liability, just as the current LAD clauses in the JCT forms do in respect of late completion due to the builder's culpable delay.

Contracts for the supply of products, collateral warranties and contracts for professional services often seek to limit liability to agreed maximum sums. Unlike LADs, these do not prescribe the amount payable for a specific breach of contract – but they do put an upper limit on the liability of the supplier, manufacturer or service provider to pay damages to the purchaser or employer for any or all breaches of the contract.

Often, insurers require these limits. For example, architects with professional indemnity insurance, when asked to enter contracts or to sign collateral warranties, should confirm with their insurers that the proposed agreements do not cause them to extend their liability beyond that for which they are insured. One condition of their insurance will be a limit either to the amount they can claim in a period of insurance, or for each claim, or both. It is advisable for all ensured professionals to ensure that any warranty they give limits their liability to levels that do not exceed those for which they were insured.

A clause limiting liability to a predetermined maximum might run as follows:

> *The warrantor's liability for any expense, loss, cost or damage of any kind whatsoever whether direct, indirect or consequential arising out of any action or proceedings whether legal, as a result of an adjudication award under the Housing Grants, Construction and Regeneration Act 1996 or any other proceedings relating to the Construction Contract and this warranty will be limited to £.....(.............) or the total amount charged by the Warrantor in respect his works whichever is the greater. This limit of liability includes, but is not limited to, breach of contract, negligence, misrepresentation and breach of statute. This limitation is the total amount of liability arising from this warranty and the construction contract to which it relates.*

Statute of limitations

In the UK, there is a limit to how much time can pass before a claim can be brought to law. This is due to a statutory instrument called the Statute of Limitations. It is not open to contracting parties to 'contract-out' of these restrictions. However, if a defendant does not plead a limitation defence, a claim may proceed after it has been timed-out under this statute. The limitation periods are as follows:

- For simple contract (also referred to as a 'contract under hand'), that is an oral agreement or a written agreement which is not sealed or executed as a deed, action must be brought within six years of the cause of accrual of action.
- For a deed (or a contract under seal) action must be brought within 12 years of the cause of accrual of action.
- In the case of fraud, limitation shall not begin to run until discovery of fraud.
- For a claim under tort rather than contract the limitation period is three years from discoverability, with a 'longstop' of 12 years.

There are difficulties in seeking to circumvent the limitation period by bringing an action in tort instead of contract and the recoverable damages may be less due to the difficulty in recovering purely economic loss in a tortious action.

The 'cause of accrual of action' is the culpable action by one party to a contract which causes a loss to another party to the contract. For an architect, engineer and the like the cause of accrual of action may lie in negligent design carried out some time before site work starts. The defect may not come to light until after the building is completed. The period between these events, on a large project, may easily exceed six years.

The duty to review design

There is case law which suggests an architect or engineer has an ongoing duty to review their designs.

> The architect is under a continuing duty to check that his design will work in practice and to correct any errors which may emerge. It savours of the ridiculous for the architect to be able to say: 'True, my design was faulty but of course, I saw to it that the contractors followed it faithfully' and to be enabled on that ground to succeed in the action.[145]

There is authority that duration of the duty continues beyond practical completion until the works are truly complete.[146] (See Chapter 4 Practical completion.)

The extent of this duty is not set out in a statute but comes from precedent drawn from a number of decided cases. There is some debate as to whether this duty arises as a matter of course or due to a specific event during a project.

Archie, having designed a wall in 1990 which would not adequately resist driving rain, goes onto site in 1992 when the builder starts to construct the wall. The building is completed in 1995 and is subject to driving rain, which causes leaks in 1997.

When he goes on site, Archie sees his design being built and has an opportunity to recognise and correct his error but does not do so. This failure to correct his earlier error is a negligent action, in respect of which a claim for damages could be brought.

If it is seen as a renewal of his earlier error, it may be argued that the limitation period for a claim for the design error runs from 1992 not 1990. If it is a new and distinct error, there may be some difficulty in sustaining a worthwhile claim against him. Arguably, the new error cannot cause a loss, the loss already having been caused by the earlier negligence in design. The amount claimable for damages is based on the loss caused. Logically, the second error, however reprehensible, is not the cause of the loss for the negligent design and causes no additional loss because, at the time the second error was made, all of the loss was already an inevitable consequence of the earlier error and, if that earlier error had not been made, the second error could not exist.

Correcting a design error, apart from the additional work done by the designer, may not result in any loss if done early enough. A correctly designed wall may not cost more to build than an incorrectly designed one. Therefore, finding and correcting the error before the wall is built to an incorrect design may occasion no loss. Once construction is commenced, the cost of correcting the error is likely to increase as work progresses and to reach a maximum once the building is finished and occupied. If it is accepted that there is a continuing duty to review, delay in finding the error can be said to increase the loss.

The above example deals with the assumption that there is a deemed duty to review design, i.e. that this duty exists regardless of events and despite the silence of the designers' terms of appointment on this subject. It is as if the designers of buildings had some overriding duty to review their designs every day until construction was finished.

Often the symptoms of a defect might become apparent to the skilled observer during construction, despite no significant damage becoming apparent until later. Let us suppose, in the above example, that during construction there is a brief period of severe weather during which rain penetrates the wall and causes a delay to the application of internal finishes while it dries out. This delay is reported to Archie in accordance with the terms of the contract, and Archie has to consider extending the contract period accordingly.

His attention has now been firmly drawn to an event which, if properly considered, would alert him to the deficiency in the wall's capabilities. He now has a compelling reason to look into the problem, irrespective of whether it arose in bad design, workmanship or materials. No doubt we would expect any competent architect to require the defects to be corrected if he found the wall's poor performance to be due to faulty materials or workmanship. It would be difficult to argue that his duty to address this problem was in any way lessened if he found the wall, built exactly as he designed it, was incapable of adequate performance. This would allow the argument that the cause of accrual of action occurred when he was effectively put on notice of the need to review his design and failed to do so.

The above considerations apply to designers who have some duty to supervise the implementation of their designs. It is probable that any architect or engineer who visits site during construction and ignores an event which would put a reasonably competent architect or engineer on notice to review their designs, would be held to have renewed the cause of accrual of action for their defective designs.

Some building projects are not administered or inspected by their designers and the designers' contracts end before site work commences. In these situations, the duty to review the design is not covered by the legal precedents considered in the preparation of this book.

Some projects are managed and administered by people who did not design the building, while the designers are kept on in a limited capacity. There is some relevant legal precedent where additional layers of management have been added to the project team, with the architect nonetheless required to provide full services.

It is difficult, from reported cases, to see how the courts will address the question of a continuing duty to review designs where the traditional role of the designer during the construction phase of a contract is maintained but at a reduced level of responsibility, by the introduction of project managers, contract administrators and inspectors who are not themselves the building designers.

Privity and exclusion clauses

A well-established principle of contract law is that only the parties to the contract can make claims against it.

> Dunlop sold tyres to Dew & Co., with a term in the agreement that Dew would not sell more cheaply to anyone else, and that Dew would not enter into a contract with anyone else except on the same terms. Dew sold tyres to Selfridge at the stipulated terms, but Selfridge sold them more cheaply. Dunlop brought an

> action against Selfridge, which failed on the basis that Dunlop had no contract with Selfridge and was not a party to the contract which had allegedly been breached.
>
> Presumably Dunlop could have taken an action against Dew, who in turn could have taken action against Selfridge.[147]

Clearly, it is fair that people should not incur obligations in respect of contracts to which they are not party and which offer them no benefits. However, the principle of 'privity' does mean that it is difficult to enter a contract that benefits a third party without taking out a separate contract with the third party.

> Woodar contracted to sell some land to Wimpey for £850,000 on the understanding that £150,000 would be paid to a third party on completion. Wimpey backed out of the deal without paying any money, leaving Woodar to make a claim under the contract. This they could not do, because Wimpey pointed out that Woodar would have no claim on the £150,000 (privity), and the beneficiary of this money would have no claim as there was no contract in place to support it.[148]

English law has been reformed by the Contracts (Rights of Third Parties) Act (1999), which provides a mechanism by which a contract can be drawn up to benefit a person or corporation that is not a party to a contract – thereby circumventing some of the problems of privity of contract. Briefly, a third party can enforce a contract if:

- the contract specifically provides for this;
- the contract benefits the third party;
- the allowed third parties are identified in the contract; and
- the contracting parties consent to the provision for third-party enforcement.

The doctrine of privity poses particular problems for exclusion clauses in contracts.

Exclusion or limitation clauses may exclude or limit the liability, for a specific breach or negligent act, of a contracting party to those it contracts with.

It is sometimes desirable to extend an exclusion clause to parties outside the contract. For example, a company may wish to protect contractors that it employs. On the whole, however, privity of contract acts to restrict the effect of such clauses on third parties.

> A manufacturer of cladding and roofing materials sells its products through builders' merchants, under a contract of sale which excludes liability for consequential loss and limits liability in any event to the amount paid to them for their materials.

Part of their cladding cracked after it had been installed on a building. The building owner, the employer under the building contract, sued the contractor who, in turn, sued the cladding subcontractor, and so on down the contractual chain until the action reached the manufacturer.

At the same time, the owner brought an action against the engineer who designed the building.

The manufacturer publishes literature in respect of their products which, in the ordinary course of events, are referred to by designers when deciding what products to specify. This was the case here and both the engineer and the owner sought to bring the manufacturers into the action, on the basis that the manufacturers had negligently misstated the cladding's capabilities and that they had relied on these misstatements when deciding what products to use.

The result was a multi-party action in which there were two lines of attack on the manufacturer. One line, the strict contractual route, had to contend with the exclusion clause (no liability for consequential damage) and the limitation clause (liability not to exceed the purchase price of the materials).

These restrictions potentially greatly diminished the value of a strict contractual claim. The merchant charged the subcontractor more than he paid for the cladding. In turn, the subcontractor charged the main contractor more than the merchant's price and, in turn, the main-contractor similarly inflated the price to the employer. The manufacturer's trading terms, if effective, would exclude liability for these inflated costs as well as the cost of the site work.

The claimed reliance on negligent misstatement did not have to overcome such restrictive terms, as these clauses applied to the contract of sale between the manufacturer and merchant only. In fact, the terms of sale between manufacturer and merchant were unknown to the other parties until they had been pleaded in the manufacturer's defence.

The manufacturer offered a warranty in similarly restricted terms. In bringing the actions for negligent misstatements reliance was not placed on the warranty, making the restrictive terms unavailable to the manufacturer in his defending this action.

The outcome of these legal arguments is not known, as the technical issues were heard first. The effectiveness of the restrictive terms excluding and limiting liability did not have to be tested, as the case against the manufacturer was dismissed once the arguments on the cause of cracking and misuse of the products had been heard by the trial judge.

For an exclusion clause to be enforceable, the following conditions must be met:

- it must be validly incorporated in the contract;
- its meaning must be clear, and match the nature of the defence to which it is to be put;
- it must not be prevented by statute; and
- the contract must remain sufficiently intact that the clause still has some legal force.

For an exclusion clause to be valid, at least one of the following conditions must be met:

- it must form an explicit part of the contract, of which all parties are aware;[149]
- if the contract is not explicit, an exclusion clause can be inferred to be incorporated if the party that will be affected has been given adequate warning of the fact;[150]
- the incorporation of standard terms and conditions into a contract can be made, providing:
  (i)   notice is given before creating the contract,[151]
  (ii) the terms are intended to have a contractual effect,[152] and
  (iii) if the contract terms are implied, then reasonable attempts have been made to alert the affected party to the existence of exclusions.[153]

In general, the more onerous the terms of the exclusion clause the more effort that must be expended to alert the affected party.

Sometimes the use of an exclusion clause can be supported by 'prior dealings' between the parties. For this to be supported the dealing needs to be 'regular' and 'consistent'.

Excluding liability involves foresight and skilled drafting of the terms to be used. If the risk to be excluded cannot be foreseen, then using broad, all-embracing, cover-all language may not be sufficient. It must be clear that the words used apply to the case, as the rule of *contra proferentum* will apply (meaning that an ambiguity will be construed in favour of the party disadvantaged by the clause). For example, if one wishes to exclude claims for negligence, then specific words to the effect must be used; a blanket disclaimer is not adequate. On the whole, a clause that tends to limit, rather than wholly exclude, liability is more likely to be accepted in the event of breach of contract – even if not entirely precise.[154] The reasoning here is that such a clause probably reflects the division of risks agreed by the contracting parties.

Statutory provisions to strike out exclusion and limitation clauses are now contained in the Unfair Contract Terms Act (1977) and the Unfair Terms in Consumer Contracts Regulations (1999). The latter deals with unfair terms in contracts with consumers, and allows them to be struck out.

The Unfair Trading Terms Act limits the applicability of an exclusion clause which attempts to limit liability for negligence and in breach of contract. The main provisions are that any clause attempting to restrict negligence liability for personal injury or death is void – as are the following, unless shown to be reasonable:

- any clause that attempts to restrict negligence liability for loss or damage;
- any clause that limits liability for breach of contract, where the contract refers to standard terms or conditions or one of the parties is a consumer;
- any clause that requires a consumer to indemnify any other party (whether a party to the contract or not) for negligence of breach of contract.

What is meant by 'reasonable' is not defined, but some guidance is given as follows:

- reasonableness will be assessed with reference to what the parties could be expected to know when the contract was formed;
- the 'reasonableness criterion' will act in favour of a party with relatively weak bargaining power;
- a clause is more likely to be assessed as reasonable if the party affected could have acted to protect themselves, e.g. by insurance; and
- the burden of the proof of reasonableness lies with the propounder of the clause – it is not for the person affected to prove unreasonableness.

The effect of statutory restrictions on exclusion and limitation clauses in contracts is to act in favour of the weaker party. The House of Lords has tended to uphold the right of two roughly equal contracting parties to bind themselves to such terms as they wish, however unreasonable and damaging. If you agree to take on risks when freely entering a contract, you will have to live with the consequences.

Law Reform (Contributory Negligence) Act 1945 and the Civil Liability (Contribution) Act 1978

The architect's, engineer's, builder's etc. liability to the employer for negligence may be reduced to the extent that the employer has also been negligent and, in so doing, has contributed to the damage suffered. This arises under the Law Reform (Contributory Negligence) Act 1945.

> *Where any person suffers damage as the result partly of his own fault and partly of the fault of any other person or persons, a claim in respect of that damage shall not be defeated by reason of the fault of the person suffering the damage, but the damages recoverable in respect thereof shall be reduced to such extent as the court thinks just and equitable having regard to the claimant's share in the responsibility for the damage.*[155]

It is well established that this applies to claims in tort. It may apply to a breach of a general duty of care under a contract, which duty is the same as would exist in common law, but it most probably is not applicable to a claim in respect of a breach of a strict contractual duty: *'Provided that this subsection shall not operate to defeat any defence arising under a contract'.*[156]

It does not alter the effect on any claim of the Statute of Limitations:

> *Provided that where any contract or enactment providing for the limitation of liability is applicable to the claim, the amount of damages recoverable by the claimant by virtue of this subsection shall not exceed the maximum limit so applicable.*[157]

The Civil Liability (Contribution) Act provides, subject to certain other provisions, that *'any person liable in respect of any damage suffered by another person may recover contribution from another person liable in respect of the same damage.'*[158]

Subject to the exact meaning of *'the same damage'* this gives a wide scope for actions for damages being brought against architects, engineers and the like by people they have not even met – let alone contracted with.

Risk control

In considering defects and the related questions of liability and claim, there are two approaches which can be taken. One is to rely on the judicious use of carefully worded exclusions and warranties, and then to wrap everything up in all-embracing, expensive insurance policies. The other is to ensure that the work is done properly. The first approach is of questionable merit, but is often essential where work is carried out under cost constraints – placing an economic bar to a thorough and rigorous approach to all aspects of the tasks undertaken.

Where the input into a project is limited by cost constraints, it is important to maximise effort in those areas which most commonly give rise to defects and claims.

The perception of the designer as a necessary evil – required to demonstrate compliance with statutory regulations, rather than to add value and ensure quality in construction – is at the root of many problems. It is essential to a well-run building project for adequate resources to be invested at the outset, to ensure a properly planned and co-ordinated approach.

Similarly a competent construction team is vital to good work. Designers tend to know more about the qualities required of the finished product than they do about the process of creating it. Practical site experience and trade skills are an equally important part of achieving a satisfactory product which meets the brief and satisfies the user.

Above all it is teamwork, communication and co-operation which allow the skills available to a building project to be fully utilised. The effective and appropriate use of human resources should allow the production of high-quality, low-risk building without premium cost or the avoidance of innovation. Where the most skilful focus on personal liability and reward – to the exclusion of adopting a common goal with the rest of the project team – they increase the likelihood of a trouble-ridden project, leading to dissatisfaction and dispute. Organizing a project so that the team all benefit from its success is the surest approach to good building. The best outcome from investing in construction comes from empowering competent people to contribute positively to all stages of a project.

135 *Sahib Foods Ltd and Co-operative Insurance Society Ltd.* v *Paskin Kyriades Smith (A Firm)* [2003] EWCA Civ 1832.
136 JCT Standard Form of Building Contract (Incorporating Amendments), 1998 edition, Clause numbers 22, 22a, 22b, 22c and 22d.
137 There is a footnote in the JCT Standard Form of Building Contract conditions which acknowledges that the policy wordings of insurance companies are not standardised. This recognises the potential for variation in the extent of cover which is obtainable.
138 JCT Standard Form of Building Contract, 1998 Edition, clause 22c·1.
139 JCT Standard Form of Building Contract, 1998 Edition, clause 22c·2.
140 The substitution of one party for another in respect of a right of claim.
141 JCT Standard Form of Building Contract, 1998 Edition, sub-clause 22c·1.
142 JCT Standard Form of Building Contract, 1998 Edition, clause 22d.
143 A loss is 'fortuitous' if it happens by chance or accident, occurring unexpectedly or without known cause.
144 See Chapter 1, Relationships.
145 L. J. Sachs in *Brickfield Properties* v *Newton* [1971] 1 WLR 862, p. 873.
146 Judge Bowsher QC in *University Court of Glasgow* v *Whitfield* [1988] 42 Build LR 66.
147 *Dunlop Pneumatic Tyre Co Ltd* v *Selfridge & Co Ltd* [1915] AC 847.
148 *Woodar Investment Development Ltd* v *Wimpey Construction UK Ltd* [1980] 1 WLR 277, [1980] 1 All ER 571.
149 *L'estrange* v *Graucob* [1934] 2 KB 394.
150 *Olley* v *Marlborough Court* [1949] 1 All ER 127.
151 *Thornton* v *Shoe Lane Parking* [1971] QB 163.
152 *Chapelton* v *Barry Urban District Council* [1940] 1 KB 532 and *McCutcheon* v *David Macbrayne Ltd* [1964] 1 All ER 430.
153 *Parker* v *South Eastern Railway* (1877) 2 CPD 416.
154 *Ailsa Craig Fishing Co. Ltd.* v *Malvern Fishing Co. Ltd.* [1983] 1 All ER 101, [1994] 67 BLR 25 1994 GWD 9–521.
155 130 Law Reform (Contributory Negligence) Act 1945 (8 & 9 Geo. 6 c.28) s.1 (1).
156 Law Reform (Contributory Negligence) Act 1945 (8 & 9 Geo. 6.) c.28 s.1 (1) (*a*).
157 Law Reform (Contributory Negligence) Act 1945 (8 & 9 Geo. 6.) c.28 s.1 (1) (*b*).
158 The Civil Liability (Contribution) Act 1978, s.1 (1).

Bibliography

Addleson, Lyall, *Building Failures: a Guide to Diagnosis, Remedy and Prevention*, 3rd Edition, Oxford, Butterworth Architecture (1992).

Adler, David, *Metric Handbook – Planning and Design Data*, 2nd edition, Oxford & London, Architectural Press (1999).

American Society of Civil Engineers, *Reducing Risk and Liability Through Better Specification and Inspection*, New York, ASCE (1982).

Anderson, W. E., Roberts, J. J. and Watt, P., *Efficient Masonry Housebuilding – Design approach*, London, Cement and Concrete Association (1985).

Bonshor, R. B. and Bonshor, L. L., *Cracking in Buildings*, Watford, Herts., Construction Research Communications Ltd. (1996).

British Academy of Experts, *Members' Handbook*, London, British Academy of Experts (1992).

Broomfield, John, *The Repair of Reinforced Concrete*, Tisbury, Wiltshire, The Building Conservation Directory (1996).

Building Project Information Committee, *Common Arrangement of Work Sections for Building Works*, 2nd Edition, Newcastle Upon Tyne, NBS Services Ltd. (1987).

Building Project Information Committee, *Production Drawings – A Code of Procedure for Building Works*, Newcastle Upon Tyne, NBS Services Ltd. (1987).

Building Research Establishment, *BRE Research Series Volume 5: Practical Studies from the Building Research Establishment: Building Failure*, Lancaster, Construction Press (1978).

Building Research Establishment, *DIGESTS – Vol 4: Design and Site Procedures, Defects And Repairs*, London, HMSO (1983).

Building Research Establishment, *BRE Digest 25: Assessment of Damage in Low-Rise Building,* London, Building Research Establishment (1985).

Burberry, P., *Practical Thermal Design in Buildings*, London, Batsford Academic and Educational Ltd. (1983).

Chappell, D. and Cecil, R., *Concise Encyclopaedia of Architectural Practice*, London, Legal Studies & Services (1985).

Chappell, D. and Hoxley, M. (eds.), *Construction Companion – Building Surveys*, London, RIBA Publications (2002).

Connell, L. R. and Callahan, M. T., *Construction Defect Claims and Litigation*, Maryland, USA, Aspen Publishers Inc. (1995).

Connell, L. R. and Callahan, M. T., *Construction Defect Claims and Litigation 2001: Cumulative Supplement*, New York, Aspen Publishers Inc. (2001).

Cook, G. K. and Hinks, A. J., *Appraising Building Defects – Perspectives on Stability and Hygrothermal Performance*, Hong Kong, Longman Group UK Ltd. (1992).

Cook, G. K. and Hinks, A. J., *The Technology of Building Defects*, London, E. & F. N. Spon (1997).

Cornes, D. L., *Design Liability in the Construction Industry*, 4th Edition, London, Granada, Blackwell Scientific Publications (1983).

Cox, S. and Clamp, H., *Which Contract?* 2nd Edition, London, RIBA Publications (1999).

Bibliography

Crowter, Harold, *Introduction to Arbitration*, London, LLP Reference Publishing (1998).

Egan, John, *Rethinking Construction: the Report of the Construction Task Force*, London, Department of the Environment, Transport and the Regions (1998).

Eldridge, H. J., *Common Defects in Building,* London, HMSO (1974).

Emery, Peter, *Butterworth's Step-by-Step Guide to High Court Actions*, London, Butterworth (1998).

Genn, Hazel, *Court-Based A.D.R. Initiatives for Non-Family Civil Disputes: the Commercial Court and the Court of Appeal*, London, Lord Chancellor's Department (2002).

Harrison, H. W., *BRE Building Elements: Roofs and Roofing: Performance, Diagnosis, Maintenance, Repair and the Avoidance of Defects*, London, Construction Research Communications Ltd. (1996, 2000).

Harrison, H. W. and de Vekey, R. C., *BRE Building Elements: Walls, Windows and Doors: Performance, Diagnosis, Maintenance, Repair and the Avoidance of Defects*, London, Construction Research Communications Ltd. (1998).

Harrison, H. W. and Trotman, P. M., *BRE Building Elements: Building Services: Performance, Diagnosis, Maintenance, Repair and the Avoidance of Defects*, London, Construction Research Communications Ltd. (2000).

Harrison, H. W. and Trotman, P. M., *BRE Building Elements: Foundations, Basements and External Works: Performance, Diagnosis, Maintenance, Repair and the Avoidance of Defects*, London, Construction Research Communications Ltd. (2002).

Health and Safety Commission, *The Approved Code of Practice (ACoP) for the control of legionella bacteria in water systems,* London, Health and Safety Executive (1985).

Health and Safety Commission, *Managing Health and Safety in Construction: Approved Code of Practice and Guidance*, Norwich, Health and Safety Commission (2002).

Hinks, J. and Cook, G., *Technology of Building Defects*, London, E. & F. N. Spon (1997).

Hollis, Malcolm, *Surveying for Dilapidations*, London, The Estates Gazette Ltd. (1988).

Howard, Michael, *Phipson on Evidence*, 15th edition, London, Sweet & Maxwell (2001).

Joint Contracts Tribunal Limited, *Standard Form of Building Contract 1998 Edition, Series 2: Practice Note 5: Deciding on the Appropriate JCT Form of Main Contract*, London, RIBA Companies Limited, trading under the name of RIBA Publications (1998).

Kaye, G. W. C. and Laby, T. H., *Tables of Physical and Chemical Constants*, London, Longmans, Green & Co. Ltd. (1959).

Keiller, A. P. and Brown, J. H., *Technical Report 535 – Thermal and Moisture Movements in Two Small Aerated Concrete Block Walls*, Wrexham Springs, Canada, Cement and Concrete Association (1980).

Knowles, Roger, *Partnering Contracts Compared*, Daresbury, Cheshire, James R. Knowles (2005).

Levy, Matthys and Salvadori, Mario, *Why Buildings Fall Down*, New York, W. W. Norton (1994).

Lucretius (tr. R. E. Latham), *The Nature of the Universe Book 1 – Matter and Space*, London, Penguin (1951).

Lupton, Sarah (ed.), *Architect's Job Book*, 7th Edition, London, RIBA Publications (2000).

McKay, W. B., *Building Construction: Volumes One and Two together*, London, Longman Group Ltd. (1971).

McKay, W. B., *Building Construction: Volumes Three and Four together*, London, Longman Group Ltd. (1971).

Mildred, R. H., *The Expert Witness*, London and New York, George Goodwin (1982).

Murdoch, Richard, *The Lead Sheet Manual – A Guide to Good Building Practice: Volume 1 – Lead Sheet Flashings*, Tunbridge Wells, Kent, Lead Development Association/Lead Sheet Association (1990).

Murdoch, Richard, *The Lead Sheet Manual – A Guide to Good Building Practice: Volume 2 – Lead Sheet Roofing and Cladding*, Tunbridge Wells, Kent, Lead Sheet Association (1992).

Murdoch, Richard, *The Lead Sheet Manual – A Guide to Good Building Practice: Volume 3 – Lead Sheet Weatherings*, Tunbridge Wells, Kent, Lead Sheet Association (1993).

Property Services Agency, *Defects in Buildings*, London, HMSO (1989).

Pye, P. W. and Harrison. H. W., *BRE Building Elements: Floors and Flooring: Performance, Diagnosis, Maintenance, Repair and the Avoidance of Defects*, Watford, Herts., Construction Research Communications Ltd. (1997).

Ransom, W. H., *Building Failures*, London, E. & F. N. Spon (1981).

Richardson, Barry A., *Defects and Deterioration in Buildings*, London, E. & F. N. Spon (1991).

Scott, G., *Building Disasters and Failures,* Lancaster, Construction Press (1976).

Stainsby, R. and Pope, R., *Commentary on the Fourth Edition of the National Structural Steelwork Specification for Building Construction,* London, British Constructional Steelwork Association Ltd., in association with the Steel Construction Institute (2003).

Styles, Keith, *Working Drawings Handbook*, London, Architectural Press (2003).

Wallace, D. (ed.), *Hudson's Building and Engineering Contracts*, London, Sweet and Maxwell (1995).

Useful organizations/addresses

The Association of Consultant Architects, 98 Hayes Road, Bromley, Kent BR2 9AB: *www.acarchitects.co.uk*

Civilinfo.Net knowledge integrator is a site developed and promoted by the Jemi Group of Companies based in Chennai, India: *http://203.197.88.82:8080/civil/index.jsp*

The Concrete Centre: *www.concretecentre.com*

Council of Europe Treaties and Conventions: Arbitration Law: *http://conventions.coe.int/treaty/en/reports/html/056.htm*

European Aluminium Association, Brussels: *www.aluminium.org*

International Aluminium Institute, London: *www.world-aluminium.org*

International Chamber of Commerce, Paris – Rules of Arbitration: *www.pbh.org.uk/PDF/rules_arb_english.pdf*

RMC Group plc. is a leading international producer and supplier of materials, products and services used in the construction industry: *www.rmc-group.com*

United Nations Commission on International Trade Law (UNCITRAL): *www. uncitral.org*

www.jrklibrary.co.uk/
www.blissuk.com
www.steelconstruction.org

Index

ACA *see* Association of Consultant Architects
ad hoc contracts 16–17
adjudication 217, 223, 225–9, 256–67
admissibility of evidence 209
agreement letters 21–2
agreement terms 23–6
Agrément Certificates 62
alloys 125–6
alternative dispute resolution 217–29
aluminium 129
arbitration 225–9, 241–55
Arbitration Act (1996) 242, 246–7
arbitration clauses 244–6
architects' responsibilities 6–7, 305–7
Association of Consultant Architects (ACA) contract form 77, 244–5
awards (arbitration) 253–4

Barbour compendium 141
betterment 205, 206–7
blame *see* liability
bricks 130–2 (*see also* masonry)
briefing, project 27–30
building insurance 299–300
building regulations 20, 35–8, 90–2

Calderbank Offers 235
cameras 145–7 (*see also* photographic records)
carbonation, concrete 175–6
cathodic protection 178–9
'cause of accrual of action' 196
cement 113–15
ceramics 106, 107, 130–3
Civil Liability (Contribution) Act (1978) 311–12
Civil Procedure Rules (1999)
    section 20 actions 200–1
    section 36 offers 235–8
claims for damages 193–213, 215–40
coatings, protective 127
collateral warranties 18–19, 88
companies
    legal status 9
    liability 302–3
completion, defined 85–6

composite materials 124
conceptual design 50–2
conciliation 222
concrete 103–4, 112–18
    corrosion 175–8
condensation 60, 81, 128–9, 135–6, 180–1, 189–90
'consolidation' 232
Construction Act *see* Housing Grants, Construction and Regeneration Act (1996)
Construction (Design and Management) Regulations (1984) 35, 36, 88, 141–2
construction management contracts 15–16
construction procedures 78–82
contract law 229–30
contractor's responsibilities 6, 20, 24, 179
contracts
    arbitration clauses 244–6
    exclusion clauses 308–11
    insurances within 298–9
    rights of third parties 307–8
    roles and relationships 10–13
    standard forms 13–26
Contracts (Rights of Third Parties) Act (1999) 308
corrosion 125, 127, 128–9, 136–8
    reinforced concrete 115, 116, 118, 175–8
corrosion fatigue 138
cost-benefit analysis 182–5
costs of proceedings 202–3, 215–16, 247
    cost-benefit analysis 182–5
    insurance cover 299
covenants 44–5
cracking
    concrete 115, 116, 117
    investigation 169–75
    masonry 131
    stress-corrosion 138

damage *see* defects
damages (*see also* awards (arbitration); claims for damages)
    assessment 201–2
    pre-estimated 304

Index

dampness 136
  investigation 143–4, 148–52
  treatment 185–6
defects
  causes 101–6, 134–9
  diagnosis 141–53
  liability period 86–8
  schedules 163–7, 164–6
  statistics 93–7
  symptoms 133–4
design
  avoiding errors 46–64
  detailing 77
  duty to review 305–7
  modifications 7–8
design-and-build contracts 14–15, 69
designer-user relationship 7–10
detailed design 53–6, 77
'determination' 25
diagnosis of defects 141–53
differential movement (*see also* cracking)
  design for 58–9, 106–7, 130–2
dimensional stability of materials 106–7,
  122–3
'discovery' of documents 211
dispute resolution 26, 217–29
dispute review boards 223
drainage, improvement 186
drawings
  investigations 278
  specifications 53–6, 71–2, 78
dry lining 170

early neutral evaluation (ENE) 223
easements 41–4
efflorescence 136
employer's responsibilities 17, 18, 20,
  24
equipment for investigation 142,
  144–8
'estates in land' 40
evidence 208–11, 273–5
exclusion clauses 307–11
exfoliation 138
expert determination 219–21
expert witnesses 209, 211–12, 269–85
express terms 20–1

facts 'in issue' 211
failure mechanisms 101–2 (*see also* defects,
  causes)
finishes, wood 123
fixed-price contracts 66
floors 99–100, 118
'flying freehold' 41
forensic reports 157, 198–9
foundations
  movements 97–8, 170, 171–3
  site investigations 33–5
frost damage 135
fungal decay 60–1, 136, 153, 186, 188–9

glass 129–30, 132–3

health and safety file 88–9, 142
healthy environments, design for 59–61
Housing Grants, Construction and
  Regeneration Act (1996) 225–6,
  256–7, 258, 259–61, 263
hydration, cement 113–14, 115–17
hygroscopic effects 136

illustrations, in reports 157 (*see also*
  drawings; photographic records)
independent interventions 223
indoor environments, design for 59–61
insect attack 121–2, 152, 188
inspections
  on-site 82–3
  responsibility for 6–7
  site inspection sheets 148, 158–62
insulation 128, 180–1, 191
insurance 25, 287–313
international rules, for arbitration
  241–2
interstitial condensation 81, 128–9, 135–6,
  180–1, 191
investigation of defects 141–53

'joinder' 232
joint arbitrations 250–3
Joint Contracts Tribunal (JCT), Standard
  Building Contracts 18, 19, 86, 244
  Agreement for Minor Building Works 16,
  23

Joint Contracts Tribunal (JCT), Standard
    Building Contracts (continued)
    Building Contract for Home
        Owners/Occupiers 22
    With Contractor's Design contract 15
judicial appraisal 223

land ownership 40–1
Law Reform (Contributory Negligence) Act
    1945 311–12
lead 128, 129
legal constraints 35–46
legal proceedings see litigation
liability (see also claims for damages)
    defects schedules 166–7
    establishing 179–80, 196–9, 203–5
    limiting 303–4, 308–13
    personal and company 302–3
licences 45–6
lime mortars 119, 131–2
limited liability 9, 302–3, 304
'liquidated and ascertained damages' (LADs)
    304
litigation 215–17, 225–9, 230–4
    costs 202–3, 215–16, 299

maintenance 89–90
maintenance manuals 88–9
maintenance period 86–8
management contracts 15–16
masonry 130–2, 169–75 (see also walls)
materials, characteristics 106–33
med-arb 223
mediation 222
metallic materials
    characteristics 124–9
    corrosion 136–8
    protective coatings 127
mini-trials 222
mitigation 205–6
mortars 131–2
mould see fungal decay
movement
    differential 58–9, 106–7, 130–2
    foundations 97–8, 170, 171–3
multi-party arbitrations 245, 250–3
multi-party litigation 201

negotiation 212
neutral fact finding 223

occupation, damage during 89–90
'offers to settle' 234–5
on-site see site
'open offers' 235
operating manuals 88–9
oral agreements 66–9
outline design 50–2

paints 123
part 36 offers (Civil Procedure Rules 1999)
    235–8
partnering contracts 13
partnerships, legal status 8–9
party structures 38–40
'payment into court' 235
payments, project 24–5
performance specifications 77–8
personal liability 302–3
photographic records 145–7, 208–9, 278
pitting corrosion 137
plastics 108–12
Portland cement 113–15
practical completion 85–6
practicality in design 56–8, 71–6
pre-estimated damages 304
preservatives, wood 122, 124
'privilege' 211–12
'privity' 307–8
procedural law 230–2
product assessment 60–3
product information 141
product insurance 296–8
professional indemnity insurance 294–6
programming of construction 79–81
proof 207 (see also evidence)
property rights 38

records of investigations 145–8, 208–9
'refusal of a stay' 233–4
reinforced concrete, corrosion 115, 116,
    118, 175–8
'relevance' of evidence 209–10
remedial work 169–91, 179–80
renders 116

Index

repairs 169–91
reports of investigations 153–7, 274–84
responsibilities 1–13
rising damp 136
risks, minimising 311–13
roles and responsibilities 1–13
roofs
    defects 99, 187
    tiles 132, 226–8
rubber 108–10

salvaged materials 63
schedules
    defects 163–7, 164–6
    remedial work 278
Scheme for Construction Contracts
    (England and Wales) Regulations
    256–7, 265
Scott schedules 166–7
screeds 117, 118, 134, 228
second-hand materials 63
section 20 actions (Civil Procedure Rules
    1999) 200–1
services, building 100–1
settlement, foundations 97–8, 170, 171–3
sick-building syndrome 59–61
site inspections 82–3
    inspection sheets 148, 158–62
    responsibility for 6–7
site investigations 30–5, 143
site supervision 6–7, 69–71
specifications 53–6, 71–2, 77–8
stainless steels 125–7
standard forms of contract 13–26
standards
    building 35–8, 90–2
    professional 2–5
'state-of-the-art' defence 200
statistics, defects 93–7
Statute of Limitations 305
statutory regulations 35–40
'stay of proceedings' 232–4
steels 125–6 (see also reinforced concrete)
stress-corrosion cracking 138

subcontractors
    liability 179–80, 201, 245, 251–3
    responsibilities 6, 10–11, 18–19
    supervision 70
subsidence see settlement
substantive law 230
substructure see foundations
supervision, on-site 6–7, 69–71
supply and build contracts 13–14

taxation of costs 202–3
technical reports 154–7
techniques for investigation 142–5
thermal stresses 106, 130–2
third party actions 200–1, 307–8
tiles 106, 132, 226–8
timber 103, 107, 120–4
tolerances, design 71–6
tribunals 222, 226, 248–9

Unfair Contract Terms Act (1977)
    310–11
Unfair Terms in Consumer Contracts
    Regulations (1999) 310–11
upgrading of old buildings 180–1
user-designer relationship 7–10

ventilation 59–61, 180–1, 189, 191

walls 98–9, 131–2, 169–75
warranties 288–93
water damage 134–8, 148–52 (see also
    corrosion)
'without-prejudice' exchanges 212–13,
    272–3
'without-prejudice' offers 234
witnesses 208–9, 250 (see also expert
    witnesses)
wood see timber
wood-boring insects 121–2, 152, 188
workmanship, design for 56–8
works contracts 15–16

zinc 127–8, 129